'Spurs or Halo'

Homeowners guide to avoiding a 'cowboy builder'.

'Spurs or Halo'

Homeowners guide to avoiding a 'cowboy builder'.

An alphabetical guide to the building industry, covering all the different trades.

Brian Tugwell.

LastResortPublishing.com

In Association with the Daily Express

First published in 2000 by Lastresortpublishing.com
Text © Brian Tugwell 2000
This edition © Lastresortpublishing.com
Line drawings © Brian Tugwell
Main drawings © Graham Sherwin

ISBN 0 9539381 0 7

First edition

October 2000

Printed and bound by
Barnwells of Aylsham
Printing Works
Aylsham
Norfolk
NR11 6ET

For the publisher
Last Resort Publishing.com
PO Box 246
Aylsham
Norwich
Norfolk
NR11 6GW

Edited by	Tom MacKeown (reformed 'cowboy') & Brian Tugwell.
Cover design by	Tim & Susan Morgan (Litcham High School, King's Lynn, Norfolk.
Digital editing of cover by	Barry Cawthorne (Cawtec Computer Services).
House and detail drawings by	Graham Sherwin B.Sc. (Environmental studies), Dip. Arch., RIBA parts I, II, III.
Other drawings by the author	Brian Tugwell HND (Business Studies), BA (law with Business).

Note:
The material contained in this book is set out in good faith for general guidance. No liability can be accepted for loss or expense incurred as a result of relying on particular circumstances or statements made in this book. The laws and regulations are complex and liable to change. Readers should check the current position with relevant authorities before making or entering into any arrangements.

Contents

Acknowledgements

Preface

Foreword

1   **Large labelled diagram identifying all areas of a house**

2   **Start of main content of book in alphabetical order**

3   **Chapter on contracts and the law surrounding them**
Sample domestic building works contract

4   **Continue with main contents**

5   **Conclusion**

6   **Glossary of building abbreviations and trade jargon**

7   **Glossary of Legal terms**

8   2 further copies of the Domestic building works contract

9   Metric to imperial conversion chart

11   **Index**

Plates

M: 1 Common Building Elements

L: 1 Semi-circular Brick Arch

L: 2 Flat Brick Arch

R: 1 Closed Eaves with Timber Soffit

R: 2 Corbelled Eaves

R. 3 Double Rafter or Purlin Roof

R: 4 Typical Roof Truss

R: 5 Typical Trussed Rafter

R: 6 Up-stand Verge to 'Cold' Flat Roof

R: 7 Projected Eaves to 'Warm' Flat Roof

Acknowledgements

A special thank you to Jillinda Tiley and all the staff at Anglia Law School, Cambridge.

To Dr George Turner MP, for your time and invaluable assistance to ensure the successful outcome of this book.

To Barry, your technical input has been invaluable.

To Graham, for the drawings to make sense of my text!

To Tom and Wendy, true friendship is very hard to find, but rewarded when deserved.

For Shirley, Adam and Jemma

Preface

The aim of this book, is to look at both the construction industry and how the current law is applied when contracts are made. The reader will then be able to use this book as a guide to control any building work they intend to have done on their property, and to reassure themselves that what is happening to their home is being done in the correct manner. This book is also designed so that the prospective new homebuyer can use it as a guide when inspecting their proposed new home. It highlights the common faults and problem areas of speculative house builders, more importantly what you should legally expect with regards to quality of workmanship and materials.

The inspiration for this book is gained from having recently studied law. I now realise how unfair the current situation is for the homeowner and that without a written contract they have no real protection against 'cowboy builders' when they have building work done on their home.

The book explains the failings of the current situation with regards to the private building contract, and the relationship between the individual and builder. The Government has plans to outlaw 'cowboy builders' by using a 'quality mark' licensing system. However, they do not say when it will pass through parliament, or if it will be a compulsory system.

Even if it does pass through the legislative process quickly there will still be those unscrupulous members of society that will slip through the net and avoid the proposed licensing process. The real problem will be the policing of any successful legislation, as the proposed system is complicated. For it to be effective, it needs to be kept simple with easy to use standard forms and procedures. This book will endorse and run along side any actions that the Government takes to solve the problem of 'cowboy builders'. The book will provide the consumer with the knowledge they need to combat the problem, but more importantly it will give them a contract to use if the builder has not joined up to the 'buildmark' scheme.

After reading the book, any homeowner, however practically minded they are, should be able to spot a possible building fault. Anyone wishing to create a construction contract could use this book as a guide, and feel assured that the contract they formulate would be fair on both parties and be sufficient as to provide for most problems that could arise. The contract contained within this book is designed to protect both the homeowner and the builder; it is not always the builder who creates the fault!

This book is written with personal experience and knowledge gained from a twenty year career within the construction industry. Beginning as an apprentice carpenter and joiner with a bespoke conservatory manufacturer progressing to site manager of speculative housing projects and on to technical manager for a large structural aluminium building fabricator. The experience has included large commercial contracts with values exceeding £10.5 million, at one extreme, and small private contracts with only a couple of hundred pounds value at the other.

The book is based on the experience of the formal procedure with commercial contracts, their advantages and pitfalls and who really benefits from the contractual arrangements. The knowledge has been further enhanced through reading Law at Anglia University, Cambridge. A large area of the study covered the fields of Contract, Commercial and Construction law.

If the home owning population is made aware of their rights and are given access to the knowledge needed to combat the scourge of 'cowboy builders' this will assist in any proposals made by the Government. All the technical details are explained in an easy to understand format.

Hopefully after reading this book you won't hear the spurs rattling as the builder walks down you path or if the builders already on the premises, see a large nail knocked into your lounge wall to hang his saddle, whip and mastic gun holster on!

Finally, this book is written to aid the consumer. It is for this reason that many of the building techniques and processes are simplified, to make them more easily understood. All the drawings are for explanation purposes only, and are not to scale, it is not intended to aid the DIY expert! It is not an instruction manual, more of a quality assurance check list, that the homeowners can enforce themselves.

M:1 Common Building Elements

by Graham Sherwin

Labels:

ridge tile
tiles or slates
rooflight or 'Velux' type window
verge
valley
eaves
hip tile
hipped roof
gutter
rainwater pipe (rwp)
fascia board
brick corbel
balustrade consisting
balusters + handrail
balcony
flat roof
coping
parapet forming balustrade
stepped flashing
mono-pitch roof forming 'lean-too'
patio doors
hopperhead + rainwater downpipe
soil vent pipe (svp)
waste branch pipe
soil branch pipe

dormer window
purlin
rafter
ceiling joist
ridge board

cold water storage tank
apron flashing

ridge tile
tiles or slates
rooflight or 'Velux' type window

chimney pot
chimney stack
mansard roof
tile battens
roofing (or sarking) felt
gable end
semi-circular arch
barge board
outer rafter
soffit board
flat arch
brick quoin
oriel window
sheet flooring
herringbone strutting
suspended floor joists
soldier arch on
concealed lintel
window cill
plaster finish
skirting board
load bearing internal wall
concrete raft foundation

sand/cement screed
concrete floor slab
insulation
damp proof membrane (dpm)
damp proof course (dpc)
compacted hardcore
strip foundation

ground

brickwork column or pillar
external cavity wall
outer brickwork skin
loadbearing blockwork inner skin
insulation
trench foundation

Foreword

Every MP has a story to tell of constituents victimised by 'cowboy builders'. I am certainly all too aware of homeowners dreams shattered at considerable personal and financial cost. Brian's contribution for the better education of the consumer is both timely and welcome. Even the simplest of the precautions he recommends would have prevented the disasters known to me.

Brian has produced a clear and simple guide to the many pitfalls facing the householder in dealing with the building industry. Time and again my casework has illustrated the importance of the advice he gives and I would particularly recommend the section on contracts. A lack of written quotations or agreements has been the biggest downfall for many that have fallen into the clutches of the worst elements of the trade. There are many reputable builders and I have never known one who did not understand the request 'to put it in writing'.

The book benefits considerably from Brian's extensive knowledge of both the industry and the law. He successfully avoids the use of jargon and many readers will welcome his translations. There is a wealth of information to help the homeowner who is contemplating anything from a modest alteration or extensions to the purchase of a brand new home.

Both Government and the reputable industry recognise the damage done by the 'cowboys'. At the time of writing fresh initiatives are being piloted under a Quality Mark initiative aimed at raising the standard of workmanship. The scheme will help consumers identify reputable builders, independently assessed as to their competence and workmanship. This scheme will include protection by third party warranty against defects and unfinished work.

Brian is to be congratulated on his work. I am sure it will be a useful guide to those contemplating or undertaking home improvements. As ever I would advise 'buyer beware' but this book will help raise awareness!

George Turner

Dr George Turner MP for North West Norfolk

Foreword

Trading Standards Departments across the country have played a very significant role in the last few years highlighting the misery and financial loss suffered by consumers at the hands of less scrupulous traders involved in the building and home repair industry. So I am delighted that a book of this nature is available to the public to help redress the balance.

Technology is such these days that we have to trust the people who are carrying out jobs for us because we are not, and indeed would not wish to be, experts in all the products and services that we purchase. So here is a guide that we can easily dip into to give us some basic information on the nature of the work, and the legal remedies if something goes wrong.

The author has advisedly not covered the criminal law, but I think it would be remiss to go to press without some mention, and indeed reassurance, that the full weight of the criminal law can be brought to bear in some of the more obvious cases. If someone has falsely stated that parts have been replaced, or the work is completed to a recognised standard, when it is not, then these are issues Trading Standards can investigate.

Trading Standards Departments along with Citizens Advice Bureaux can also provide advice on the civil law and how to make a small claim in the County Court without necessarily involving a solicitor.

The information derived from consumer complaints help target the resources of Trading Standards Departments and so it is always worth informing them if you experience a problem with a trader. They can be found easily in the telephone directory or by going online and searching for Trading Standards.

(Surrey County Council's Trading Standards Department worked with Granada's World in Action team to produce the original "House of Horrors" programme that highlighted the issues and "named and shamed" the culprits.)

By Peter Denard,

County Trading Standards Officer, Surrey County Council

Aggregate

What is aggregate?
The name used by the construction industry to describe the group of materials that are extracted from the ground in open quarries. The type of quarrying used to extract aggregate is some times called crushed stone quarrying. Aggregate is sometimes referred to as ballast.

Aggregate is probably the main material used in conventional construction in the UK, not only is it used greatly in the various stages of building, it is the base material for many of the products that combine together to build homes. Sand is used in the manufacturing of bricks, roof tiles and paving slabs. Sand and gravel are used together with cement to manufacture concrete products such as beams and foundation piles. At the other end of the scale sand is also used to manufacture sandpaper and as an ingredient in the manufacture of other abrasive products.

There is aggregate on many drives in the form of gravel or shingle and many people use sand to lay paving slabs. Concrete is made using a blend of 20mm stone and sharp sand, mixed with Ordinary Portland cement; this type of aggregate is generally called 'pre-mix'. Cement render is made with cement and sharp sand. Mortar, for laying bricks or blocks, is made with soft sand and masonry cement.

Some aggregates available are recycled products; the most commonly used are crushed concrete and crushed metalled road surface. These are not used as ballast for concrete products but as base materials for paths, driveways and roads, this is because they bind together very well and compact to give an excellent stable base or support for construction purposes.

What sort of bad practices do you look for?
Builders even the 'cowboy' variety generally uses soft sand for mortar, sharp sand for rendering walls and 'pre-mix' containing crushed stone for concrete. This is mainly due to the fact that each type of aggregate does a specific job, if the wrong aggregate is used the job is likely to fail.

It has to be said that it is very difficult for a 'cowboy builder' to take shortcut with aggregate, as it is one of the cheapest materials used in construction. If a builder tries to cut down on aggregate they will have to add another material to make up the quantity needed. Bad tradesmen do bulk-out concrete by adding rubble and building rubbish to the mix, some even throw any rubbish into the mix including wood, plastics, glass, even soil and clay!

What can you do to prevent the wrong aggregate being used?
The only way to spot this happening is to keep a close eye on the rubbish heap and skip. It is also a good idea to ask the builder to keep the site clean and tidy by disposing of the rubbish regularly; this can prevent bad practices happening.

It also may be advisable to check with the local gravel pit to see what the current prices are per tonne as many unscrupulous builders load the price heavily to increase their profits.

Which type of aggregate should be used for each job?

It would take several pages to cover this subject thoroughly so the list below gives a good overview explaining which aggregate is used for the most common building tasks encountered on the average home building project;

- **Fence posts**   If they are going to be fixed in place using concrete this should be done with 20mm 'pre-mix' or 'ballast' mixed with ordinary Portland cement. If they are going to be fixed in place dry, this could be done by using crushed granite, crushed concrete, or 40mm rejects (cobblestones not suitable for building walls). All of these are placed around the post and compacted heavily to keep the post secure in the ground.

- **Over-site preparation**   This is the 'hard-core' or 'hoggin' placed within the boundary or the foundation walls to support the concrete ground floor. This material may differ regionally, but is generally sand-based ballast in its natural state. It may be a mixture or sharp sand and large cobbles or boulders sometimes called '100mm down rejects' ballast. In another region of the country this could be a mixture of crushed granite and '100mm down granite lumps'. Whichever is used, the preparation is the same, i.e. being heavily compacted to give a firm base.

- **Over-site concrete**   This is always made using 20mm 'pre-mix', or ballast mixed with Ordinary Portland cement.

- **Brickwork mortar**   Soft sand is the only option here, if sharp sand is used the pointing will not be smooth and the large particles of sharp sand would make the mortar more porous.

- **Wall rendering**   Sharp sand is used for this for three main reasons. The larger particles will give the dry mortar greater strength, it also allows easier working of the wet mortar when spreading it on the wall, but more importantly the sharp sand gives a better key for the plaster finish.

- **Paving slab laying**   If the slabs are going to be laid dry, i.e. not on mortar, sharp sand is normally used. If they are laid on concrete 'dabs', 10mm pre-mix is the ideal aggregate to use as the small stones allow easier levelling and bedding of the slab. Some builders use standard 20mm pre-mix, which is acceptable.

- **Foundation concrete**   This is always made using 20mm 'pre-mix' or ballast.

- **Concrete lintels**   Always made using 20mm 'pre-mix' or ballast.

- **Paths and driveways**   Generally 20mm 'pre-mix' or ballast is used with the cement.

- **Underground pipe bedding**   When sewer pipes are laid, they are laid in and surrounded by 10mm pea shingle.

Appearance

It is traditionally said that it is wise to judge by first impressions. This may not be the case when attempting to spot a 'cowboy builder'. Some are masters of disguise and will cleverly present themselves as reputable tradesmen. They will often have the gift of persuasive talk and the ability to dominate a situation. It is true to say that a good tradesman may have these qualities too. But how can you tell which is which?

What to look for

When the builder arrives at your doorstep, look at their vehicle and its general presentation, taking special attention to the ladders and other access equipment and if possible any tools. Most access equipment will last for many years so it would be normal for ladders and steps to be covered in dried cement, concrete and paint, this suggests that the builder has been trading for a considerable period and should be experienced. A vehicle carrying all new access equipment should put you on guard immediately; this type of equipment is expensive and generally not replaced all at once. Ask why theirs is new; there may be a genuine reason such as theft replacement.

Any tools should have clear signs of wear and tear, however good tradesmen will have looked after their tools and they should appear clean and in good order. A tidy van or work place usually identifies a person who is methodical and organised; this should be reflected in their work. A tradesman who visits you equipped with a writing pad instead of a cigarette packet should be more reliable. At least they will be able to read their notes and so give an accurate estimate!

What things should start the alarm bells ringing?

One of the biggest problems for homeowners, especially older people, is the scourge of the so called 'ladder gangs'. They are opportunists who drive around looking for likely targets; homes with building faults, and 'cold call' offering to do the repair work. They generally operate in gangs, sometimes watching their 'prey' for several days, observing their routine, before moving in for the 'kill'. They find a small fault and offer to rectify it. This often escalates and becomes a major and very costly disaster. If a person 'cold calls' at your home does not agree to anything. This is not the way in which a reputable builder conducts business.

When you have contacted a builder to price a job, they should visit your home to carry out a survey of the proposed work. A good builder will carry out a thorough survey talking you through the stages of the work, answering questions you may have and give you time to study a 'written' quotation before commencing the agreed work. Some may even offer a written contract! If this is not the case, look for another builder as this one has rattling spurs.

The key issues to watch for

- The 'builder' may try to baffle you with technical and trade jargon, not only will they have no idea what they are saying! but they will expect you to be 'clue-less' as well.

- They will have a 'phobia' of paper work, using verbal agreements only. If you mention the word 'contract' they will probably give a 'vacant' expression and if you are really lucky develop a severe case of shock!

- They will become very anxious if you ask for references, skirting round the subject, and avoid giving names.

- They will claim to be expert at all areas of construction. A favourite saying of the average 'cowboy builder' is "no problem, we can do all of that, no worries". 'Jack of all trades, Master of none'!

- They tend to have a low opinion of qualified tradesmen, and claim to be able to do the job cheaper.

- They will prefer to be paid in cash - are they allergic to cheques.

- Clearing up any mess that they make is like destroying their scent markings! The average 'cowboy builder' will leave the property as if a 'scud' missile had been dropped nearby.

- If you try to contact them, you will have more chance of finding the 'Holy Grail'.

- They never return your telephone calls.

- They are convinced that VAT is a contagious disease!

- It is highly likely that your home will become an ashtray, as they never ask if it is all right to smoke, they just take it for granted!

Architect

Why do you need to use an Architect?

If you are planning a large building project it is wise to employ the services of an architect or an architectural technician, as they are trained and experienced in all areas of construction design. More importantly they are usually able to spot the bad builder. Architects are aware of reputable builders and, more importantly, which builders should be avoided.

   The best reason for using an architect is that any work will be insured and guaranteed against faults, so they will have ensured that all workmanship on the project is of the highest standard. A good architect can spot a 'cowboy builder' in a very short period of time. He will produce working drawings, bills of quantities, specification data and any other document necessary for the satisfactory completion of a building project.

How do you find an Architect?

There are usually several hundred architects advertising their services in 'Yellow Pages', some advertise in local papers. A list of architects can be found at your local library. Architects must be registered with ARB, (The Architects registration Board). A lot are members of the RIBA as well, (The Royal Institute of British Architects). The RIBA sets the exams parts I and II the equivalent of a degree, and diploma stages, Part III is usually taken after one or two years in practice.

How do you know that the architect will do their job properly?

As a registered architect they owe a duty of care to you, their employer. To use all reasonable skill and care in the design work they do, and if specified at the time you instruct them to do the work, this duty of care can cover many other areas as well.

What are their duties and responsibilities?

As previously stated architects owe a standard duty of care to you as their employer. However, if you want this duty to be more than the reasonable duty expected it must be specified at the time the contract for their services is made. These extra responsibilities could include:

- Delegation of design work. They will be responsible for checking all design work that is delegated.

- They are responsible for warranty of the project. However you must ensure that they obtain further warranty for work undertaken by each sub-contractor.

- Deciding how long the period of warranty is, and that all contractors working on the project are sufficiently insured to cover their responsibilities under the terms of the warranty.

- Supervision and inspection of quality control and assurance.

- General project supervision and administration.

- Acting as a quantity surveyor if one is required.

- Payment valuations, this means they will be responsible for ensuring that any invoices submitted by contractors are correct and that the materials on the invoice(s) are on site and/or work has been completed satisfactory.

Bay window

What is a bay window?
A window with more than one aspect, usually with two side facing and one front facing, there are other combinations. Many have 90-degree corners but it is not uncommon to see bay windows with different angles, some may even be curved in aspect.

Why use a bay window?
There are two main reasons for using bay windows:

- To let more light into a room, this is why many blocks of flats and apartments use them, and

- To give the room extra space, and a feeling of airiness.

What problems do you need to be aware of?
On new build projects, unless specifically designed, they are not load bearing, so any roof or floor above should be self-supporting. A lean-to roof can be supported on a bay window but it must be tied into the face of the building behind it. The hole where the bay window comes through the face of the building must have a lintel supporting the brickwork above.

Some bay windows have no supporting brickwork below them and are supported on timber or brick brackets, with a large window board (sill) on the inside. On this type of bay window there must be a space between the cladding underneath the bay and the window board, this is for insulation purposes, the space between these is normally in excess of 150mm and filled with fibreglass or similar insulation material. If this is not done condensation will form on the board in cold weather, with potential for rot.

Common faults in this type of bay are the timber brackets being too weak, or badly jointed, to hold the weight of the window (glass, especially in sealed units is very heavy). Not only is there the weight of the window but there are also timber joists that the window sits on top of, which in turn support the window board and the underside cladding. The other main problem is that the window board is made of material that is too thin. In time the board sags and in bad cases it comes away from the window frame, exposing the insulation, or worse, the elements!

Problems with replacement 'bay' windows
Lots of older properties have bay windows that continue through to the first floor giving a bay on top of a bay. Many of these were designed and built to be part of the structure of the house and are consequently load bearing, the lower bay supporting the floor and wall below the first floor bay and in many cases they support the roof as well.

There have been some major disasters where poorly trained and inexperienced window companies have removed the old windows and replaced them with non-load bearing uPVC windows. For a short time there are no apparent problems but soon cracks start to appear in the walls and plaster starts to crack on the inside. There have been some extreme cases where the bays, floors and roof have totally collapsed.

Where there are bay windows of this design, the replacement uPVC or aluminium windows, if not custom made from matching timber, must always have the upright sections of the frames reinforced with steel or aluminium ensuring that any floor joists between the floors are supported again. This applies to the roof wall plate as well.

6

When fitting is finished inspect the work thoroughly, looking for secure fixing, gaps between window and wall and good sealing with mastic. If you are not happy with the work complain and don't pay until the work is completed properly. Two further pieces of advice are:

(i) When the old bays are removed, it essential that the floor and roof are supported with 'Acro-props' to prevent straining and stressing of the structure prior to fitting the new window, and

(ii) Where the bay extends to two or more storeys, the bottom, or ground floor, bay window must be replaced first. This is to ensure that the work on the upper storeys is adequately supported.

Bill of Quantities

What is a 'Bill of Quantities'?

Simply a list of all the materials required for a construction project. Historically used to enable sub-contractors to quote for building contracts, as it not only lists the quantity but also the quality of the products to be used.

What is their purpose?

On a large building project they are used as a means of valuing 'interim' or 'stage payments'. This is to say that if a project is to take several weeks or months the builder can be paid for materials on site as well as for completed stages of work. The main use is as a reference guide as to the quality of work and limit of contractor liability under the terms of the contract they have agreed to.

How can one protect me from a 'cowboy builder'?

Using a bill of quantities can give some protection against an unscrupulous builder. However, it should be noted that a bill of quantities does not normally form part of a contract, it merely acts as guide to payment and a clear instruction to the specifications of the building project.

Many 'cowboy builders' probably would not be able to tell the average homeowner what a bill of quantities was and would probably not agree to work with one, even if the homeowner asked them too.

Blocks and Block-work

What are blocks and how do you recognise block-work?

Construction using blocks is one of the main forms of building found today. Blocks are available in many different sizes and types, made from many different materials and are used for many different types of building. Most blocks used for private dwellings are made from cement based products, light weight blocks for cavity walls or internal dividing walls and generally heavy concrete and aggregate blocks for constructing foundations or load bearing walls.

There are now large lightweight blocks available for building foundations, made for their ease and speed of construction. They can be purchased up to 1m long with, widths varying depending on the type of wall that is going to sit on them, above the foundation level.

How do you identify the blocks be used are correct for the type of wall?

As a general guide, any internal leaf of a cavity wall on a domestic dwelling can be constructed with lightweight blocks with a minimum thickness of 100mm. Some cavity walls now have 125mm blocks for better thermal value, some even have insulated pockets built into them. Any internal wall can be built with lightweight blocks, however if it is to be a load bearing wall then it must be constructed with blocks with a minimum thickness of 100mm. Any other internal walls must be constructed using blocks of a minimum thickness of 75mm.

Foundation blocks are normally 275mm thick to allow for the thickness of a cavity wall, these again are available in various sizes to suit different uses. If the wall to be built is a retaining wall, or is around a room below ground level, it has to be constructed from dense concrete blocks with a minimum thickness of 100mm.

What do you look for when checking blocks?

One of the most common 'cowboy builder' tricks is to use 'seconds' or cheap blocks. The main problem with this is the original stack from which the blocks came from may have been dropped or knocked into in the builders yard, they would have been re-stacked in the yard in smaller quantities and then sold for a sum much less than the full retail price. In the first instance this seems like a good deal, but that may not be the case as lightweight and solid concrete blocks when dropped or knocked into crack very easily. Damaged or cracked blocks could give problems at a later date such as cracking plaster or at the very worst, loose or unstable walls.

One final factor to be aware of when checking blocks is the bonding of the block-work; this means the layout of the blocks when they are laid on top of one another. It is imperative that the joints of mortar are staggered and the blocks are not laid directly on top of each other. The diagram below explains:

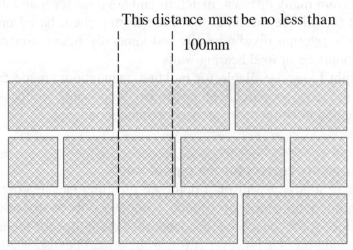

This distance must be no less than 100mm

Drawing shows mortar joints staggered to give greater strength to wall

It is not necessary for the mortar joints to be evenly spaced; the important factor is that they are staggered by a minimum of 100mm. It should be noted that the better the bond pattern the greater strength the wall will have.

Key points to look for when checking block-work

- When blocks are used to build internal partition walls, they must be bonded to the external wall every second course or row of blocks. This means that they are interlocked with the outer wall to prevent the internal wall from falling over. It is standard practice by a bricklayer to leave out blocks in the external walls to allow for the internal walls to be built at a later date, once the internal walls are interlocked using these spaces both walls will achieve full strength.

- Internal walls can be built not using the interlocking method explained above; this is achieved by using stainless steel or galvanised 'profile ties'. These are slotted steel profiles that are screwed to the external wall, ribbed or perforated ties are then inserted into the profile and built into the mortar courses at every third block course. These provide adequate lateral stability, has the added advantage of being cheap to install and cutting down on labour costs.

- Always ensure that there is sufficient mortar between the blocks, bad tradesmen have the attitude that block-work is going to be rendered or covered with dry lining, so the work does not have to be good quality. Gaps or spaces in badly applied mortar can create a weak wall.

- Where lintels are placed over door openings you must ensure that the lintels are supported by a minimum of 150mm of block-work.

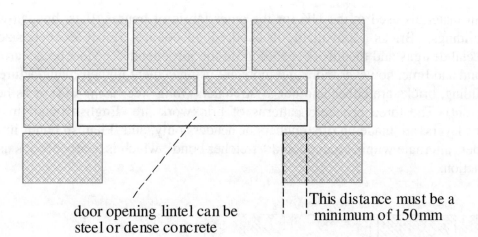

door opening lintel can be steel or dense concrete

This distance must be a minimum of 150mm

Bricks and Brickwork

What are Bricks?

Bricks are the main materials used in the UK for the outer fabric of houses, flats, bungalows and their associated buildings. Bricks are available in hundreds of colours, finish textures, sizes and materials, with special designs and qualities depending on the job intended. Most bricks are made of baked clay or sand and lime, however more and more are using cement in their manufacture.

In wall building, bricks are either laid out as stretchers (long side facing out) or as headers (short side facing out). The three principle patterns of brickwork are 'English bond' in which alternate courses, or layers, are made up of stretchers or headers only, and 'Flemish bond' in which stretchers and headers alternate within courses, and 'stretcher bond', which is nearly always used on cavity wall construction.

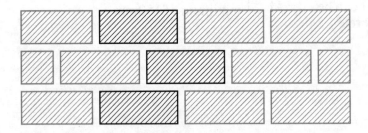

Stretcher bond

English bond

Flemish bond

Very hard engineering bricks are manufactured for building 'manholes' and for using under lintels and load bearing beams. Engineering bricks are often used instead of copings on walls, as an ordinary brick used in this situation would deteriorate very quickly due to the effects of the weather.

There are construction salvage yards that specialise in the supply of reclaimed bricks, commonly used in renovation and repairs of old buildings. These are normally cleaned and checked for damage and there is nothing wrong with using them again. Most old buildings where these bricks are salvaged from will have lime based mortar, which is soft and very easy to clean off the bricks to enable their re-use.

Even if the bricks are very old they will be very durable once they are laid with modern mortar. In some cases the bricks used in a building may no longer be available. More and more old buildings are being protected by Local Authority preservation orders, so when repairs or renovations take place it will be a local planning requirement that the bricks used match the existing areas of brickwork. Local Authorities normally give no alternative when brickwork has to be matched and it is only right that this is enforced by their planning departments.

How do you know when the wrong bricks are being used?
Because reclaimed bricks can be very expensive this can create an opportunity for the unscrupulous builder to use unorthodox methods to avoid buying them. The builder may try to convince you that it is all right to use coloured mortar and shape it to look like a brick to repair a wall, this is not correct and you should not allow him to do this under any circumstances. They may also try to use a modern faced brick that looks similar, again you should not allow the builder to do so, as old handmade bricks vary in size and modern bricks are usually uniform and would stand out, looking very out of place.

It is important on a new build project that the bricks used for face-work are not 'seconds' or that they have damaged edges and faces. A brick with a damaged face or edge will deteriorate quickly in frost and wet weather; the face will split away from the brick and allow water through the wall. Bricks that are classed as 'seconds' are suitable for foundations or rendered walls, where they will not be seen, and will save money.

How do you know if the bricklayer is using bad practices?
The inspection of new brickwork for faults and bad workmanship is a very challenging task for the best building inspector, so to make the task simpler this section will show the key points to look for;

- If it is a large building project with several packs of bricks being used, make sure that the packs are mixed together when they are laid, this will avoid dramatic shade changes in the colour of the bricks.

- If the project is an addition to the existing building, ensure that the brick courses line up old with new.

- Ensure that the joints between the laid bricks line up vertically and that they are plumb, paying special attention to the bonding pattern in the brickwork. This ensures that the wall obtains maximum strength throughout its entirety, that there is lateral stability and resistance to side thrusts, and there is an acceptable appearance to the completed brickwork. (see following drawings)

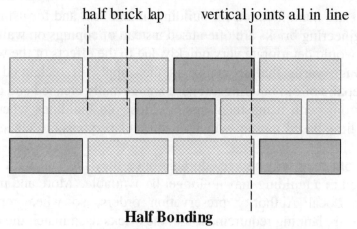

Half Bonding

usual bond for cavity wall construction

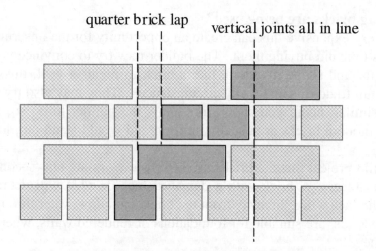

Quarter bonding

used as the minimum bond with standard bricks

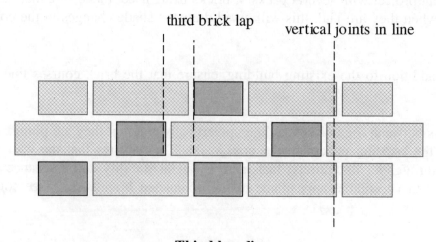

Third bonding

generally used with metric bricks

Bricklayer

Who is a bricklayer?

A tradesman, who builds with bricks and blocks, usually has served a three to five year apprenticeship. A very skilled person, whose workmanship generally improves with experience, some specialise in decorative and stone walls. They have to be aware of many rules and skills, so correct training is essential. All the other trades on a building project rely on them to be accurate with their work, since all the other stages of building follow brickwork.

What sort of questions should you ask a bricklayer?

All the quality issues are listed in the section on brickwork, however there are some other pointers to help you prevent problems:

- Ask to see proof of qualifications or experience, some may have served a good apprenticeship but have no formal qualifications, there is nothing wrong with this.

- A good bricklayer will be proud of their work, ask to see any photographs or if possible, other customers' completed work in the area.

Are there any tell tale signs to help recognise a bad bricklayer?

It is not really possible to spot a 'cowboy' bricklayer without actually seeing them laying bricks. The best advice is to ask someone who has recently had brickwork completed on their property, if the work completed was of a good standard, 'word of mouth' is a good recommendation, if they're good they will come highly recommended.

A list of important things to look for

Obvious signs to look for as the work commences are:

- Clean, accurate tape measure

- Clean, well used tools

- A good spirit level

- Good quality building lines or strings

- An organised work area.

- That he hasn't got a case where he stores his holster and spurs while he's working!

- If there are bricks with chipped corners or cracked faces complain and ask that they be changed.

- Pointing of the brickwork should be neat and tidy and match any existing brickwork for colour and style (pointing will be explained further in the book).

- If the weather is cold and frosty insist that the fresh brickwork is covered at night with old sacks, this prevents the frost from freezing the water particles in the mortar and rendering the brickwork useless. Also insist that a frost inhibitor be added to the mortar when it is being mixed.

Building Contract

I would like to mention that while this section is the longest in the book, it is also the most important!

What is a building contract?

The definition of a building contract is much the same as any other form of contract. It is a legally binding agreement. The agreement arises as a result of an offer from one party, which is accepted by the other party, and each party must contribute something to the bargain. There are, however, other requirements that need to be satisfied to make a contract legally binding but I shall discuss these later.

A building contract is applicable for the fitting of a door on a private house or building an extension onto a house, or equally, on a larger scale where it could apply to building a dwelling from Architect's drawings and on to a complete housing project for a speculative developer.

The contract could be one small part of a large project, or for the construction of one small component of the building, there really is no defined description of the size or nature of a building contract only that it will involve constructing something or some part of a building.

Why should you use a contract?

With regards to 'cowboy builders' it is imperative that more and more people get into the habit of using a written contract of some nature. It is much easier to solve problems when they arise with a construction contract when the agreement is in writing, because when there is a verbal agreement between parties it is often one person's word against the other's. The strongest argument for using a written contract is that most unscrupulous traders will avoid one like the plague.

There are different elements that come together to make a valid contract, I will explain them briefly, with reference to examples applicable to a building contract. If you are able to understand the elements that go together to make a contract, it will be easier to ensure that the contract you use is correct and fair to both parties.

The elements required to formulate a successful contract
Consideration

There must be consideration by both parties, unless the contract is by deed. The consideration can take the form of performance of work, payment of money or the provision of goods.

This can also take the form of any benefit to one party or detriment to the other, put simply 'this for that'. The consideration must not be something that has already been done and must be more that he is already bound to provide. For example If a building project was behind schedule and you as the customer offer additional payments to speed up the work, this will be seen to be consideration, the extra money being the benefit to the builder for work being finished on time or sooner. The work may be part of the original contract but the builder agreed to speed up the work, this is seen to be 'valuable consideration'.

This can amount to be a 'promise', the consideration being the benefit to the builder. Even though this will be nothing more than he has already agreed to do, the fact that it will be an agreement to speed up the contract will be enough to amount to good consideration, as he was not obligated to complete the contracted work faster.

An intention to create legal relations

When a contract takes place between an individual and a commercial enterprise or between two businesses, it is presumed that there was an intention to create legal relations, however, it is possible that the intention may be rebutted. If wished, the parties can make it an express condition that the contract is not binding in law. This however, could make the contract void and unenforceable - both 'fool hardy' and not recommended.

Explained simply if you pick-up the telephone and contact a painter you have found in the Yellow Pages, he then visits and gives an estimate to paint your house which you then accept, this will be an intention to create legal relations.

Important note:

If the contract was domestic, between members of a family or close friends, it is normal to presume that domestic arrangements are not intended to create legal relations. It is the responsibility of the party seeking to enforce the contract to rebut the presumption, i.e. to prove that there was an agreement and that it was intended that the agreement would create a legally binding contract.

Capacity to contract

This means the competence to enter into a legally binding agreement. A minor (person under the age of consent) would not be able to make a contract for building work. A contract made by someone who was drunk would be voidable if the other person knows that the condition of the person is preventing him from fully understanding what he is doing or agreeing to. The same principle would apply to someone with a mental disorder or illness caused by age.

The agreement must comply with any formal legal requirements

In general there is no particular formality for building contracts, they can be written or oral or a combination of both. As a general rule most commercial contracts between main contractor and subcontractor are written in the form of a JCT contract (see glossary).

Many people presume that all contracts must be in writing, this is not however the case, simple contracts may be made in writing, verbally or a combination of both and despite the absence of documentation may still be enforceable.

With 'cowboy builders' I feel this is the real problem area at present, as proof of what was agreed will be very difficult to show.

This is the area of current law that I think needs urgent attention!

The agreement must be legal

This means that it must comply with building and planning regulations. What is being asked for must be in keeping with easements that are part of a property's deeds or title. All local authority rules and regulations must be adhered to.

The agreement must not be rendered void either by some common law or Statutory rule or by some inherent defect

This could be something such as a tradesman's mistake. A contract, though valid, may be liable to be set aside by one of the parties on such grounds as misrepresentation or undue influence, these points of law will be explained further on.

The terms of a contract

This does not apply to contracts that involve the sale or 'disposition' of land or interests in land; these must be by deed or evidenced by written documentation. When a contract is being formulated, the final stage will be agreement of the terms and the effect they will have. If the contract is mainly contained in writing, there may not be any problems but often when contracts are negotiated, the parties may make further statements and these may have a contractual effect.

It should be remembered that statements made during the negotiations of a contract might amount to representation. Explained further if a carpentry sub-contractor during the contract negotiations simply makes a statement as to their future conduct when on site, and later fails to do what they said, they do not misrepresent a fact of what they said would be done. Circumstances or events may have prevented them from carrying out their intentions.

If, however, when they make the statement, it is of their present intentions and they later fail to carry out the promise because they never intended to, they could be misrepresenting the facts, this could create a contractual problem. This can be a very 'grey' area when it comes to prove what was said if it has not been recorded in writing. Therefore it is more likely that a statement made before an agreement has been reached, or if the statement maker had special knowledge, that a statement will become binding on the parties.

These provisions of a contract agreed to by the parties are known as the 'express terms'. They may constitute either a 'condition' of the contract (a major term of the contract that goes to the root of the contract) breach of, which entitles the injured party to treat the contract as discharged. Or they could be a 'warranty', (a term or promise in a contract), breach of which will entitle the innocent party to damages but will not allow the parties to treat the contract as discharged. It could be that there are other terms that are implied into the contract, although not specified by the parties, they will nevertheless be as binding as the 'express terms' agreed to.

These terms are 'implied' on the basis of an intention by the parties from their actual circumstances, meaning there is no question of imposing a legal obligation irrespective of the parties' intentions. A term will only be implied if the contract becomes incomplete without it. An 'implied term' refers to something that while not directly stated in the contract never the less forms part of it by virtue of its necessity. For example a statutory planning requirement, or by past dealings of the parties, which can be either by conduct or a special relationship that exists between parties, this is generally called common law contractual duty.

Implied terms within a construction contract could be:

- Completion of the contract in a reasonable time, i.e. handing the finished building to the owner at the agreed time,

- To communicate with others involved with the contract in a reasonable manner,

- To use proper skills and judgement and care,

- Materials and labour used should be of a good standard and fit for the purpose.

These are just some of the examples of what could be implied into a construction contract by the parties. It must be remembered that where a building has been designed by architects or engineers, it is not implied that the contractor who constructs the building is responsible for design defects or not following the construction techniques suggested by the design team. Design defects will be the responsibility of the designer and construction techniques are not compulsory, after all, the site labourer doesn't tell the design team how to do their job!

Again an 'implied term' can be a 'condition' or a 'warranty' and the rules are the same as those for an 'express term'.

Privity of a contract

It must always be remembered that The doctrine of privity of contract states that a person (company) may not enforce a contractual promise, even when the promise was expressly made in their favour, when they are not party to the contract. Furthermore, it is also the rule that a person (company) who is not a party to a contract may not have their rights diminished by that contract.

This appears to be a very unfair area of the law when it relates to construction contracts, as an 'Agency' situation can arise where there is a main contractor, the 'Principal', and a site manager, the 'Agent'. Because the 'Principal' is able to sue or be sued because of contractual agreements made by his 'Agent' the site manager.

The site manager could agree with subcontractors to pay them extra money for work because of difficult working conditions. The main contractor may not like this agreement but will be duly bound by his agent's actions, as this will be accepted as the normal role and responsibility of a site manager. This will also apply to goods purchased by the site manager, i.e. cement, timber, all the usual items used when construction projects take place, as this is also considered to be a normal duty of a site manager.

It should be noted that this relationship will not exist between homeowner and builder but an unscrupulous builder could try to pass on these extra costs incurred by his manager to the homeowner. The homeowner is not however responsible for these costs and should not under any circumstances agree to pay them.

Mistake

As a general rule the effect of a mistake in a contract is to render the contract void, in effect there is no contract and there never has been. There is however two defined legal types of mistake:

- When both parties have made the same common mistake, and if both are in agreement, they may extricate themselves from the contract. This could be complicated if one of the parties, although mistaken in the instance the contract was made, is now unwilling to relinquish a benefit gained under the apparent contract. If this is the case it is very difficult to prove, except by the admission of the parties.

- The second type of mistake occurs where the parties have different intentions; it may be that it is not possible to ascertain what has passed between the parties. Again, if both parties are in agreement that they have failed to reach a satisfactory conclusion, they may extricate themselves from the contract without the use of the courts. Litigation may arise where one of the parties claims that an agreement exists on the terms as he understands them to be, this can be where the parties are honestly at cross-purposes or where one party is aware that the other is labouring under a mistake.

It must be remembered that if a court has to resolve a situation where there is a mistake it will try to ascertain the true essence of the contract, if this cannot be done then the contract will be void.

Misrepresentation

Misrepresentation is an untrue statement of fact(s), made by one party (the representor) to the other (the representee) in the course of negotiating a contract, which induces (the representee) to enter into the contract. A false statement of law, opinion, or intention does not constitute a misrepresentation; neither does a statement of fact known by the representee to be untrue. Furthermore, unless the representee relies on the statement so that it becomes an inducement to enter into the contract, it is not misrepresentation.

The remedies for misrepresentation vary according to the degree of culpability of the representor, if the representor is guilty of fraudulent misrepresentation the representee may, subject to certain limitations, set the contract aside by rescission and may also sue for damages. If the representor is guilty of negligent misrepresentation the representee was formerly entitled only to rescission, but may now under **The Misrepresentation Act 1967** also obtain damages.

If the representor has committed an innocent misrepresentation the representee is restricted to rescission, subject to the discretion of the court under **The Misrepresentation Act 1967** to award him damages in lieu. It should also be remembered that a representee entitled to rescind a contract for misrepresentation might decide instead to affirm it.

Exclusion clauses

This is a term in a contract purporting to exclude or restrict the liability of one of the parties in specified circumstances. In general courts do not regard exemption or exclusion clauses with great favour, and if such a clause is ambiguous, they will interpret it in the narrower sense rather than the broader. Explained further, if a contract is written in a deceptive manner, the courts will deal with it so as to treat both parties in a manner, which can be regarded as being more reasonable and fair, considering the circumstances in which the contract was made.

If an exclusion or restriction is not recited in a formal contract but is specified or referred to in an informal document, such as a notice displayed in the site office of a builder, it will not even be treated as a term of the contract, unless reasonable steps have been taken to bring it to the attention of the person affected at the time of making the contract.

The **Unfair Contract Terms Act 1977** contains complex provisions that limit the extent to which a person can exclude or restrict his business liability towards consumers. More information can be found in a good consumer law book, try your local library.

Performance of a contract

This means the carrying out of obligations under a contract and performance by both parties to discharge the contract completely. If obligations are only carried out by one party this will discharge them alone. The rules relating to performance fall into two categories, divisible contracts where the obligations of the parties are independent of each other and therefore one party can demand performance by the other without rendering performance themselves, or, indivisible contracts where the obligations are interdependent, where neither party can demand performance unless they themselves have performed or they are ready and willing to do so.

At common law, complete and precise performance was originally required, so that a party who performed anything short of this could recover nothing for their efforts. Related to construction, a builder who carries out the contract work, but defectively in some respects, would not have been able to recover anything even if substantial parts of the contract were completed correctly.

This somewhat unfair and extreme position was subsequently modified by The **Doctrine of Substantial Performance**. This allows a party who has substantially performed his obligation in a contract to recover the contract price for the parts completed in a satisfactory manner.

With building contracts there can be 'vicarious performance', this is where a subcontractor completes the work that the main contractor agreed in the contract to do, this will still be held to be good performance, unless personal performance was specified in the contract.

Frustration

This is where the unforeseen termination of the contract takes place as a result of an event that renders its performance impossible, illegal or prevents its main purpose from being achieved. This could occur in a construction contract where the specified materials that are only available from one supplier become destroyed by fire, or severe weather halts building work.

A frustrated contract is automatically discharged and the Law Reform (Frustrated Contracts) Act 1943 in most cases governs the position of the parties. Where money paid before the event can be recovered and money due but not paid ceases to be payable **s.1 (2)** a party who has obtained a valuable benefit under a contract must pay a reasonable sum for it **s.1 (3)**.

The modern approach to frustration was reached by Lord Radcliffe, who said *"Perhaps it would be simpler to say at the outset that frustration occurs whenever the law recognises that, without default of either party, a contractual obligation has become incapable of being performed because the circumstances in which performance is called for would render it a thing radically different from that which was undertaken by the contract...but, even so, it is not hardship or inconvenience or material loss itself which calls the principle of frustration into play. There must be as well such a chance in the significance of the obligation that the thing undertaken would, if performed, be a different thing from that contracted for".*

Other remedies

I have shown some of the remedies already in the cases highlighted, however damages are usually the primary remedy for breach of contract, and there is no guarantee that the amount awarded will be any more than nominal. It is normal that, when damages are awarded, the court will try to put the plaintiff in the position he would have been in if the contract had been performed correctly.

When seeking a remedy 'remoteness' and 'causation' (see glossary of legal terms) must always be considered, the basic rules for this were laid down in the case of **Hadley v Baxendale [1854]** '...the contracting party is liable for losses if either...

1. Arising naturally, i.e., according to the usual course of things, or
2. Such as may reasonable be supposed to have been in the contemplation of the parties, at the time they made the contract, as the probable result of the breach of it'...

Causation was highlighted in the construction case of **Quinn v Burch Bros. [1966]**. A sub-contractor was carrying out work. It was argued that the defendant (the main-contractor) should have supplied the necessary equipment (ladder) to enable the sub-contractor to carry out his tasks. No ladder was supplied and the sub-contractor fell-off the trestle he was using and injured himself. It was held that it was not the fault of the defendant and that it was not his breach of contract that caused the accident to happen, but the plaintiff's actions. This is actually contributory negligence on the part of the sub-contractor, and removes the liability completely from the defendant.

Another important remedy to consider, where construction contracts are involved, is that of 'Quantum meruit', this enables a party who has provided a benefit to someone else, but for some reason cannot obtain payment under the terms of the contract, to recover a reasonable value for the benefit provided.

The leading construction case showing this rule in operation is **British Steel Corp v Cleveland Bridge & Engineering Co. Ltd. [1984]** *'Where work had begun on a major construction before all the elements of the contract had been agreed. Both sides confidently expected to reach agreement without difficulty. Final agreement was never reached. The plaintiff ceased performance and claimed a quantum meruit for the work completed'*, their claim was successful.

All of the points of law I have covered on the previous pages are based on what we call 'English Common Law'. Explained briefly this is the part of our legal system that was developed by the royal courts during the first three centuries after the Norman Conquest (1066), it was created as a system applicable to the whole country, not, as it was previously, linked to local customs. This part of our law is however derived from customs and moral views improved over the years by decisions reached in cases that have passed through our legal system.

Applicable Legislation

There is however another side to our legal system which is based on legislation, although much of it is not specifically created for the construction industry and homeowner, parts of it can be used as remedies in an effort to resolve disputes. The following section will give a quick overview of the legislation and sections, which may be used as solutions to problems.

European Communities Act 1972 s.9

Provides that a person who deals with a company in good faith can rely that the work or service is something that the company has capacity to do. That a person does not have to make inquiries of the company's memorandum as to what their company was formed to do. An act outside a company's objects is *'ultra vires'* and void. After all you would not expect your gardener to service your car, but if he did and there were problems he could be held liable.

Limitations Act 1980

s.5 States that an action established on a simple contract (not necessarily in writing) must be brought within six years of the date at which the breach or fault occurred. **s.8** states that if the contract was made by deed (in writing) then action has to be brought within twelve years. If there has been a concealment by the defendant the period of limitation begins from the time the concealment is discovered by the plaintiff.

The Latent Damage Act 1986

The act introduced new sections to the **Limitations Act 1980**. **S.14 (A)** was created to assist the award of damages for negligence, where an action could be bought within three years of a reasonable person being able to conclude that proceeding could be instituted and **s.14 (B)** which allows for a long stop period of fifteen years added to the initial action for further negligent claims that may occur from the initial fault or defect.

S.2 provides that an action of tort will not be brought after six years from the date on which the event occurred, and **s.11** states that, if the claim involves negligence, nuisance or breach of duty resulting in personal injury, the action must be bought within three years of the event taking place.

Sale of Goods Act 1979

As amended by **The Sale and Supply of Goods Act 1994** apply to construction contracts, the important sections are as follows:

S.12 (1)

In a contract of sale, there is an implied condition on the part of the seller that in the case of a sale he has a right to sell the goods, and in the case of an agreement to sell he will have such a right at the time when the property is to pass.

S.13 (1)

Where there is a contract for the sale of goods by description, there is an implied condition that the goods will correspond with the description.

S.14 (1,2,6) as amended 1994

That where the seller sells goods in the course of a business, that they are of 'satisfactory quality' and fit for the particular use;

S.15

That the bulk will correspond with the sample.
(It should be noted that these sections apply to the goods or materials supplied and not the workmanship on site)

S.17

    (i)   Where there is a contract for the sale of specific or ascertained goods the property in them is transferred to the buyer at such time as the parties to the contract intend it to be transferred.

    (ii)   For the purpose of ascertaining the intention of the parties, regard shall be taken as to the terms of the contract, the conduct of the parties and the circumstances of the case.

S.18

Unless a different intention appears, the following are rules for ascertaining the intention of the parties as to the time at which the property in the goods is to pass to the buyer.

Supply of Goods and Services Act 1982

There are some important sections of this Act that apply to construction contracts, they are contained within sections **13,14 and 15** and are specifically aimed at ordinary building contracts between the 'builder' and the ordinary 'citizen'. They provide that contracts are subject to implied terms that **"the supplier will carry out service with reasonable care and skill, in the absence of agreement, and the service will be carried out within a reasonable time and for a reasonable cost".** This is only effective if homeowners are aware of this legislation, and the rights inferred by it to them.

Unfair Contract Terms Act 1977

Lastly, this legislation is aimed at clauses excluding or restricting the implied rights of a buyer, as to their description, quality, fitness, in the main, aimed at the consumer sale, but also applicable to building contracts **s.7**. Section **2(1)** provides that liability of death or personal injury may not be excluded where it results from negligence and **s.2 (2)** extends this further to allow for loss from negligence, limited by that considered

to be fair and reasonable. Section **3** applies to written standard terms and makes them enforceable, so far as is fair and reasonable, this will apply to a private individual who contracts with a builder using his normal commercial standard form of contract, the JCT contract, (see glossary).

All of these points of law, if required, can be found in any good business or contract law book at a local library.

Conclusion

If you have managed to read this far then it is reasonable to assume that either you have an existing building problem or you are thinking positively and are going to prevent problems arising. By far the best way to prevent problems arising when taking up the services of a builder has to be by putting any agreement in writing. A written contract is much easier to work with when things go wrong in comparison with a verbal agreement, which often, as the book has already shown, will result in one party's word against the other's.

Does the size or value of the building project determine if you should use a written contract ?

In our society there are two misconceptions:

- That only complex agreements necessitate a written contract, and that,

- Verbal contracts are not always legally binding.

However neither is the case.

A verbal agreement however trivial, provided it complies with all the formalities shown on the preceding pages, will result in a legally binding contract. The problem will be proving that the contract existed if a dispute occurs.

Any agreement, for any project from painting a door, fitting a lock to a large house extension, can be made into a written contract. A letter confirming the details of the work, time scale and price with provision for both home owner and builders signatures will constitute a written contract. It may not be very detailed but if problems occur for either party it could be the difference between dispute and solution to the problem.

What is the next step you take

The best advice to any one contemplating construction work on their home has to be, 'Put any agreement in writing', thereby formulating a written contract. A simple written contract will suffice, it may not address every problem, but it may help to solve them.

On the next page there is an example of what I consider to be a good, simple contract with the most important issues and terms laid down. There are also 2 more copies at the back of this book for your use.

Is there anything else you can do to prevent problems?

If any changes to the initial building contract are to be made after work has commenced, you must confirm these with the builder and if agreed add them to the contract with the changes to price, time and any terms and conditions. These changes must be confirmed in writing and signed by both parties.

Contracts for Homeowners and Private Occupiers.
(For building works, repairs and maintenance only)

This building contract is between ....(Home owner)
and   ....(Builder)

                  ....(Builder's Address)

                  ....

                  ....

The address where the building work is to take place is:

                  ....(Home owner's address)

                  ....

                  ....

                  ....

The contract is for   ....

....

....

....

....(nature of the work)

All plans, specifications, variations must be attached to this document, and will comply with all
current planning and building regulations

The agreed sum for the completed work is...

The contract is to commence on...

The contract will be completed by...
Unless a further date is agreed to in writing by the parties

**Payment will be made to the builder within 14 days of the completion of the contract. If the
contract is to run for more than 28 days then there will be weekly payments made to the
builder from the commencement of the contract, on a valuation of work completed basis, paid
a week in arrears**

**Any changes to the specification must be made in writing with a minimum of seven working
days notice.**

**If the builder/home owner is going to incur delays then he will give the homeowner/builder a
minimum of seven working days notice.**

**The homeowner may retain 10% of the total contract value for up to 28 days after completion
and this will be paid when both parties have inspected the work and satisfactory completion
has been agreed.**

Builder...   (Signature)   as per terms over the page

Homeowner...   (Signature)   as per terms over the page

This contract was agreed and signed on this...(date)

Terms and conditions of the contract

(1) The homeowner will provide any 'mains' services required enabling the builder to carry out the work. If unusual requirements are needed the builder will give reasonable written notice.

(2) The homeowner will, where practical, make sure that there are no obstructions that will prevent the work from taking place, such as a blocked access or internal furniture and fittings.

(3) The builder will be fully responsible for all the work undertaken by himself, his operatives and any other sub-contractors that he appoints. If sub-contractors are to be used the builder must notify the homeowner of this intention in writing. (minimum of 7 days notice)

(4) It is the builder's responsibility to ensure that they comply with the minimum insurance requirements to undertake building works for a homeowner. This is to include cover to provide for injury to a third party, or their property in the form of public liability insurance. Proof of this insurance must be shown at the time the contract is agreed.

(5) The builder will be responsible for all aspects of Health and Safety for the duration of the contract in accordance with the current regulations laid down by the Health and Safety Executive.

(6) Payment details are as agreed to on the front page of the contract, unless another agreement is made at the time of contracting.

(7) All waste that is the result of the building work is the responsibility of the builder, they are responsible for its safe disposal and for cleaning the site area when the building work is complete.

(8) When the building work commences the builder must give a guarantee to complete the work to a satisfactory standard, or to a standard a reasonable person would expect. Any faults or bad workmanship will be the responsibility of the builder and they will be responsible for any costs incurred by this bad workmanship for a period of two years, to commence once the work is completed.

(9) The contract can be terminated in writing by the home owner if;

    (i)   The work is not being completed with reasonable care, skill or if the work is not being completed in the time scale agreed to; or

    (ii)   There is failure to follow the homeowner's written instructions within a reasonable time (reasonable can be determined by the agreed duration of the initial contract).

(10) The contract can be terminated in writing by the builder if;

    (i)   They are delayed from completing the said works by the home owner without reasonable cause; or

    (ii)   The homeowner does not make the payments to the builder as agreed this includes any stage payment agreements as specified on page one of this contract.

(11) In the event of sections 9 or 10 taking place the home owner must pay for work completed and materials purchased for the work, up to the time of the termination, this will be calculated on a 'quantum meruit' basis.

(12) If, when the work is completed, there is disagreement as to whether the work is completed to a satisfactory standard, a 'third' party, qualified to inspect the work should be called in to adjudicate the decision (adjudicator must be acceptable to both party's). The cost of the inspection should be taken out of the retention payment, and when a decision has be made, if it is decided the work is of a satisfactory standard the cost of the inspection should be paid for by the home owner. If it is found that the work is sub-standard the builder should correct it, or in the event that they will not do the work the retention should be used to pay another builder to complete the work. Should any funds be left after the faults have been corrected they must be paid to the original builder.

Building regulations

What are building regulations?

Most building work or repairs are not usually affected by statutory rules however all building work has to comply with the building regulations that are part of the Building Act 1984, which has been amended by the Building Regulations Act 1991. Details of these requirements can be obtained from the local authority responsible for the area in which the building work is to take place.

What areas of construction do building regulations effect?

Current requirements are primarily aimed at thirteen specific areas of construction and are very precise as to the correct way of constructing a building.
The areas are as follows:

* Type of structure

* Fire safety

* Site preparation and resistance to moisture

* Resistance to passage of sound

* Toxic substances

* Ventilation

* Hygiene

* Drainage and waste disposal

* Stairways, ramps and guards

* Heat producing appliances

* Conservation of heat and Power

* Access and facilities for the disabled

* Glazing materials and protection

This list is not in order of importance neither should it be considered as the preference in which the areas of regulation should be examined when planning building works.

All of the areas of construction in the list are covered in more detail in a handbook, available from the local authority-planning department. Please note that a reputable builder should have a copy of the current regulations.

One important factor to bear in mind is that when building work takes place as an addition to an existing building, it is only the new work has to comply with building regulations, there is no obligation to bring the existing parts of the building in line with current requirements.

How are building regulations controlled?

Any building works that are subject to building regulations have to be authorised and made available to inspection, this inspection is usually done by one of two bodies. The local Authority planning department will have a sub-division called 'Building Control' whose job it is to inspect projects subject to control, the cost of this is levied in the form of a fee which is payable when you apply for building regulation approval.

The alternative is to use the NHBC, The National House Building Council. This is a private organisation licensed to operate a building control authorisation, advice and inspection system, much the same as the local Authority. This is initially aimed at the large developer, however an individual can use them too.

The advantage of the NHBC is that they endorse the inspection process with a 10 year guarantee on building work that is up to the required standard when completed. It should be noted that some local authority building control departments also run a guarantee scheme to match that given by the NHBC.

Do building regulations effect all building work that you have done on your property?

Any building work has to comply with current building regulations, however sometimes only projects that have been subject to planning approval have to be inspected for compliance of the regulations. In some cases a project can require building regulation approval and inspection, but no planning approval. This subject is covered later.

If the work to be done is just interior or exterior decorating, fitting a new door, fitting an outside light or any other general building repair or maintenance there is no requirement to inform the local building control department at the local Authority.

Note:

On a listed building or where a domestic dwelling is located in a conservation area, planning permission may be required for any improvements or alterations. Always consult your local planning authority.

Cavity and cavity walls

What is a cavity wall?
Most houses built since the late 1940's will have been constructed using cavity wall construction. This means that the external walls of your house, if built after this date, will consist of an outer and inner wall with a gap between them, 'the cavity' see diagram below. (If your property is timber framed or similar this may not be the case, see later in the book).

Inside

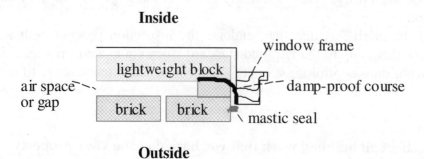

Outside

What is the purpose of the cavity?
There are several roles for the cavity in a wall, they are:

- A space to allow water that penetrates the outer bricks to run down and drain to the outside; this prevents damp walls, which can be found on older properties where there is no cavity.

- A void giving the wall a greater heat retaining property ('U' Value).

- A space in which more insulation can be placed to give the wall an even better insulation.

- In the summer the thermal role is reversed, it helps keep the house cool.

How do you know if your building project requires a cavity wall construction?
Any brick or block construction that contains a living space or is part of a domestic dwelling will have to be built with a cavity wall. Garages do not require a cavity wall construction, however if the garage is integral to the house and there are rooms above it, the walls will need to be cavity walls.

Is there a minimum size for the thickness of the cavity?
The minimum thickness of a cavity is 50mm, this can be greater, obviously the thicker the cavity, the higher thermal value of the wall (see section on insulation). One important factor to be aware of is that with a small cavity, building regulations may require thicker inner thermal blocks to bring the wall up to the minimum thermal value required.

How do you know if the builder is creating faults in the cavity construction?
There are some very important things to watch for, all of which can be looked for when the builder is out of the way as this allows a thorough inspection of the work and maybe more diplomatic. The faults are:

- There must be no obstructions in the cavity, pieces of broken brick or large masses of dried mortar.

- Every effort must be made to prevent large amounts of mortar falling down the cavity and filling the space at the bottom to bring it above the level of the damp-proof course. This will allow damp to bridge across to the inner block work. (see diagram below)

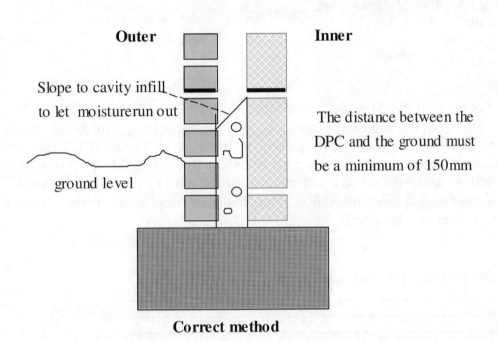

Outer · Inner

Slope to cavity infill
to let moisture run out

The distance between the
DPC and the ground must
be a minimum of 150mm

ground level

Correct method

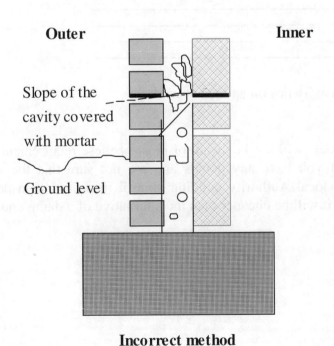

Outer · Inner

Slope of the
cavity covered
with mortar

Ground level

Incorrect method

31

- The cavity must be a continuous void with no bridges across from outer to inner leaf at any point apart from wall-ties. Where window and doorframes are placed, the cavity should be closed as in the diagram below, with the damp-proof course acting as a barrier between inner and outer skins of the wall.

Inner

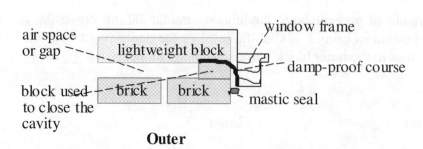

air space or gap — lightweight block — window frame — damp-proof course — block used to close the cavity — brick — brick — mastic seal

Outer

- The inner leaf of the wall should be tied to the outer leaf by means of cavity wall ties. These are available in various types, but most commonly made from twisted wire in the shape of a butterfly (these can only be used on cavities of between 50 to 75mm, if a larger cavity is required galvanised vertical twist type ties must be used). They should be placed in the mortar joints every 900mm along the courses and stepped every fourth to fifth course of bricks. The twist in the tie must hang downwards; this is so any moisture drops or runs to the outside skin of the wall, thus preventing a damp wall.

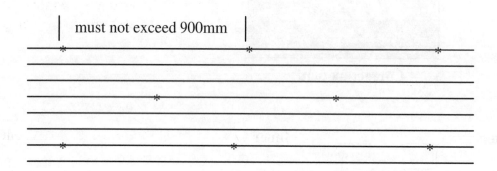

must not exceed 900mm

shows spacing of cavity ties on an area of wall

It has to be said that a 'cowboy builder' will not be aware of most of these requirements for a cavity wall. It is imperative that if you have any doubts and are not sure that the wall is constructed correctly that you get a local Authority building control inspector to inspect the wall. Even if this costs you £150.00 it will be cheaper than the alternative of a damp and faulty wall.

Carpentry

How do you know if the work needed is carpentry?

This is the name given to all work on a building project that involves the fitting of wooden or wood based products that form part or parts of a building. The main items of carpentry in the average home are as follows:

- Roof trusses and/or rafters

- Floor joists and floors

- External doors including specially made window and door frames, Internal doors and door lining

- Skirting and door lining architraves

- Bath panels

- Kitchen and other room units

- Garage doors and frames

- Archway profiles and concrete shuttering

It should be noted that there are many more areas of building that could be entered on this list that would fall quite normally under the heading of carpentry. A carpenter normally completes carpentry, however some general builders are also competent carpenters.

How do you know if the work being done is of a good standard?

When the carpentry being done is of a 'first fix' nature it will not be very obvious by appearance of the work if it is of a good standard, however quick checks that can be made while the carpenter is off the site are:

- Check that the work is plumb or upright, faults can cause problem later.

- Ensure that door linings are securely fixed, this will ensure better hanging of the doors. Also check that they are square, this can be done by placing a tape measure across the lining diagonally (bottom left to top right and then bottom right to top left), the measurement of each diagonal should be the same.

- Check that floor joists if used are sufficiently braced with 'noggins', usually at the midway point of the floor. This is done with timber placed in a scissors fashion between the joists; to prevent joists twisting and causing problems like cracked ceilings and squeaking floorboards. 'Noggins' are now available in mild steel or aluminium.

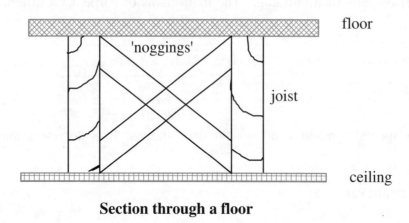

floor

'noggings'

joist

ceiling

Section through a floor

- Make sure that all unused materials are stored in a dry and clean environment.

When the work to be carried out is of a 'second fix' nature its appearance will normally be sufficient to tell if the work is of good quality. There are checks that can be made and to be diplomatic they could be done while the carpenter is off the site, they are:

- Mitre joints should be clean and accurate with no gaps between the pieces of wood that are joined.

- Ensure that the gap around doors is even, 2 or 3mm at the top and sides. The space at the bottom will vary depending on the type of floor covering used. A carpet will require a greater clearance than linoleum tiles, because the pile of the carpet will catch on the door if there is insufficient space.

- Skirting board should be fitted tightly to the wall and 'scribed' (fitted to any discrepancies in the floor surface) where any unevenness occurs, internal corners should not be mitred but 'scribe' jointed. (Scribe jointed means to fit one piece over the other, to cut out the shape of the moulding on the end of the skirting that abuts the skirting running the adjacent direction).

- Kitchen units or other fitted furniture should be secure and level, continuous lines of cabinets should be in line and level. All doors on kitchen units should be level and flush across their faces when a straight edge is placed against them.

- If doors are polished veneer finished it is advisable to leave the polythene wrapper on until any decorating is completed.

- Check that all sharp or rough edges to timber have been removed with sandpaper or similar, this is sometimes referred to as removing the 'arriss'.

- If nails securing skirting or architrave, or badly fitted screws in any timber have caused splitting; ask for the timber to be replaced. Do not accept the excuse of filler, this is bad building practice when the job you have paid for is supposed to be new. After all, split timber will not be secure and could come away from what it is fixed to.

Carpenter

Usually a skilled person, having served traditionally an apprenticeship of between three and five years of which up to three years would have been spent gaining a City and Guilds certificate of qualification.

Carpenters are usually very flexible members of the construction industry, as their skills have to cross over the many other trades. For example building a water-tank stand for a plumber or timber fuse-mounting boards for an electrician.

How do you know if the carpenter is good at his job?

Nearly all carpenters are apprentice-served qualified trades persons, generally 'City and Guilds' qualified. Though more recently these have been replaced with 'NVQ' courses. Carpentry covers a large field of construction and necessitates that all carpenters are both experienced and knowledgeable. This is the reason that most have served a three to five year apprenticeship.

Their customers always recommend good carpenters. Once a carpenter has been found ask for references.

It should be noted that not all carpenters are qualified with City and Guilds or similar qualifications, but may come highly recommended by customers, if the result is good use them.

Ceiling 'textures' (Artex)

What is 'ceiling texturing' (Artex)?

'Artex' is the trade name given to the textured finish on ceilings, usually mixed from a dry powder and water by a professional 'texturer'. Various patterns are made, using different application techniques. The wetter the mix, the greater the stippling effect will be. This is also governed by the quantity of 'Artex' applied prior to the pattern being made.

What problem areas do you need to look for?

'Artex' is usually placed on plasterboard which has a side identified for plastering and texturing. Always check for this, as the wrong side has poor adhesion qualities. A ceiling will have several joints where the sheets of plasterboard meet; these have to be jointed with a flexible bandage called 'scrim'. The 'scrim' is applied to the boards using mixed 'Artex' which is then smoothed using a trowel, if this were not used the ceiling would be susceptible to cracking.

If coving is not used in the room, 'scrim' must be placed around the room between the wall and ceiling to prevent cracks appearing as the building settles. This jointing is normally done at least the day before the textured ceiling is applied, this is because sagging can occur where the joints are, due to the extra quantity of 'Artex' that has been applied to level and smooth the two boards.

How do you know if the 'texturer' is qualified or experienced?

Until recently there have been no formal qualifications such as City and Guilds available to 'ceiling-finishers'. Various courses are run in colleges that award certificates on completion of the course, but these are very short and don't give the person experience. Most 'ceiling-finishers' are trained 'in-house' by large specialist companies who normally have their own standards of proficiency and control this by training new personnel 'on-site' with experienced trades persons

The best way of finding a ceiling 'texturer' is to ask someone who has recently had some work done and see if they are happy with the finished work. Because the job is artistic most are good at their chosen profession and take great pride in the quality, however there are some 'cowboys' so beware!

Cement

What is cement?

This is the 'glue' that binds sand to make mortar for brick laying, or sand and stone together to create concrete. It is made from a mixture of lime and clay, which when blended with water, sets like stone. The aggregate acts as a reinforcing or binding agent that gives mortar and concrete its strength.

Are there different types of cement?

There are two main types of cement used in construction, 'Ordinary Portland' for concrete or floor screeds and 'Masonry' for mortar. Masonry cement has additives to make laying of bricks and blocks easier as well as the smooth pointing of joints between the bricks. Masonry cement is slightly more expensive than Ordinary Portland, so this is an area where the 'cowboy builder' can try to save money.

How do you know what to look for to prevent problems occurring?

It is a favourite trick of the 'cowboy builder' to save money on a building project by not using the correct amounts or type of cement in concrete and mortar mixes. As a rule of thumb concrete for a driveway, floor or over site would consist or a 4:2:1 mix, this means 4 parts graded stone (shingle), 2 parts sieved sand and 1 part cement. Concrete for foundations would use a 6:3:1 mix, 6 parts graded stone, 3 parts sieved sand, and 1 part cement.

Mortar for laying bricks or blocks is generally a mix consisting of 4 parts soft sand and 1 part cement, this can vary depending on the wall down force loads and the crushing strength of the bricks, (please refer to local Authority building control or design architect). A floor screed or rendering to a wall would consist of 4 parts sharp sand and 1 part cement. If paving slabs, brick 'pavers' or 'sets' are to be laid on a bed of concrete or mortar the strength of the mix is not important as the bed only acts as a stable and secure anchorage for the slab or brick. A mix consisting of 10 parts sharp sand and 1 part cement will do the job satisfactorily. Some builders when laying paving slabs like to substitute three parts of the sharp sand with soft sand, this makes laying the slabs easier and has no effect on the finished patio or path, it also makes the pointing smoother.

Note:

When concrete is purchased from a specialist supplier rather than mixed on site, there is a coding system used to specify the different types of concrete; this is covered in the section on concrete.

Cement storage

Domestic building contracts will normally have a short duration, but proper provisions must be made for the storage of bags of cement. It should be raised off the floor, usually by means of a pallet and a vapour barrier should be placed on the pallet prior to the cement being placed on it. The cement must be covered with a waterproof barrier to protect it from the weather. If the weather is damp and stormy any coverings must be weighted down.

Ceramic tiling

What is ceramic tiling?

To most ceramic tiling is self explanatory, it is the application of tiles to walls and floors. In most cases they act as a protective cover to walls and floors, but occasionally glass and mirror effect tiles are used for decorative purposes.

Does this area of construction attract 'cowboys'?

Most tilers have no formal qualifications, but this does not mean that they are not good at their chosen trade. Good ceramic tiling is almost an art form in itself, and is the result of skilled experience rather than qualifications. Carpenters and painters, whose own trades are to some degree also artistic, do much of the ceramic tiling work in the construction industry.

Unfortunately ceramic tiling is a profitable area of the industry and so attracts cowboys who price low to get jobs. It is not until the work is complete that many people realise they may have employed someone from a horror movie props-department to tile their walls!

What problems can you look for?

This is one of the main areas of construction where problems arise through lack of training, little experience, poor quality control and use of inappropriate equipment. Experience in the construction industry has shown many bad techniques used to cut and shape ceramic tiles. Cutting the tiles with glass cutters, hacksaws and masonry drill bits, but even more surprisingly, shaping the tile outside someone's kitchen on the exterior wall and concrete path using the wall and path as a giant sanding block.

A professional wall and floor tiler will use a 'bed tile slide cutter' and breaker, tungsten abrasive fret saw and electric angle grinder to cut and shape the tiles, a pair of special sharp ceramic pliers will be used to breakout tight corners.

Some skills of the trade highlighted

The first task to be undertaken is to find the levels on the walls to be tiled, for example in a kitchen where there are work tops, a level line is drawn the height of one tile above the work top around the walls to be tiled. A temporary support is then fixed to the wall to support the tiles while the adhesive sets, and to hold the tiles in a level line around the wall.

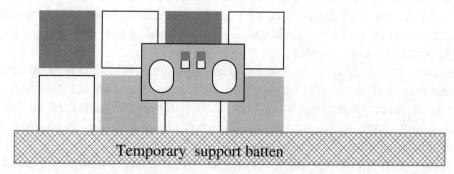

these tiles are placed on the wall once the tiles above have set

Any variation in levels around the room will be taken up in the bottom row of tiles after the batten has been removed, these would be cut to size between the Worktop and first row, placing the cut edge of the tile against the work surface. The theory is that a cut tile shows less against a work surface than it would if it was on the top row. More importantly if the worktop had been used as the level the tiles may have been out of level over the length of the work surface. The same principle applies if the tiling starts at skirting board or floor level.

Where there is to be tiling around an electrical socket the tiles should pass below the face of the socket, long socket screws will allow for the socket face to sit over the tiles. By using this method the job looks neat, and seals around the socket better than if the tiles had been cut around the socket. Tile grout may crack and allow water to enter the socket, if this procedure is not followed.

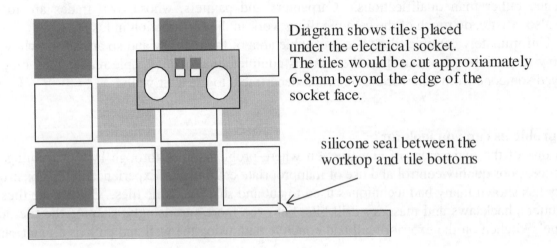

Diagram shows tiles placed under the electrical socket. The tiles would be cut approxiamately 6-8mm beyond the edge of the socket face.

silicone seal between the worktop and tile bottoms

Some tiles have built-in spacing lugs on their edges. However, most tiles are spaced using plastic cross-pegs or sticks. Some tilers use matchsticks, which are fine and should not be seen as a 'cowboy' method. Many have the opinion that wooden sticks don't slip whereas plastic pegs do, it is a matter of personal preference.

Tiles are fixed to the wall or floor using tile cement, either ready mixed or dry powder that is mixed with water. The cement is placed on the wall or floor using a comb trowel; this allows the tiler to press the tiles down more easily and creates suction to hold the tile in place until the cement sets. The more important reason for using the trowel is that it allows the tiler to level out any unevenness on the wall surface, furthermore an experienced tiler can straighten a slightly curved wall with the cement as the tiles are positioned giving the wall an even finish.

Grouting of the joints between the tiles can be done using either ready mixed grout or dry powder mixed with water, a water proof grout should always be used as this does not go mouldy in damp conditions and is generally more durable.

Grout is spread over the whole tiled area with a damp sponge, working it well into the joints, and any excess is removed before it sets in hard in lumps on the face of the tiles. After approximately twelve to eighteen hours (this may vary with different products) the surface of the tiles are polished with a soft cloth, this removes any dullness created by the dried grout residue. Any stubborn areas can be removed with a damp cloth and slight pressure.

On completion the joints should appear level and square, if a straight edge is placed against the tiles there should be no gaps. Where the tiles adjoin work surfaces the gap should be sealed with high modulus silicone sealant. If the tiling looks bad then it probably is, complain and don't pay until the work is completed to a reasonable standard.

Chimneys and flues.

For the purposes of clarity in this book a 'chimney' refers to the masonry construction, while a 'flue' is the passage through which the exhaust gases (smoke) pass.

Where are they located on a dwelling?

There are three locations that chimneys are located:

- Built-in as part of an external wall

- Built-in as part of an internal wall

- Free-standing in the centre of a property

Steel flues when not enclosed within a chimney may be bolted to an outside wall.

What is their purpose?

The purpose of a flue is to provide a means of escape for the fumes and gases that result from combustion.

Rules applicable to an open fireplace.

Open fireplaces, room heaters or back-boiler burners like 'Parkray' all use the same kind of flue. It will comprise of a recess at the bottom where the hearth fire bricks or back-boiler burner will be located.

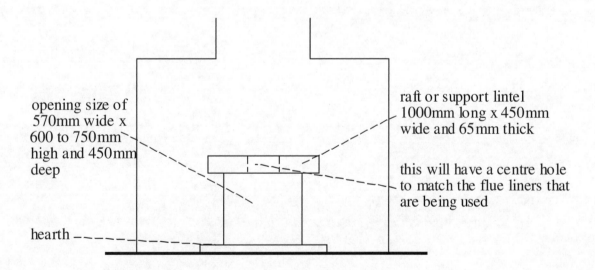

A lintel is placed on top of the opening to support the flue liners; this can be cast or made on site using shuttering and concrete. The fireplace opening should be lined with a pre-cast throat unit at the top and the sides and back should be protected using a pre-cast fire-back manufactured to BS1251. The void between the fire-back and the brick flue should be filled using a mixture of lime, sand and small brick rubble or 'vermiculite' flue lining insulation.

The fire-back and hearth are normally built-in once the plastering is completed on a new property.

Key rules that apply to flues as part of the Building Regulations Section J.

- For maximum efficiency, flues should be straight.

- There should be a minimum distance of 4.0metres from the support lintel to the top of the chimney, to ensure that the flue works efficiently.

- If bends have to be incorporated in a flue they should be at angles of no more than 45 degrees to the vertical, with a maximum angle of 30 degrees.

- Flue liners must have a minimum internal dimension of 185mm for square liners and 200mm diameter for round.

- Flue liner sleeves must have joints that are rebated together.

- Flues must extend at least 600mm beyond the ridge tiles.

- When the flue exits the roof on the slope and not at the ridge, the flue must extend a minimum of 1.0metres beyond any roof lights. Ideally the top should finish level with the ridge tiles.

- If the flue exits through a roof that is shadowed by a higher part of the building, for example where a boiler is located in the garage, the flue must extend beyond the slope of the higher roof.

- There must be an adequate supply of air into a room where a fire or boiler is located to a vertical flue; normally an air vent will be incorporated into the external wall of the room.

External and top of chimney details.

When a flue or chimney extends beyond a roof it will match the brickwork on the rest of the property. It will be weatherproofed to the slope of the roof using flashing, probably a combination of stepped flashing up the slope, apron flashing at the front or lower edge of the chimney, and a back gutter and cover flashing at the rear. These are made from code 5 lead or other suitable material.

The tops of flues are normally finished in one of two ways:

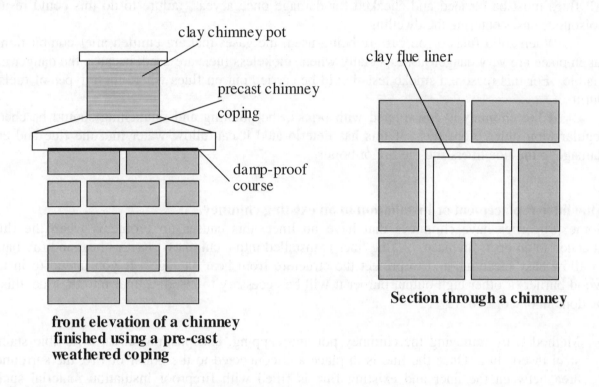

front elevation of a chimney finished using a pre-cast weathered coping

Section through a chimney

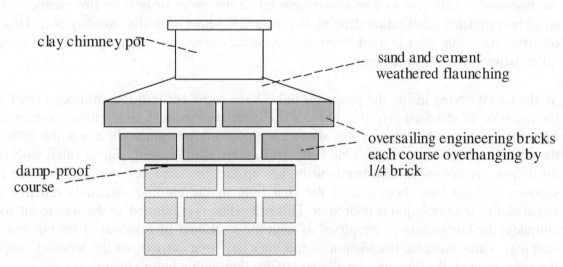

Flaunched oversailing brick chimney

External metal flues.

Some boilers have metal flues fixed to the external wall of a dwelling, often because the boiler or room heater has been added as an improvement to the property. These are normally manufactured from stove enamelled steel or plain stainless steel, and are securely fitted to the wall with the appropriate brackets.

This type of flue is normally between 100 and 150mm in diameter, this is determined by the boiler manufacturer.

Balanced flues.

Some gas or oil fired room heaters and boilers have a balanced flue system. These do not have a vertical chimney; they vent and breathe through a horizontal flue on the wall to which they are mounted. The flue for expelling fumes and gases is in the centre; the air intake is around the perimeter of the flue grill.

Maintenance.

All flues must be cleaned and checked for damage once a year, failure to do this could result in poisonous gases entering the dwelling.

When solid fuels or oil/gas are being used, the gases that are emitted after combustion has taken place are very dangerous, especially when smokeless fuels are used, because the danger is not visible. For this reason, a smoke test should be carried out on flues where these types of fuels are burnt.

If the chimney is constructed with bricks, the pointing and flaunching should be checked regularly on older properties. If this has deteriorated it can allow water into the flue and cause damage to the flue liners and the fire or boiler.

Flue liner replacement or installation in an existing chimney.

Some properties have chimneys that have no liner; this causes no problems when the flue is attached to an open fireplace. A flue liner is installed into a chimney to act as heat and fire barrier, to allow easy cleaning, and to protect the structure from heat damage. If you intend to install a wood burner or other high output burner it will be necessary to install a liner into the flue, this can be done in one of two ways;

- Method 1 by removing the chimney pot and capping, and pushing down a flexible stainless steel insert flue. Once the flue is in place and connected to the boiler or fire, the surrounding area between the liner and existing flue is filled with fireproof insulation material such as 'vermiculite'. This acts as a secondary barrier in the event of heat or fire escape. Once this stage is completed the weather capping is replaced together with the chimney pot. This method of installing a flue liner is used often; it is relatively easy, very cost effective and causes very little disruption inside the property.

- Method 2 Working inside the property, holes have to be cut into the chimney-breast to allow the insertion of standard clay flue liners. These are inserted and joined using cement, working from the bottom of the chimney just above the pre-cast throat unit at the top of the fireplace. As the clay liners are installed the void between the liner and existing flue is filled with fireproof insulation. A hole will have been cut higher up and the sequence is repeated, once the next sections of liner have been joined the first hole in the chimney-breast is repaired and the remainder of the insulation is poured in. This procedure is continued all the way to the top of the chimney, the last section is completed as with the steel liner by removal of the pot and weather capping. Once compete installation of the liner has been carried out the weather capping and pot are relocated, the flue must be allowed to dry thoroughly before using.

Concrete

What is concrete?

Concrete has many uses in construction, mainly foundations, over-sites, floors, driveways, kerb laying, securing posts etc., protecting shallow drains and for structural frame work in large buildings. There are many different types of concrete and specialist data can be obtained from most bulk pre-mixed concrete suppliers. Concrete is made from a mixture of sharp sand, course graded stone, cement and water, the quantity of each of these is determined by the job it is intended for. (See section 'cement')

Faults caused by lack of experience

For concrete to be strong it is imperative that it is mixed both correctly and thoroughly, an even colour shows that it is mixed correctly and plenty of water assists in the mixing process, however too much water can affect the strength of the concrete. A dry mix is required for paving slabs or floor screeds and takes longer for the cement to mix with the aggregate thoroughly. The most commonly used mixes are covered in the section on cement, other mix requirements are more specialised and will require technical data available from bulk concrete suppliers.

Standard construction concrete mixtures.

The list below gives a brief description of specialist grades and their codes, this is only a guide, please refer to specialist supplier;

Grade	Use
C7.5 and C10	Non-reinforced plain concrete
C15 and C20	Plain concrete or if reinforced containing Lightweight aggregate
C25	Reinforced concrete containing dense aggregate
C30 and C35	Post-tensioned reinforced concrete *
C40 and C60	Pre-tensioned reinforced concrete *

* These grades are not generally used for the construction of domestic dwellings, but several products that may be purchased such as pre-fabricated beams may use these grades.

There are four different categories of concrete mix, they are:

- **'Prescribed mix'** concrete that is made to a predetermined recipe, meeting required standards of strength, this is shown by adding a 'P' to the grade, e.g. C20P, used for suspended slab floors.

- **'Standard mix'** concrete intended for minor works.

- **'Designated mix'** concrete selected for specific applications. General graded 0-4 is specified at 7.5 - 25 N/mm squared; this is used for floors, foundations and external works such as driveways or garden paths. Foundation graded 2, 3, 4A and 4B specified at 35 N/mm squared, generally used where the foundations need to be sulphate resisting.

- **'Designed mix'** concrete designed to give a guaranteed performance. Criteria can include workability, durability and/or strength. The supplier will design and supply the appropriate mix.

How do you know what faults to look for?

Concrete is an area of building that can attract the 'cowboy builder', mainly because it is very easy to disguise shortcuts and the faults don't show until he is long gone. The added problem is that spurs don't rattle when they are splashing about in wet concrete!

The favourite trick is to put insufficient cement in the mix to save money, this makes the concrete weak when set, liable to cracking and, if it is on a drive or similar exposed situation, it is susceptible to quick wearing of the surface. This problem is very difficult to detect while work is in progress, however in general a concrete mix with insufficient cement content will appear sandy in colour, and this is only a guide as colour is determined by the colour of aggregate available in the locality. Some parts of the country have very grey sand, therefore even a poor mix will look cement coloured.

A good way to test is to put a trowel full of mix onto a dry surface where the air can dry it quickly. This will enable you to see the dry colour of the mix sooner. A good mix will already have started to bond together when pressure is applied at this stage and should break into pieces rather than just crumble.

This may not be very effective if the aggregate is grey in colour or the sample is left for a long period, but it will let the builder know that you are aware of the potential problem and encourage him to ensure the mixing is correct.

Another favourite shortcut is to make the mix very wet to enable it to run round foundation trenches more easily thus needing less effort from the person dragging it around the trenches. Many people within the industry will argue that this does not harm the concrete mix, others will disagree as it has the same effect as making a cake mix too wet. All the fruit will settle at the bottom of the cake when cooked, with the concrete mix all the stone or aggregate will sink to the bottom of the trench and the sand and cement will settle at the top, thus creating a weak foundation.

It is the stone in the mix, which gives concrete its strength.

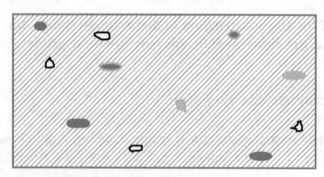

Section through correctly mixed
concrete showing the aggregate
distributed evenly thoughout the mix.

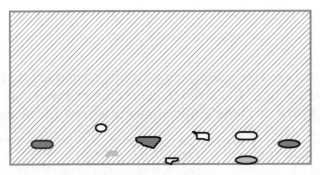

Section shows a very wet mix of
concrete, with all the aggregate at the
bottom of the trench.

Why it is better to use pre-mixed concrete by a specialist supplier

When a project involves foundations with a concrete capacity exceeding 0.5 cubic meters, a reputable builder will often buy in concrete ready-mixed, as it is more cost effective and he is able to put any risk of failure onto the concrete supplier. Concrete bulk suppliers check their mixing process regularly throughout the day to prevent problems. The lorry drivers are skilled in the delivery process to ensure that what leaves the lorry is not contaminated or that the mix is altered in any way, for example by the adding of excess water.

The main advantage to using ready mixed concrete is the time and cost saved by the builder not having to mix it himself. It would cost far more in labour costs, as a site mixer can not mix the quantity of concrete a bulk lorry can.

Concrete covering a large area is much better finished in one go, batch mixing the same area can take far longer, often days, resulting in joints which may weaken the completed foundations, drive or floor area.

It should be noted that it is not always possible or practicable to lay large areas of concrete all at once! Either from lack of labour or because the area is too large. However, structural-building items such as over-sites and floors must be poured in one day, there must not be any joints other than properly positioned expansion joints.

Note:

A small site mixer will have a capacity up to 100 litres. A ready-mixed concrete lorry can deliver 6 cubic metres in one visit, however the site must be suitable to accommodate a concrete lorry of some 20 tonnes who's turning circle is as much as 20 meters diameter.

Coving

What is coving?

It is the shaped finish used in many rooms between the ceiling and walls, its main role is to hide any shrinkage cracks that are often seen around ceilings. It is fixed to the ceiling and wall with 'Artex' or 'coving bonding' and is normally fitted by the 'texturer'. Sometimes plasterers fit coving.

Are there any faults to look for?

There are several problems to look for; bad training and/or lack of experience cause all:

- The corner mitres should be accurately cut and jointed.

- The bottom edge of the coving must be level.

- There should be a 25 to 30mm smooth border between the 'Artex' and the top edge of the coving.

- The pattern should not touch the coving as it will make future painting difficult.

- Any joints in the length of a wall must be mitred together not butt jointed, a straight joint will crack easily.

- The coving must be primed prior to painting.

Curtain battens

What are they?
They are pieces of timber fixed above windows for anchoring curtain tracks, poles or wires to. Timber used for curtain battens is normally softwood because it is easy to fix screws into.

Why are they there?
It is difficult to drill accurately into concrete or metal ('Catnic') lintels. You could end up with a curtain track that is both uneven and not level. Fitting a wooden curtain batten overcomes the difficulty.

What are the important points when fitting curtain battens?
If possible they should be fitted at least 75mm above the window opening, this is to prevent the wall edge from splitting away. They can be fitted with masonry or cut nails, however most carpenters fix them with masonry plugs and wood screws. The batten should run past the vertical reveal by a minimum of 150mm, to allow enough space for the curtains to hang during daylight hours.

The batten should be a minimum size of 45mm x 25mm, this to allow fixing screws of the track enough depth in the wood to hold, and to give a sufficient surface area on the timber to fit the curtain brackets to.

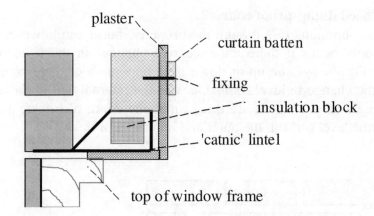

Section through a wall showing curtain batten fixing position.

Faults to look for.
These usually suffer from two problems, lack of fixings and insufficient fixings. Grasp hold of the batten and pull on it, if it is fixed correctly it will not move. Poor fixings will pull out of lightweight blocks very easily, so this is a worth while check.

Damp-proof Course, or 'DPC'

The name given to the black line that may be seen around your house approximately two brick courses above ground level.

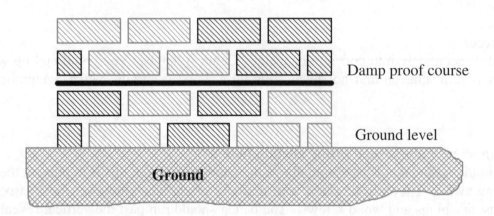

Damp proof course

Ground level

Ground

If your home is built on a sloped site it may be that there are more than two courses of bricks showing between the damp proof course and the ground. However there should never be any fewer than two courses. This is the Building Regulation minimum requirement.

How do you identify a correctly placed damp-proof course?

The damp-proof course should be a continuous ring around the property, but it can however have steps in the run. Steps normally only occur if there are excessive changes in the level of the surrounding ground. The steps should however be up or down by a maximum of three course of facing bricks at a time. This is so the change in levels coincide with the internal leaf of the cavity wall lightweight block courses, as lightweight blocks are three times the depth of bricks, and the damp-proof course must be at the same level on both the outer and inner leaf of the wall.

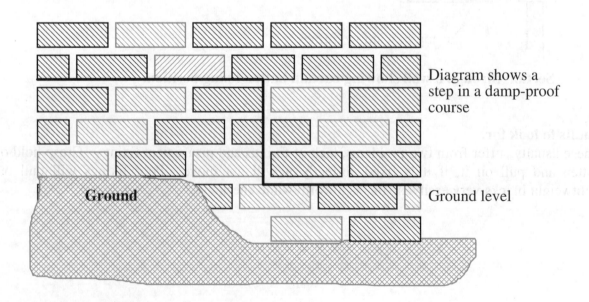

Diagram shows a step in a damp-proof course

Ground

Ground level

Steps in the damp-proof course normally only occur in a block of terraced properties or where the dwelling covers a large area of ground. The internal floor level is at the same level or just above the damp-proof course, so if steps occur in the damp-proof course within one property the floor levels could be different throughout the ground floor. On steeply sloping sites this is why dwellings with split level aspects are built, as this overcomes the problem of different floor levels and utilises the sloping ground without creating the need for access steps to enter properties, internal staircases are used between levels.

Explained further the ground at the front of a property may be only two courses of bricks below the damp-proof course, but at the back of the property due to the slope in the site, the ground could be six or more courses below the damp-proof course. Thus creating the need for steps to gain access.

The diagram below is a section through a wall showing the relationship between floor level and damp-proof course. Floors whatever nature of construction always have to be level, there is no instance where a floor is allowed to slope on a new construction apart from an access area.

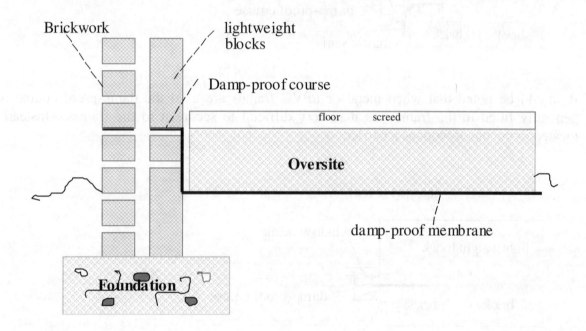

What is the purpose of the damp-proof course?
The damp-proof course is there to provide an impermeable barrier, in a wall to prevent damp areas developing. They are normally made from PVC or 'bitumen' based products. Where a joint is needed, the two ends must overlap at least 200mm to prevent any breach of the barrier. The joint can be glued using 'bitumastic' paint but this is not currently a compulsory building regulation requirement.

Other uses of Dpc

- Damp-proof course has many other uses in construction

- To resist moisture penetration from below (rising damp)

- To resist moisture penetration from horizontal entry, such as a seal around a door frame, (see later in this section)

- To prevent moisture penetration from above, (where a cavity is closed above a window)

The list below explains some common uses:

- Under the coping stones or tiles on external boundary walls to prevent damp areas developing down the wall where water soaks through the mortar joints, (mortar is porous). Many builders don't use damp-proof course for this and that is why on many new housing developments you see areas on walls that have large areas of moss growing on them. It is not just the small builder who uses bad construction methods!

- It is nailed to the sides of wooden window and doorframes to act as a barrier preventing moisture crossing over to the inner leaf of the cavity wall. Some frames have a mortar groove in which the Dpc can be located.

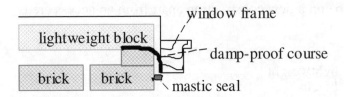

- It should be noted that when metal or uPVC frames are used the damp-proof course is not generally fitted to the frames, as it is very difficult to secure it to the frames. Instead it is located in the block-work as a barrier.

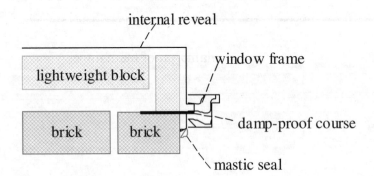

- Many houses are now having their windows replaced with uPVC frames and it is quite normal for the seal around the between brickwork and frame to be mastic or low modulus silicone sealant. Foam insulation is sometimes inserted behind the mastic to prevent draughts.

- If timber stud-work walls are constructed on concrete floors Dpc is placed on the floor between the stud-work wall and floor, again to act as a moisture barrier. Normally this is only done on older properties where the history of the building is not known, when the builder can not be sure that there is a damp-proof membrane in the floor its self.

- A damp-proof course will be placed above a window frame to prevent moisture in the cavity entering the building, this only occurs when a concrete lintel is used because pre-formed steel lintels are designed to act as a barrier. When a Dpc is used over a door or window opening it must extend beyond the ends of the lintels by a minimum of 150mm.

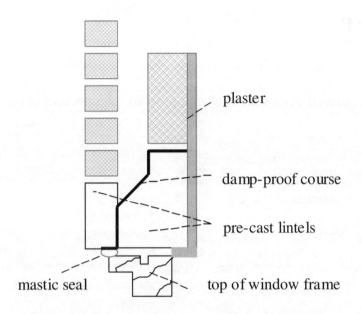

plaster

damp-proof course

pre-cast lintels

mastic seal   top of window frame

Why does failure of the Dpc occur?

Problems should not arise with damp-proof courses as long as the areas outlined are checked and the guidance given is followed. Problems generally arise not from the cost of DPC, but through lack of training and inexperience, e.g. running a wheelbarrow over an unprotected Dpc could puncture it, allowing moisture to penetrate by capillary action.

The problem that occurs most often with damp proof courses are caused after it has been installed, placing of the top-soil around the property or positioning of patio slabs. These or any other permanent materials adjacent to the property must be a minimum of two courses of brickwork below the damp proof course, this measurement is taken from the underside of the Dpc to the top of the slab or soil surface. If the surrounding area of a property is above the Dpc any moisture can cross the barrier and rise up the walls and create damp patches.

Other materials that can be used as Dpc

- Lead complying to BS1178

- Copper complying to BS2870

- Slates complying to BS680

- Engineering bricks complying to BS3921

- Emulsion Dpc paint

- All asphalt based Dpc must comply to BS6925 and BS6577

Damp-proof membrane, 'DPM'

What is a damp-proof membrane?
Like a Dpc, an impermeable barrier, placed across an over-site prior to the concrete being poured in.

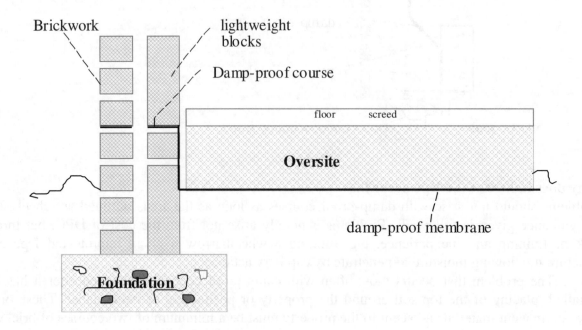

Where the Dpc and Dpm meet, they must overlap to continue the barrier.

Why does failure of the Dpm occur?
Failure normally occurs for the same reasons as shown in the section for Dpc, so the same care should be taken.

What materials can be used to create a damp-proof membrane?
The main material used for Dpm is polythene; it must comply with building regulation requirements and is known as LDPE - 1200 gauge (0.3mm). Bitumen is sometimes used to form membranes in existing properties; this has to comply with BS743 and BS8102 and requires 3 coats, usually applied cold.

Note:
Some properties are built in areas where there can be a problem from methane and Radon gases escaping from the ground. Methane gas is caused by organic waste decaying in the ground, a hazard of landfill sites, where a mixture of carbon dioxide and other gases blend together to form 'landfill gas', the risk from this could be fire or explosion.

Radon occurs naturally and is formed from the radioactive decay of radium. It is said to increase the risk of cancer and is found in granite areas of Scotland and Northern England.

Precautions can be taken to prevent damage to the building and injury to the occupants from these gases;

- An airtight seal needs to be built within the ground floor and surrounding walls. A damp-proof membrane of LDPE - 0.3mm specification is sufficient, provided that it is bonded at the edges to create a permanent seal.

- It is better to use a membrane of LDPE - 1200 gauge (1mm thickness).

- LDPE's are available reinforced with aluminium foil and non-corrosive wire, to prevent puncture.

- If the problem with gases is very severe, an extraction system can be incorporated as part of the property's permanent structure. This will require a containment tank being built below the ground floor, to store to extracted gas in. This type of system is costly because it must run continuously, therefore creating a permanent maintenance problem, caused by the disposal of extracted gas and servicing of the extracting unit.

Doors

It would be possible to write a book on this subject alone, however it should be said that it wouldn't prove very interesting reading to all but a few 'sad' carpenters. This book will attempt to address the most important factors, and what to look for if you think that there may be a 'cowboy builder' lurking!

How to identify the type of door to be used
There are two main types of door used in construction, internal and external. The main difference is that the materials internal doors are constructed from may not durable if used externally. Very often internal doors are assembled with glue that is not waterproof and are faced with man made board not designed for external use. As a general guide doors are stamped on one of the edges, giving their intended use. If you are not happy or are unsure of the door get the builder to confirm its suitability, the invoice should say the type and use of door, if not ask the supplier.

Storage precautions and the first stages of use
All doors purchased should be protected and stored properly. They should be kept dry and clean and stored flat with level supports underneath them. A door should never be stored in an unsupported fashion. Any door for external use must always have a base coat applied prior to the carpenter hanging it; this will afford protection until it is painted.

Cost saving ideas and special offers to avoid
Due to the economic climate some builders' merchants appear to sell cheap doors. These are not always as cheap as they seem as problems often arise once they have been fitted. Sometimes they are cheap because there are stain marks or bruises on them; they may be storm damaged and should not be used by a builder because he will not be able to guarantee the normal life expectancy of the door. The door may look fine, but on closer inspection or when they are placed in a frame, many of these cheaper doors are twisted and bowed which means however good the carpenter may be at his job the door will never close properly.

Is there a correct procedure for fixing a door?
Fixing a door to its frame is called 'hanging'. It is a very skilled process and there are defined ways of 'hanging' external and internal doors.

External doors
Must always be hung on three 100mm hinges (Butt hinges), that are housed into the edge of the door. Three hinges are used to give greater security and to prevent the door from bowing. An Insurance certified British Standard 5-lever lock or similar should be fitted, preferably with a lever type handle, as these are easier to use. It is advisable to fit a security bolt to the top and bottom of the door.

Once the door is fitted there are some quick checks to ensure a 'cowboy' is not about to make a swift exit!

- The door should open and close with ease without force.

- There should be an even gap of between 2 and 3mm between the frame and the door; this should only be at the top and sides (for bottom of door see section on carpentry).

- Bolts, if fitted should slide into position with only slight resistance, this prevents the door from rattling in strong winds.

- Any key operated locks should turn easily and once locked there should be no movement in the door.

- If a letter plate (letterbox) is fitted it should open and close fully; poor fitting may not permit this. The hole that has been cut out for the letterbox should be smooth with no sharp edges.

- Any glass fitted to a door must either be 6mm toughened or laminated; the very minimum requirement is 6mm float (standard) glass.

- Many external doors have weather boards fitted at the bottom on the out side face, they are there to throw driving rain away from the door and prevent it blowing under the door in severe weather. It must be securely fitted with good clearance.
  As a general rule where a weather-board is used there will be a water bar fixed into the sill, this is a metal bar to prevent water being blown between the door and sill. It must not touch the underside of the door, as this would allow capillary action of the water. The bottom of the door will be rebated to pass over the water bar; this is the other reason for the weather-board as it helps to hide the rebate.

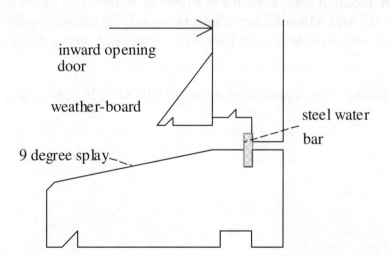

If any one of these points has not been completed in a satisfactory manner, prevent the builder from leaving. Under no circumstances should they be paid before the job is completed satisfactorily.

Internal doors

Many of the same principles apply to internal doors; again they are generally hung on 100mm butt hinges, however two can be used instead of three, as internal doors are usually lighter. The gap around the door should again be 2 to 3mm, but the gap at the bottom of the door should allow for the floor finish. For example if there is going to be carpet, there would need to be an allowance of approximately 12 to 15mm, whereas if the floor were of ceramic tiled finish, a gap of only 4 mm might be necessary.

Most internal doors use mortise lever latch type catches and the same inspections should be carried out on completion of the job as were discussed for external doors.

Door sizes.

All the doors on new properties must be made to comply with standard sizes, both in width and height. When a door and frame is being installed to older properties it may not be possible because the opening is not a size to match standard sizes available, this is allowed, and specially made doors and frames will have to be made. When doorframes are replaced in property where the opening will take a standard size, but the existing frame is larger in section and the door is non-standard this should be altered. A standard frame and door should be fitted, firstly it is much cheaper than having a door and frame specially made and secondly it is much easier.

Properties that were built more than 25 years ago received much heavier and larger joinery timber sections; this is now overcome by better grading of timber and preservation techniques. If a property has openings that are slightly different to standard sizes, the frame should be manufactured to fit the opening, but it should be rebated to receive a standard sized door, this may mean that the timber sections of the frame will have to be larger. This will reduce the cost, but more importantly if the door has to be replaced, it will be easier to fit a standard door to the frame.

The most commonly used standard sizes of doors available are:

External doors They are normally 1982mm high, available in widths of 762mm (the minimum width permitted for an external door) 813 and 838mm. Some joinery manufacturers still produce large height doors measuring 2032mm, the old 6 foot eight inch size. This large size is not used very often on domestic property.

Internal doors these are again 1982mm high, available in widths of 610, 686, 762 and 838mm.

Door linings

What is a door lining?

The name given to the timber frame supporting internal doors, these are of a totally different construction from external doorframes. The sections below explain the difference.

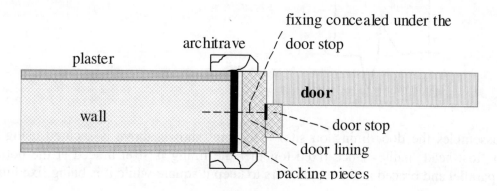

Internal door lining

Inside

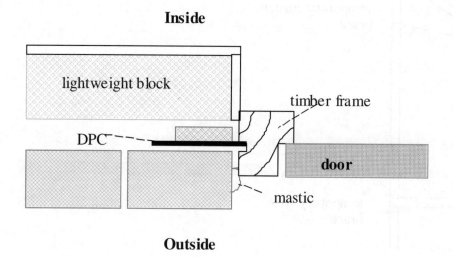

Outside

External door frame

How are door linings constructed?

Door linings have a very simple structure, being just three pieces of square edged timber. The two side upright timbers are called jambs and the top timber is called the head. The width of the timber section is determined by the thickness of the wall to which the door lining is to be fixed, the thickness of the door lining timber is normally either 21mm or 27mm. Door linings are not generally delivered to site assembled; they are supplied in kits, ready jointed and cut to a standard door size. Where the head meets the jambs there is a housed joint to give the lining greater strength.

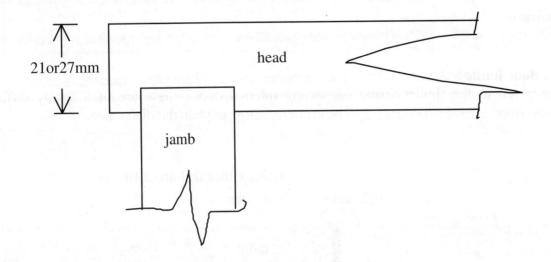

The carpenter assembles the door lining on site. The joint shown above is secured using either wood screws or 'lost head' nails. Once fixed together the lining is strut-braced at the bottom to keep the jambs parallel and braced at the top corners to keep it square while it is being fixed into the opening.

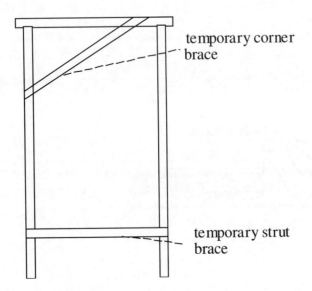

temporary corner brace

temporary strut brace

Fixing of door linings

If a door lining is fitted correctly it can shorten the time it takes to 'hang' a door by up to one third. The apertures left in the internal walls for the door linings are usually over-size, so before the lining is secured in place it must be wedged in place, square and upright using thin pieces of wood. There should be sufficient packing to hold it tightly in place and to prevent the jambs pulling out of shape once the fixing screws are positioned and tightened. Sometimes door linings are secured using 'cut nails' and provided that care is taken when wedging in place, this method of fixing is fine. A conscientious carpenter will usually fix door linings in place using screws, the advantage being that if adjustment is required when the door is hung, the screw can be loosened and the lining packed out to get over the adjustment. This is far easier than trying to loosen a nail to get over the same problem.

What problems should you look for?

There are five problems to watch for, any of which can cause difficulties when the door is being 'hung':

- Use a large set-square and check that the head is at 90 degrees to the jamb.

- With a long straightedge check that the jambs are straight and that the fixings have not twisted the jambs.

- Take hold of the lining and ensure that it is securely fixed, there should be no movement

- Check that the measurement across the top of the door lining is the same at the bottom (the jambs are parallel).

- No fixings are placed through the head.

Door frames

Generally used for external doorways, they are available in hardwood and softwood in different sizes. External doorways are normally made to a minimum opening width of 765mm and height of 1982mm, this is to allow for ease of access with furniture, to prevent injury to tall people and allow wheelchair access. (This applies to new building not the replacement of existing doorframes).

The bricklayer usually puts wooden doorframes into place in a new building, but it should have been squared and braced by the carpenter beforehand. To tell if this has been done properly look for a piece of wood across one of the top corners of the frame. It should be nailed onto the top of the frame (the head) and the side of the frame (the Jamb) thus forming a triangle in one of the top corners of the frame. This is the same method already described in the section for door linings.

How do you know if the door frame is fitted correctly

It should be securely fixed using frame ties, sometimes called 'owlets'; these are screwed into the frame and then placed in the mortar as the bricks are laid. Once the mortar has set they hold the doorframe securely in place. Each door should have a minimum of three fixings in the jambs.

There should be an even edge of bricks showing from the face of the brickwork and the face of the doorframe of approximately 30 to 60mm. This is dependant on the thickness of frame used and what depth of reveal (the internal wall abutting the door frame) is required on the inside of the doorway (see diagram below).

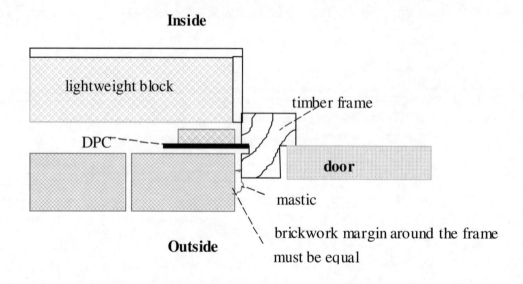

Horizontal section through a wall, viewed from above

What problems should you look for?

There are five problems to watch for, any of which can cause problems when the door is being 'hung' into the frame, the checks made are very similar to those made for door linings;

- Use a large set-square and check that the head is at 90 degrees to the jamb.

- With a long straightedge check that the jambs are straight and that the fixings have not twisted the jambs.

- Take hold of the door frame and ensure that it is securely fixed, there should be no movement

- Check that the measurement across the top of the doorframe is the same at the bottom (the jambs are parallel).

- No fixings are placed through the head.

Drains and drainage

A description of drains and drainage systems Drains are a system of channels and pipes in and around a property, falling into two categories;

- Foul water or sewage systems and

- Storm water systems.

What is their purpose?

Their purpose is to enable the disposal of sewage and storm water from a property. Sewage is disposed of either in a septic tank (see separate section) in the grounds of the property, or the drains of the property are connected to the mains sewerage system incorporated within the public highway.

Storm water, or rain water, is directed by pipes either into man made soakaways (see separate section) in the grounds of the property, or into the mains storm water system within the public highway.

Public sewerage systems are owned and maintained by local water companies, and storm water systems are generally owned and maintained by local Government Authorities or the Highways Agency in your area.

Why are there two separate systems

It is a legal requirement that storm water and sewerage be kept separate, this is because much of the rain water is allowed to enter the natural causeways and streams that disperse into rivers and the sea. Raw sewage cannot be permitted in this system, for obvious environmental reasons. After a heavy storm the amount of storm water entering a sewerage treatment plant would very quickly overwhelm the plant completely.

Who should you employ to install a drainage system?

Any good general builder can install or repair drains; large companies have special personnel known as ground workers, their jobs include digging, laying foundations, roads and paths and drainage systems. There is also a specialist field of construction called civil engineering; the above areas fall under the civil engineering elements of building.

How should drains be installed?

Building Regulations apply to any drain installations; they apply to both new work and to the maintenance and repair of existing systems. The regulations apply to both storm and sewerage water drains.

It is difficult to cover this area of building in a detailed manner appropriate to the average homeowner, so the key areas are identified with important regulations and guide lines highlighted.

Storm water (rainwater) drains. Key rules and regulations:

Most storm water naturally drains into the ground using a soakaway, sometimes a soakaway maybe shared with a neighbouring property. If this is the case it may be on the boundary of the properties concerned. As a general rule existing soakaways are not easily identified on an actual property, but they are usually shown on your deeds. This however may not be to scale or very precise. They are best located by excavating and following the pipe from the rainwater gully near the property to its end.

The gully is the point at which the down pipe enters the ground near the wall of the property. If a soak away has been properly built it should last between 25 and 30 years before it eventually 'silts up'.

What is a soakaway?

A soakaway is a man made pit or 'tank' that allows for the controlled collection of rainwater. Its main purpose is to create gradual seepage of the collected rainwater into the surrounding subsoil. Soakaways are not very successful in clay subsoil's, some Local Authorities permit their use in clay subsoil's but they have a very short life span and may have to be rebuilt as soon as ten years later.

A soakaway must be located on land that is on the same level or lower than adjacent buildings. This is to prevent water that flows from the soakaway from flooding those properties. When a new soakaway is to be constructed these are the rules that apply:

- The top of the soak away must be below the topsoil or a minimum depth of 450 mm. This is not a rule but a guide, if the top of the soakaway is above this depth, garden forks or spades could breach the top.

- The hole should be a minimum of 1 cubic metre below the point at which the discharge pipe enters the hole, the bigger the hole is the longer the soakaway will last. There is a calculation that can be used to accurately determine the size of soakaway needed;

$$C = \frac{AR}{3}$$

C = the capacity of the soakaway
A = area of the surface or roof to be drained (metres squared)
R = rainfall (mm/h) (average rainfall quantities are available from your local authority)

As an example a roof covering 80 square metres with an average rainfall of 40mm/h (0.04 m/h) would calculate as follows;

$$C = \frac{80 \times 0.04}{3} = 1.06 \text{ cubic metres of soakaway.}$$

- It must be a minimum of 5 metres from any property foundations and at least 1 metre from the boundary, if it is not a shared soak away. When soakaway is shared between properties it is normal to position it centrally on the boundary line.

- The hole should be filled with hard building waste such as broken bricks and concrete block, large flints or cobbles. Under no circumstances should lightweight blocks such as 'Thermolite' be used to fill a soak away. This is because after time they crumble and crush and the reason a soak away works is that there are lots of holes around the rubble in which the water can sit until it soaks away into the surrounding ground. The pipe, which is going to feed into the soak away, should enter the hole just below the top and should run into the centre of the hole. (see diagram below)

- In areas of good drainage, for example where subsoil is sand or gravel, the soakaway need not be filled. A hollow soakaway can be built, these are constructed using either pre-cast concrete rings on large soakaways, or by using bricks laid in a 'honeycomb' bonding pattern laid on a concrete base for single property soakaway. (see diagram)

- Once the hole has been filled with rubble it should be covered with a layer of polythene, this is to stop topsoil washing through and silting up the soak away prematurely. The topsoil can now be replaced.

- As a general rule, whatever the size of the property there will be a soakaway both front and rear. One will not be sufficient for both sides of a roof in a heavy storm, as the length of supply pipe required to reach the soakaway will slow down the flow of water.

The diagrams below show the two types of soakaway used:

A filled soakaway

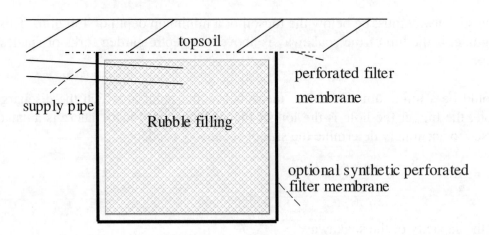

Hollow soakaway

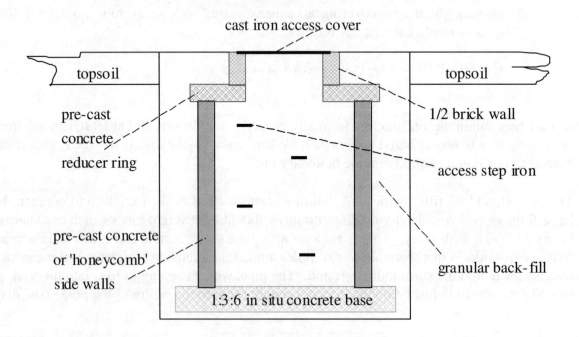

Pipes that run to a soakaway or to the mains storm drains are very straight forward, and it is easy to spot if problems exist, the key regulations that apply are as follows:

- All pipes must run in straight lines. Where there are bends they must be accessible with drainage rods if a blockage occurs. This means that an inspection eye or small chamber must be incorporated allowing access.

- The fall of the pipes must be such that the gradient will make the system self-cleaning, if the fall is too sudden silt will be left in the pipe and after a time it will build up and form a blockage.

  As a general guide the minimum fall required for drainage pipes is:

  100mm diameter pipes   minimum gradient   1 in 40

  150mm diameter pipes   minimum gradient   1 in 60

  Document 'H' of The Building Regulations provides further information and technical details.

- Any pipes less than 300mm below ground level should be protected with a layer of 'lean mix' concrete on top of them, to prevent damage from heavy traffic.

- All drainpipes should be laid on a 100mm bed of 10mm shingle and, once correctly positioned surrounded with at least 100mm of 10mm shingle.

- The tops of rainwater gullies should not be above the DPC of the property. Its cover or top should be at the same level as the topsoil.

- Any down pipes must be secured to the property wall using tieback clips, spaced along the down pipe at 1200mm minimum intervals.

Foul water (sewage)
Sewerage is disposed of in one of two ways:

    (i)   By using a septic tank in the grounds of the property, or
    (ii)   By the mains sewerage system in the highway.

A septic tank works naturally by disintegrating the waste through bacterial activity. These can be built on site using concrete and engineering bricks, or purchased pre-formed made from reinforced glass fibre or plastic.

What falls into the category of sewage?
Any water or liquid based waste that has been used within the domestic plumbing system; this would include waste from:

- Kitchen and utility room sinks

- Dish washers and washing machines

- Baths and wash basins

- Toilets and bidet

How are foul water (sewerage) drains laid? Key rules and regulations:
Many of the rules that apply to foul water drains are the same as for storm water:

- All pipes must run in straight lines. Where there are bends they must be accessible with drainage rods if a blockage occurs. This means that an inspection eye or small chamber must be incorporated allowing access.

- The fall of the pipes must be such that the gradient will make the system self-cleaning, if the fall is to sudden any silt will be left in the pipe and after a time it will build up and a blockage will form.

    As a general guide the minimum fall required for drainage pipes is:

    100mm diameter pipes   minimum gradient   1 in 40

    150mm diameter pipes   minimum gradient   1 in 60

    Document 'H' of The Building Regulations provides more information and technical details.

- Any pipes that are less than 300mm below the ground should be protected by placing (1:3:6) concrete on top of them, to prevent damage from heavy traffic.

- All drainpipes should be laid on a 100mm bed of 10mm shingle and, once correctly positioned surrounded with at least 100mm of 10mm shingle.

- Inspection chambers are incorporated where the drainage system pipes do not exceed the depth of 1.0 metres; (this is called the invert level). It is normal practice to use pre-formed plastic inspection chambers on domestic construction;

  (i) The chamber must be level, any required fall is already accommodated in pre-formed inspection chambers. It is bedded on 100mm of 10mm shingle or 150mm of (1:3:6) wet concrete, either will give a stable support.

  (ii) If a plastic pre-formed chamber is being used, the bottom must be no more than 1000mm below ground level; this is to prevent access problems occurring and the plastic sides of the chamber being crushed.

  (iii) Intersections in the chamber must run in the direction of the drain flow, see diagram, if the chamber is placed against the flow blockages will occur.

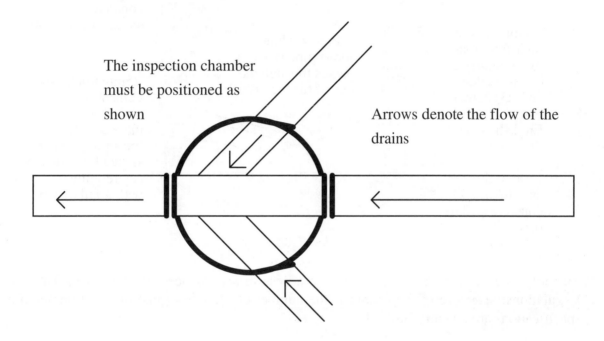

The inspection chamber must be positioned as shown

Arrows denote the flow of the drains

View looking down into an inspection chamber

  iv. If a bend is required in the pipe run to locate with the house, it must be placed near the chamber so that drain rods can access the entire pipe run.

  v. The walls of pre-formed chambers are manufactured in sections 300mm high. If stacked to give the required height they must be bonded with silicone sealant. The rim that locates the lid must be bonded as well.

  vi. If the chamber is placed in a path or driveway that is not of concrete construction or finished with a similar hard finish, the surrounding area of the chamber top wall section and lid rim must be protected and supported with 150 mm of (1:3:6) concrete.

  vii. Where a chamber is situated in a drive, the cover must be up-graded to a heavy duty cast iron type, the standard thin steel cover is not strong enough to support the weight of a car or light commercial vehicle, these standard duty covers are designed for garden use only.

  (iv) Where the bottom of the chamber is deeper than 900mm, a 'Manhole' must be used to allow access.

Where the level of the pipes (invert level) exceeds a depth of 1.0 metre, a 'manhole' is used instead of an inspection chamber. The main reason for using a 'manhole' is that it will allow a person to climb down the sides to reach the bottom. The usual design of a domestic property 'manhole' is;

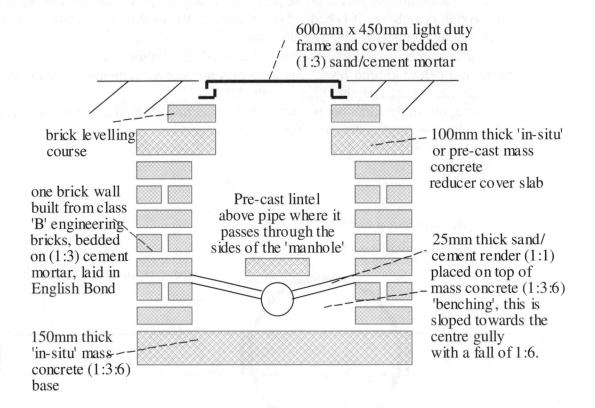

600mm x 450mm light duty frame and cover bedded on (1:3) sand/cement mortar

brick levelling course

one brick wall built from class 'B' engineering bricks, bedded on (1:3) cement mortar, laid in English Bond

Pre-cast lintel above pipe where it passes through the sides of the 'manhole'

100mm thick 'in-situ' or pre-cast mass concrete reducer cover slab

25mm thick sand/ cement render (1:1) placed on top of mass concrete (1:3:6) 'benching', this is sloped towards the centre gully with a fall of 1:6.

150mm thick 'in-situ' mass concrete (1:3:6) base

Manholes are built in this way to provide access in accordance with Part H of The Building Regulations. The size of the chamber, the number of branches (pipe intersections) and access specifications are given in BS8301.

- Trenches for drains are excavated in much the same way as foundations, the main difference being that a drain trench will be sloped to create the fall required for the system to work efficiently.

- All joints between pipes, inspection chambers and manholes must be watertight, under all conditions, and allow for expansion and movement. Most joints on drainage products must be laid in line with the direction of the flow of the system; this is marked on them.

- If rigid clay based pipes are used, their joints must be laid on top of 150mm of mass concrete. This is to prevent any movement of the joint and consequent separation.

- Once a drainage system is completed it has to be tested for water tightness, in accordance with Document H, section 2 of The Building Regulations. It specifies that a drainage system must be tested for soundness by using either an air or water pressure meter. Explained simply the system is sealed at all ends and pressure tested using a meter, if a water test is used the meter must not drop no more than 25mm in 5 minutes. This test is part of the building control inspection process.

Dry Lining

What is dry lining?

Dry lining is the application of sheets of plasterboard to walls in place of cement render and plaster or as the trade calls it 'wet plastering'. It is a relatively new concept in building created by the need to make new properties habitable more quickly and to save money.

What are its advantages over wet plastering?

The main advantage is that it requires very little drying time, a four bedroom house can be dry lined and ready for decorating in approximately seven to ten days, whereas conventional wet plastering may require up to eight weeks to dry during winter months. It is also very quick to install and to some extent there is less mess compared with wet plastering.

Dry lining does not suffer from shrinkage cracks that are a feature of conventional plaster. The expansion and contraction of wet materials drying out unevenly cause such cracks. It is also easier to fix skirting board to dry lining, nails enter and hold better than they do in rendered walls.

Another advantage is that because of the way it is fixed to the wall there is another small cavity, thus increasing the thermal value of the wall.

What are the disadvantages of dry lining?

There are a few disadvantages to using dry lining, however they are more than out-weighed by the advantages already listed above, they are;

- It is easy to dent and knock holes through the boards because there is a cavity between the board and the wall blocks.

- It is not very easy to fix things e.g. pictures and shelves, to a dry lined wall with masonry plugs and screws because of the cavity behind the board.

- Picture hooks have a tendency to fall out of dry lining.

How is dry lining fixed to the wall?

Sheets of plaster board are fixed to the wall using bonding plaster, placed on the wall in 'dabs' which are evenly distributed over the area to be covered by the sheets, rather than spread. Plaster is mixed to a creamy texture that allows it to stay in a mound when placed onto the wall, each mound or peak will stand approximately 50mm above the surface of the wall in stage one of the process (see diagram).

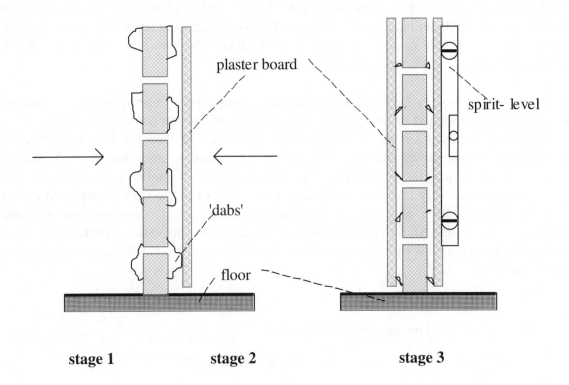

stage 1   **stage 2**   **stage 3**

The next stage is for the plaster board to be offered up to the wall touching the 'dabs' of plaster, the board is then pushed evenly against the wall so as suction is created as the 'dabs' are pushed flat by the board. The final stage is levelling and lining up the boards along the wall so the wall is straight, the wall must be checked vertically for level and a straight edge should be placed along the wall to ensure that there are no severe bumps or hollows along its length. The levelling of the boards can be made easier by nailing bitumen impregnated fibreboard pads to the wall before the 'dabs' and boards are applied. These are levelled in all directions and checked for upright, so that when the boards are pushed into place they automatically locate in the correct place.

What problems should you look for?
Most dry lining specialists are very experienced and because of the skills required for the job there are very few cowboy firms operating within the business, however common faults are:

- Not enough 'dabs' of bonding plaster being used for each board, this creates areas of the boards which, when pushed, move easily. This can create problems with fixings at a later date and more importantly the board is easily punctured when furniture is pushed against it. If you suspect the board may have insufficient support, complain and get the board removed and a new one fixed correctly. A 1200 x 2400 sheet of plasterboard should have approximately 15 to 20 'dabs' evenly spaced behind it, at 460mm centres in all directions.

- Bad vertical levelling of the boards in a kitchen will make it difficult to fit kitchen units, this applies to any other room where units may be stood against the wall, walls that are not plumb may show only when things are standing near them.

- If walls are not reasonably straight along their length, fitting of skirting boards will be made difficult, uneven walls will hamper the fitting of units. Discrepancies will cause problems with ceramic tiles, so if you suspect unevenness complain. The better the dry lining, the better quality any following work, or trade will be.

- Joints between the boards are bonded together using bandage or jointing paper, applied using a special jointing compound of fine plaster. First a layer of the compound is applied to the joint; the paper strip is placed on the compound over the joint and then levelled and smoothed by running a plasterer's trowel over it. Any excess compound is smoothed over the paper and, when dry any discrepancies sanded off. If jointing paper is not applied to the joint, cracks may occur, it is therefore very important that there are no spaces in the runs of paper on each joint. To make the application of paper and jointing compound easier, dry-lining plasterboard has recessed edges. These allow for the depth of the joint and provide a flush finish. It is not possible to dry line a wall with ordinary plaster board as each joint will have a raised finish not a smooth one.

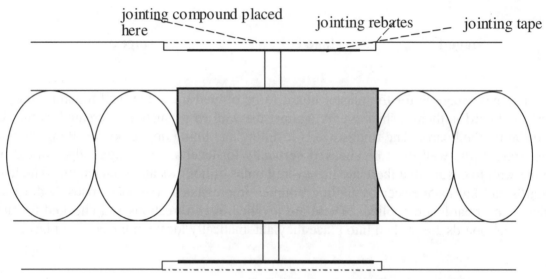

an enlarged section through the wall boards showing the rebate on the
edge of the wall sections to allow for jointing compound
this is viewed looking from the top of a wall looking downwards

- This jointing process is also applied to the joint between ceiling and walls. This prevents the usual gaps between wall and ceiling that appear even though they are filled each time you redecorate.

- Timber studs or battens can be used as an alternative to plaster dabs to hold the boards on the wall, these are nailed to the wall and the sheets of plasterboard are nailed to them. There are two main problems with this method;

  (i)   The timber may move or shrink and cause cracks to appear in the joints, and
  (ii)   There will be lots of nail holes to fill and sand level, therefore increasing the labour cost.

If timber battens are used they must be placed at maximum centres of 600mm, spaced across the wall and at the joints.

Electrical installations

What areas of domestic construction does this cover ?

This covers all areas of domestic house wiring, they are:

- Wall sockets

- Light switches

- Fuse board and circuit breakers

- Alarm systems

- Telecommunications

- Ceiling and other light fittings

- Storage heaters

- Indeed any fixtures and fittings that require electricity to function, other than those which are plugged in.

Who installs electrical installations in a property?

Only fully experienced trades persons should be permitted to install electric systems, some may have formal qualifications but many older people may have served long apprenticeships. Either form of training is adequate. Whichever form of training and experience they state they have received should be verified, as mistakes with electric can cost lives.

There are some builders with many years experience, who always do good quality work but who have no formal qualifications in any area of building. This is very common in rural areas. There is nothing wrong with this as long as you check their past dealings, ask for references or speak to someone who has employed them. Many bricklayers and carpenters while completing their formal studies will also study other areas of construction; this is because their particular expertise involves many of the other trades. This gives them a very good overview of the whole industry with regards to safety and regulatory requirements.

How do you look for possible faults?

Electrical installation is a very complicated and detailed part of the building industry. People who install electrics are normally very experienced and good at their job so this book will only highlight the real problems and safety issues that the average homeowner could identify.

There are key safety areas to look for:

- There must be a correctly installed fuse board and circuit breaking system, some older systems have separate trip units and as long as these function properly, they comply with safety requirements. Most modern systems are integral fuse, trip micro units, with a separate safety trip for each circuit. All fuses, trips and circuits must be correctly labelled.

- The steel or if surface mounted, 'cans' that conceal the electric wires behind sockets and switches must be securely fitted, usually with two screws in each. Socket outlet 'cans' must be placed a minimum of 150mm from the floor, for elderly people this can be increased to between 825 and 900mm and for disabled people the height of a socket should be approximately 300mm from the floor.

- If steel 'cans' are used, where the cable passes through the can to the socket or switch there must be a rubber grommet fitted to the hole. This is to prevent the steel from cutting the outer plastic of the wire and causing electric shock or short-circuiting the system.

- Most domestic electric cable is 3 or 4 core, this means that there are three or four cables encased in an outer plastic sheath. The live (red or brown) and negative (blue or black) are protected by their coloured identifying plastic coating, but the earth has no protective coating on it. Sometimes there is a fourth wire in lighting cable; usually coloured yellow, this is not the earth wire, this is always identified by a yellow and green stripped case, if it is ready insulated. When the wires are exposed to make connections a section of 'earth sheath' must be placed over the earth wire to prevent short-circuiting and electric shock. It is coloured yellow and green for easy identification, no other colour of sheath is permitted.

- All cables concealed behind the plaster in a wall should be protected with plastic cover conduit prior to plastering. This also permits later removal of the cables without damaging the plaster on the walls, if a fault occurs.

- All wires in walls must rise and fall vertically, to ensure that anyone drilling into the walls at future date can easily identify where electrical wires are.

- Any wiring in loft spaces or storage areas must be clipped well back to joists or stud-work and be in a neat identifiable layout.

- All sockets are on a system called a ring main, a continuous loop of cable that starts at and returns to the fuse board, all sockets are connected to this loop, which will have a fuse or miniature circuit breaker rated 32 amp on the live conductor. This means that each socket will have two cables going to them creating a continuous circuit. Normally there is a ring main circuit to each floor of a domestic dwelling.

  There is no limit to the number of sockets on one ring main; however, each circuit must be limited to 100 square metres of floor area to prevent excess loading of the cables. If an extra socket is needed at a later date it is normal for a 'spur' to be taken from one of the existing sockets and used to feed the new socket, it is not normally possible to install a new socket into an existing ring main. Each ring main can safely have several spurs installed, as long as the number of spurs does not exceed the number of outlets already installed on the circuit.

- Any joints in cables must be made using junction boxes; these are plastic boxes with clamp terminals inside to grip the wires together. Joined cables should never be left uncovered and all the joints must be insulated. Junction boxes have different ratings normally 15, 20, 32 and 45 amp these are used as follows;

  15 amp for lighting

  20 amp for sockets (ring main)

  32 amp for cookers

  45 amp for electric showers or similar

  It is normal to use a higher rated box than is needed. Never should a low rated box be used e.g. 15 amp for a cooker.

- It is very important that the correct fuse rating be used for service area of the electrical circuit and a domestic dwelling. These are the fuses that are found in the Consumer Control Unit (fuse board) the ratings are:

Type of circuit	Rating
Electric shower units	45 amp
Ring circuits for sockets	32 amp
Cooker circuit	32 amp
Immersion heater	16 amp
Central heating	6 amp-may depend on type of pump used
Lighting circuits	6 amp

- The correct cable size must also be used for each service area, this is calculated by taking into account the maximum current the cable will have to carry. This is limited by the heating effect caused by the flow of electricity through the cable (the resistance to the flow of the electricity), and the amount of voltage drop, which occurs as the current, is carried through the circuits. The cable rating is always aimed at the size needed of the live conductor. The sizes for normal domestic electrical installations are:

Type of circuit	Cable rating or size
Lighting	1mm
Immersion heaters	1.5mm
Ring main circuits	2.5mm (both live and neutral)
Cooker and shower	6mm (both live and neutral)

Electric supply

It is the responsibility of the Regional Electricity Supply Company to provide properties with an electric supply. They are only bound to bring the cable to the meter and termination equipment, which is housed in a box on new properties incorporated as part of the external wall of the property. These boxes do not have to be housed externally, but it is preferred as it permits easier access for meter reading. The property owner is responsible for the safe protection and installation of the Electricity companies equipment.

The Electricity Supply Company as part of the installation fee normally supplies pre-formed fibreglass or steel equipment boxes. There is provision on the board in the box for all the termination equipment and for the Consumer Control Unit or CCU as many electricians call it.

The consumer control unit has a very important role within the electric supply circuit of a domestic dwelling. It provides a method for distributing and controlling the electricity within a property. It is a very simple piece of equipment that consists of a main double pole control switch that is on the live supply, which then passes through individual fuse or mini circuit breakers for the protection of each individual circuit, which then connects to the neutral side of the system. Each circuit is then routed through individual fuses to provide the property with a safe, efficient system.

Floors and floor finishes

What part of a building is the floor?

This may appear to be obvious, but when discussing a project with a builder it can help if you are fully aware of the correct terminology for all the parts of a building, floors in particular is one area where it can get confusing. Used as in the dictionary the word does mean the lower surface of a room, but the word 'floor' can be used by the construction industry in some different senses, the most important are as follows;

- To describe the level of a floor, for example ground or first floor and finished floor level.

- To describe the layer placed on the structure of the building, examples are timber floor, floor screed, hollow ground floor, or floor slab.

- Floor finish, such as tiled, natural wood or manmade sheet flooring.

- Part of the structure, for example floor joist.

- It is therefore very important that when discussing floors that you are very precise as to what you actually mean.

Where do our floor finishes originate?

Stone and brick floors appeared with the first buildings during the 4th millennium BC in Egypt. Clay tiles were also used in Egypt, Crete, Greece, and Rome. The ancient Greeks made extensive use of stone and marble, and the Romans used concrete, especially as a base for mosaic floors.

What materials are used for floor finishes?

A wide variety of materials are used in modern floors. Concrete and wooden floors, the most widely used, are usually covered with carpets, rugs, for aesthetic reasons and to increase durability of the surface, absorption of sound, and ease of maintenance. Wood is still extensively used in domestic homes, especially as parquets (short, pieces of hardwood assembled in geometric patterns) or wood strip flooring. Wood tiles and joinery workshop prepared parquets can easily be installed on existing floors, they are secured with bitumen or waterproof glue.

Tiles also play an important role in modern buildings and homes. Of all floor coverings, they are the most resistant to water and humidity, and they are easy to clean. Glazed ceramic tiles are used wherever high sanitary conditions are required. In the home, this would be on the floors and walls of kitchen, utility areas and bathrooms. Synthetic, resilient floorings including linoleum, asphalt tiles, pure vinyl tiles, and rubber are all widely used to finish floors.

What are the different types of floor structure?

There are several different types of floor, the list below identifies them and describes their structure:

- **A timber beam or joist suspended floor**   The standard construction is: floor joists, parallel timber beams that stretch from wall to wall, upon which the floor is laid. This is the basic construction method used for most upper floors on domestic dwellings. The floor joists are covered with either softwood tongue and groove boarding or chip board sheets. When tongued and grooved boards are used they are laid across the joists or at right angles to them, they are secured at each joist using two 65mm cut flooring brads. If boards have to be joined in the length for wide rooms, they are butt jointed over the centre of a joist; each board is then nailed or screwed to the joist where they meet.

  Softwood floorboards are available in four thicknesses; made to comply with BS1297, the most commonly used being 19mm. The thicker the board the greater distance it will span between joists:

Dimension of board	Distance between joists	
16mm x 60mm	500mm	all width are
19mm x 110mm	600mm	approximate planned
21mm x 120mm	640mm	finished sizes.
28mm x 150mm	800mm	

  From personal experience 16mm boards should have a maximum span of 350mm, 19mm maximum span of 450mm, 21mm maximum span of 500mm and 28mm maximum span of 600mm. Spans greater than these sizes increase the risk of floor bounce. When chipboard sheets are used, much the same rules are applied. The sheets must be supported at all edges and secured along the length of a joist with the nails at maximum 450mm centres. Chipboard flooring sheets are available with tongues on two edges and grooves in the other two edges. This type of sheet flooring is normally available in a sheet sizes of 600mm x 2440mm. This size allows easy access in stairwells and corridors. They are manufactured to comply with BS5669, and are available impregnated with waterproofing for use in bathrooms, green in colour.

- **A standard dense concrete slab**   This type of floor is used for most domestic ground floor situations. It is quick to lay, cost effective and can be used on any building where the subsoil is stable and there is no more than 600mm of depth from the bottom of the over-site in-fill to the Dpc. (See drawing in section on hard-core and hoggin).

- **A suspended dense concrete slab**   These are normally used on domestic property ground floors, where the ground is sloped and the level of the finished floor height will cause the need for over-site in-fill of more than 600mm. They are used to get over the problem of ground movement, as explained in the section on foundations.

Section through a suspended slab floor

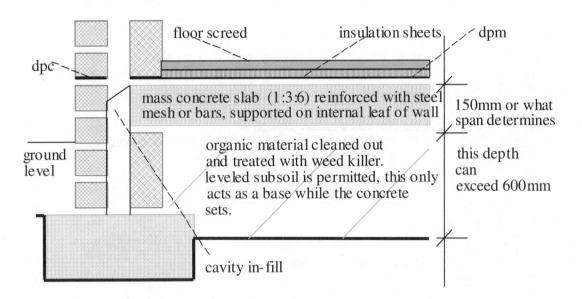

Steel reinforcing is placed in the concrete slab to give it the tensile strength that a standard dense concrete slab does not have. The steel reinforcing is placed on the over-site prior to the concrete being poured, it is placed on temporary supports allowing the concrete to totally encase it. The steel must be totally covered to prevent corrosion and to give necessary fire protection. The reinforcing must be above all supporting and perimeter walls as shown in the diagram below. If the slab is rectangular in shape the main bars of the reinforcing must span the longer of the distances.

Steel reinforcing within a concrete slab

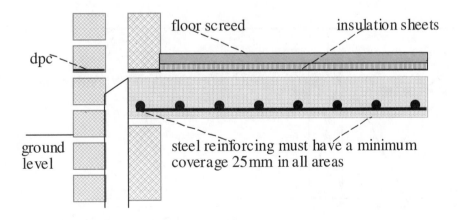

- **A concrete pre-cast floor**   These are generally used where the floor span is over 6 metres, where the ground is steeply sloped and the site is not suitable for a standard concrete slab, or where the floor is part of a block of flats. Standard construction is achieved using pre-stressed concrete joists, which have dense concrete blocks fitted between them. This is then covered with either 50mm screed, timber floorboards or sheets. It is a very strong flooring system adapted for domestic use from commercial buildings. This flooring system can be used in ground floor or upper floor situations; the preparation for ground floor situations is much the same as it is for suspended slab floors.

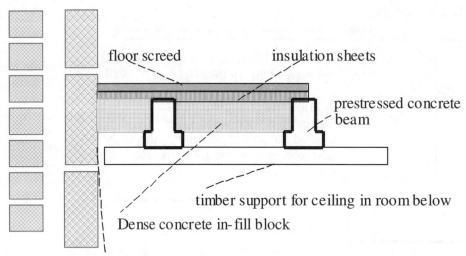

First or upper floor section of a concrete pre-cast floor.

What problems should you be aware of with floor construction?
This can be a very complex area of construction and varies with each flooring system; the list below identifies the most common faults linked to each flooring system.

A timber beam or joist suspended floor:

- **Joists that are not installed level,**

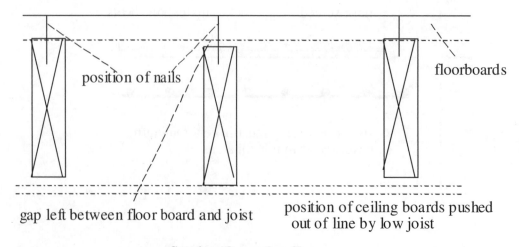

Section through a floor

The drawing above shows the effect this problem will have on the floor, it could cause squeaking floorboards where the nail does not secure the board tightly to the joist, or cracked ceilings where the plasterboard is fixed under tension to the uneven joists.

- **Twisted joists**.
This is normally a fault on floors that have a span exceeding 2.5metres. Placing strutting between the joists at the central point across the span of the floor prevents it. Two method are used to achieve this, herringbone strutting as explained in the section on carpentry, or solid timber strutting, as shown below.

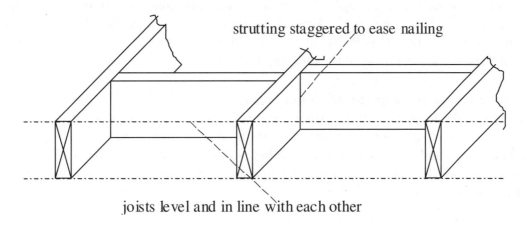

Diagram showing solid strutting

There are mild steel pressed herringbone systems available, the advantage of these is that they are very strong and there is little site preparation time, just remove from the packaging and nail in place, very cost effective!

- **Large gaps between the softwood floor board.**
This is a common fault, partly due to the use of more and more insufficiently seasoned timber in modern domestic building. (See section on timber) Once the heating is turned on in a new property, or where a new floor has been laid, the timber is going to dry out and shrink. A 19mm thick floorboard could possibly shrink up to 4mm across its width, so it is imperative that they are fixed properly. When the boards are laid they must be cramped tightly to one another, this is achieved by either tapping with a mallet and block of wood or using a special floor cramp, which uses the joist as an anchor to push the boards tightly together.

Floorboards that are not fixed in this way could have tongues that completely separate, or most annoyingly squeak.

- **Sheet flooring that squeaks and moves**
This is a common 'cowboy' fault, caused by insufficient nailing of the floor sheets. Most sheet flooring used for domestic building is tongued and grooved chipboard, this is normally 600mm x 2440mm. A sheet of this size would normally span around five joists, depending on the spacing of the joists, so it should have a minimum of 15 nails, 3 at each joist, evenly spaced across the 600mm sheet width.

Standard dense concrete slab:
These points are listed in order of installation, and must be inspected in this order, as each stage covers the previously completed work.

- The over-site area must be cleared of all organic matter and unstable soil prior to preparation. It is cleared down to the firm subsoil, but must not exceed 600mm or a suspended slab will have to be used. Failure to clear the site properly could result in ground movement or settlement, which in turn could result in concrete slab failure.

- The hard-core is placed into the area, carefully avoiding damage to the foundation wall. It is levelled out taking special care to prevent covered voids; it is generally levelled to approximately 100mm below the Dpc. A vibrating 'whacker' plate is then used to compact the hard-core, finishing 150mm below the Dpc. It is important to ensure that this measurement is even all over the over-site, areas less than 150mm thick will create a weak slab, whereas areas in excess of 150mm will eat away at the building budget!

- An over-site area can be prepared using crushed re-claimed concrete, or large stone that has been quarried in the local area, this is often used because it can be cheaper than using graded ballast. If this is the case then it is important to ensure that the top of the over-site preparation is levelled using fine sand or similar material. This is done to prevent the cement and fine sand from draining out of the concrete and settling in gaps in the hard-core, as this would seriously weaken the concrete slab.

- The damp-proof membrane can be placed in either of two positions, on top of the compacted hard-core prior to the concrete being poured, or, on top of the set concrete slab before the insulation and floor finish is laid. (See diagram earlier in this section and trench-fill diagram in foundations). If the Dpm is to be laid directly on top of the hard-core it is very important that no punctures occur from sharp stones, the Dpm is supposed to be an impervious layer to prevent the passage of moisture in to the dwelling. Sand can be used to 'blind' the top of the compacted hard-core, to prevent punctures from occurring.

- Normally concrete is then ordered from a specialist company so it is important that the builder orders the correct quantity. The quantity for an over-site 6 metres x 9.5 metres is worked out as follows;

  6 metres x 9.5 metres = **57 square metres**
  57 square metres (floor area) x 0.150 (floor thickness) = **8.55 cubic metres of concrete**

Always ensure that the quantity is rounded up to the nearest 0.25 of a cubic metre, this should allow for minor discrepancies in the preparation. Concrete delivery lorries only deliver 6 cubic metres per delivery, so it would be normal to order 8.75 cubic metres of the specified mix, this would be made in two deliveries. Remember structural concrete must be completed as one continuous job, a few hours between deliveries is acceptable, more than six in not.

- If the weather is hot and breezy, another potential problem can arise, which if it occurs has serious irreversible results, 'plastic cracking'. The wet concrete slab, after it has been 'tamped' and levelled, must be covered with a tarpaulin, this to prevent the surface drying out too quickly, causing it to crack. It should be realised if this occurs it is a major fault and should not be accepted. These drying cracks while appearing superficial can affect the whole depth of the slab. This creates a 'broken biscuit effect', so when pressure or loads are applied to the slab it could fracture completely along the fault line.

    This fault can occur with foundations subjected to the same weather conditions, but concrete slab floors do suffer more, because of their surface area: volume ratio is greater and over-site are above ground level, open to the elements.

Suspended dense concrete slab:
Most of the rules listed above for a dense concrete slab apply again along with these extra rules.

- Subsoil free from organic material can be used for over-site preparation.

- The steel reinforcing must be to the correct specification; (slabs of this type are usually designed by a structural engineer to suit the location and size of property).

- The steel must be laid in the right direction, and be supported at all edges and dividing walls.

- If the Dpm is to be placed under the slab on top of over-site preparation, care must be taken to prevent punctures. It is a lot easier to place the Dpm on the set concrete slab prior to the floor or screed being laid.

- The steel must not extend beyond the line of the concrete slab; this will allow it to corrode.

All of the above technical details are explained in the section for suspended concrete slab floors.

A concrete pre-cast floor:
These are manufactured by specialist companies who normally offer an installation service as part of the floor package, if this is not what the builder has arranged then insist that this is what you want to happen. This way if any faults occur they can be rectified by the flooring contractor.

    The flooring contractor may be following ground workers who have prepared the site, beam flooring specialists do not normally prepare the over-site area when their system is used in a ground floor situation. When the system is used on upper floors the Specialist Company will be relying on the bricklayers to have left them a level course of block-work to rest the flooring system on. (See drawing for pre-cast concrete floors)

    There are obvious faults that you can watch for even if a specialist company is completing the work; after all they can make mistakes as well!

- The pre-stressed beams have been made to the correct length for the span of the floor, they must not overhang into the cavity space or be short so that they fail to sit fully on the block support wall (100mm minimum bearing support).

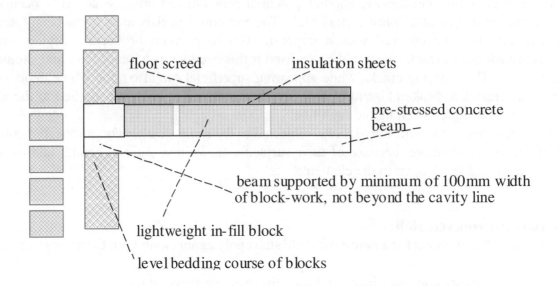

floor screed   insulation sheets

pre-stressed concrete beam

beam supported by minimum of 100mm width of block-work, not beyond the cavity line

lightweight in-fill block

level bedding course of blocks

- Where the in-fill blocks are joined together and where these join the beams there must be cement mortar grout applied, this really prevents draughts; there is no structural requirement for this.

- There are no cracks in beams, but more importantly there are no cracked in-fill blocks, these may fall out.

Faults to be aware of with floor finishes:
There are several faults that can occur with floor finishes, all unique to each type of floor finish:

Tongue and groove timber strip flooring:
- All timber must be fully seasoned, (see section on timber).

- If the floor is being laid on top of a concrete slab there must be a damp-proof membrane placed between the concrete and timber. This is advisable even if there is a membrane under the concrete slab; a new concrete slab will hold moisture for several months after construction.

- When a new wood strip floor is laid in an existing property a membrane must be used.

- The correct fixings must be used; normally 65 to 75mm cut flooring brads. However more and more timber flooring is being fixed using brass or plated screws, their advantage being that the floor boards can be tightened when shrinkage's occur, and if required, easy access is possible to the space below the floor boards.

- There must be a gap between the floorboards and the wall below the skirting board; this is to allow the boards to expand. Without this provision, if the floorboards expand in their width the floor will bulge upwards and in extreme conditions the boards will lift away from the nails.

- When the boards have been laid, if they are going to be a feature of the room, they must be protected. This can be with polythene or if the building program allows they can be treated with the specified floor finish. Dirty boot marks or wet trade spillages are very difficult to remove from softwood flooring.

Wood block or parquet flooring;

Many of the same rules apply, as for wood strip flooring; these are the extra potential faults to be aware of:

- Most parquet and wood block flooring is laid on a bed of hot bitumen, not only does this hold the blocks in place very well, but it acts as an excellent barrier against penetration of moisture. When blocks come loose on a floor it is nearly always as a result of moisture penetration where the bitumen has not covered the concrete thoroughly. Bitumen also allows the timber to move, glue is liable to fracture when movement occurs.

- Provision must be made in this type of floor for expansion, this is because it could expand and contract by as much as 10mm across a room of 3 metres. To overcome this problem a cork expansion strip should be incorporated in the floor around the edge of the room, these are normally 12 to 19mm wide.

- This type of flooring is more successful if it is tongued and grooved, if movement occurs, the top surface remains level and flat. Without a tongue and groove the blocks could lift slightly, causing a potential hazard.

Linoleum, vinyl, rubber and synthetic floor finishes:

This type of floor finish is normally available in large rolled sheets or tiles the same fitting rules apply to both. These are the faults to be aware of:

- The concrete must be level and smooth; these types of flooring will not stick to coarsely finished concrete.

- If the concrete is not smooth it can be levelled with self-levelling floor compound. This is a cement-based product poured over the concrete slab and smoothed with a trowel to give a flat, level finish. Some new properties have this as the finished floor surface.

- If the floor is level and smooth but dry and dusty, it must be sealed with a suitable product prior to applying the tiles, failure to do this could result in tiles lifting through poor adhesion.

Ceramic and quarry tiles:

Bedding and grouting procedure is very similar for both types of tiles, so the rules and procedures apply to both:

- Tile fixing cement adheres best to rough surface.

- The concrete should be sealed prior to the tiles being laid.

- If ready mixed cement is used it must be of a waterproof type.

- The grout must be waterproof.

- Special tiles for corners and edges are available for floors and tiled up-stands; these should always be used. The edges of standard floor tiles may not be glazed, and after a time if they were used on an edge or as a vertical up-stand, the edge would deteriorate and the tile will collapse.

Foundations

What are foundations?

Put simply they are, the roots of a house. Without them the house would collapse. Many dictionaries state that a foundation is the solid ground on which a property is built, but in construction terms a foundation describes the man-made structure, on which the property is built. It should be noted that many older properties have little or no 'foundations'. Churches are often found to be built on solid compacted ground and after 800 or more years are still standing. But look at the thickness of their walls, especially at the base!

Builders sometimes call them footings, but it still describes the same part of a building. There are several types of foundation. This book looks at main ones that concern domestic property building.

- Strip foundation

- raft foundation

- piled foundations

- Deep strip or trench fill

Are there any rules that govern their structure

There are many rules to be adhered to when the foundations are being built; they also fall in a defined order as the work takes place.

Strip foundations

- Most homes are built on a strip foundation that forms a closed ring beneath the walls. These are the rules that apply to this type of foundation;

When the trench is dug, usually with a mechanical digger, the width of the trench is normally 600mm. The trench is sometimes called the 'footing'. There is a calculation used to determine the width of trench needed for a strip foundation,

Width of trench = $\dfrac{\text{load per metre}}{\text{bearing capacity of soil}}$

Note: In all instances the width of the trench must provide a sufficient working space for the bricklayer, for simplicity two sizes of trench are used, 450mm and 600mm. These are standard sizes of mechanical digger buckets. It is also important to remember that when a trench is deep that the width should be increased to prevent the sides from collapsing.

- The depth of the trench to be dug is determined by the soil structure exposed and surrounding objects such as trees. The trench has to be dug down to the sub-soil; this varies depending where in the country the building is taking place. There are strict guidelines for foundation excavations to prevent serious problems from occurring.

Ground movement:

This problem is caused by a combination of several factors. It only affects foundations where the base of the strip is 600mm or less below ground level,

(i)   At this shallow depth the subsoil directly below and adjacent to the foundation will be subjected to the weather elements very easily. As the ground becomes wet and dry the strip foundation will be subjected to severe movement. This is a particular problem with clay based subsoils, whereas compact granular soils like gravel suffer very little from this fault.

(ii)   Severe changes in the ground may result as water in subsoil freezes; this is called 'frost heave'. To overcome the problem of subsoil movement all strip foundation bases must be at least 600mm deep, working to a depth of 1.0 metre or more will ensure even less ground movement. When ground movement occurs it can create faults such as tilting foundations, which cause walls to crack horizontally, or in severe cases cause the wall to push out at the damp-proof course and collapse. It is therefore imperative that foundations are deep enough so that ground movement does not occur, the guidelines above will ensure this in most instances.

Trees:

Trees can cause severe problems to properties in various ways. Good planning and effective use of Building Regulation guidelines will ensure that problems are avoided:

(i)   **Direct contact**   This is where the roots of a tree penetrate the sub-structure of a property.

(ii)   **Moisture shrinkage or 'heave'**   Shrinkage occurs when the tree sucks all of the moisture out of the surrounding ground in dry weather, causing the sub-soil to shrink. Trees such as poplar, willow, oak and elm can cause severe problems, especially in very dry weather. Once the ground shrinks, ground movement occurs and the foundations may be disturbed.

'Heave' occurs in extremely wet weather, especially where trees have been removed. These trees, previously may have assisted in the natural drainage of the land, once removed the balance is upset and the ground swells, causing ground movement. A tree or group of trees as far away as 25 metres can have an affect on foundations, so steps must be taken before they are removed or before building commences.

Issues and points to remember;

1. As a guide most deciduous trees such as those listed have a root spread area approximately the same as the spread of the branch canopy. A mature oak standing 35 metres could have a root spread of up to a 12-metre radius of the trunk. This will have an affect on the foundation type and design, if building is planned close to or within this area.

2. The type of soil structure will also be a factor where trees are close to proposed building work. If the subsoil is of a compacted granular nature such as gravel, it will suffer less from the effect of tree growth or removal.

3. There may be tree preservation orders in place, always ensure that the Local Authority planning department has been consulted. The only trees that can be felled without permission in areas where preservation orders are in operation are fruit or 'crop' trees. If a tree needs to be felled the builder will have to apply in writing for a felling licence. If a tree has a preservation order, felling is usually only granted if;

    *   It is endangering an existing property,
    *   On new developments, it will be in the interest of economic well-being of the local community, and
    *   New trees will be planted on the site to replace any felled.

4. If trees are in the close proximity of a proposed building, conventional strip foundations will not be suitable. The usual alternatives are deep trench-fill or short pile and beam foundations, (see following sections).

*   Any soil structure that appears disturbed or contains foreign or organic materials must be removed until clean undisturbed ground is found.

- Once the trench has been dug, pegs will be knocked into the bottom of the trench to give a levelling point around the trench at 1 to 2m intervals to finish the concrete to. From the bottom of the trench to the top of the peg the minimum measurement should be 150mm. It is imperative that the pegs are level from one end of the trench to the other to prevent problems when the bricks are laid on top of it.

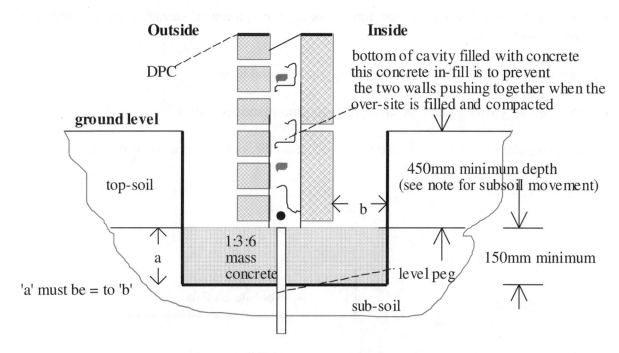

A cross section through a strip foundation

- If at any point a step has to be incorporated into the foundation it must be ensured that the concrete complies with current building regulations in all places. It must also be the correct dimensions to coincide with brickwork courses.

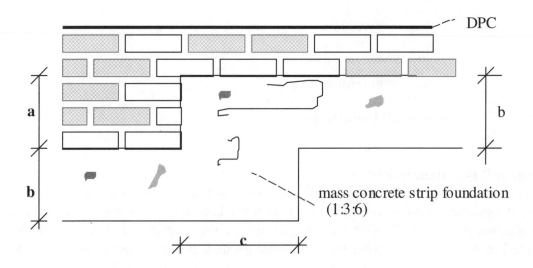

'c' (length of step) must be twice 'a'
'a' (height of step) should match brick courses, with a maximum depth not exceeding 'b'
'b' minimum depth of 150mm

Deep strip or Trench-fill foundation

This type of foundation is becoming more widely used, because it has important advantages over a conventional strip foundation:

- Fewer man-hours are required for construction.

- Uses ready mixed concrete, therefore reducing the amount of storage area required on site for bricks and blocks.

- Expensive skilled trades are not required until ground level.

- They are very strong and less susceptible to ground movement.

The same regulations as a strip foundation are applicable, other than those shown on the diagram:

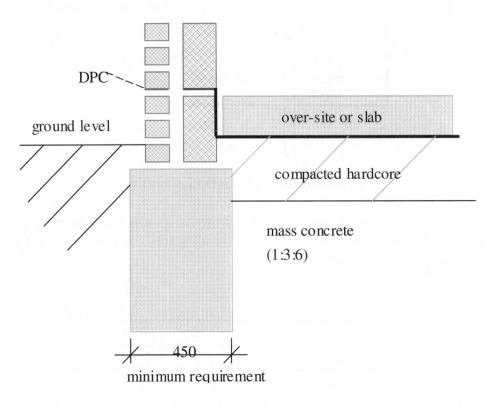

Trench-fill foundation

Solid slab or raft type foundations

These are probably the second most commonly used type of foundation for domestic property being used where the ground could be unstable or where there is a likelihood that the ground has been reclaimed at some time. The Fens in East Anglia are a good example of where a raft foundation might be used to overcome the problems of unstable ground, in this instance the ground has been reclaimed.

What is a raft foundation

A raft foundation is exactly what the title suggests, a concrete raft on which the property is built. Raft foundations are specifically designed for use on land where the subsoil is of poor quality. Basically it is the over site concrete and strip foundation linked together with reinforcing steel rods and sheet mesh. The theory behind a raft foundation is that if there is any movement in the ground the whole property moves, lessening the chances of walls cracking or in extreme case's collapse of the building. It probably is the strongest of all foundations used in domestic building, it is however considerably more expensive than strip foundations.

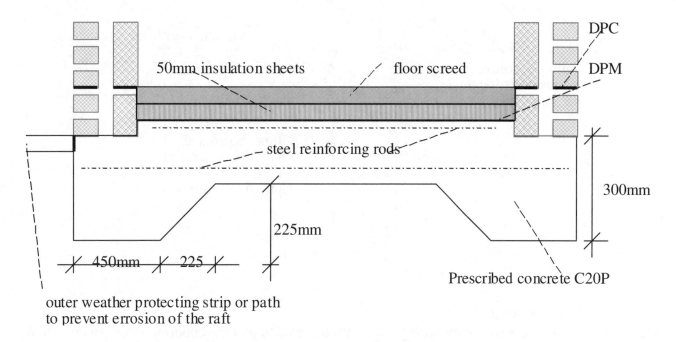

Section through a typical reinforced raft foundation

'Piled' foundations

This type of foundation is used when a raft foundation will not overcome the severe ground conditions, usually when the building is very heavy or tall, the ground is very wet or boggy, or the ground has been re-claimed at some time, perhaps an old pit. This type of foundation is very expensive when used just for one property, this is the reason that many reclaimed sites are used for flats, apartments and commercial property as the cost of the piling can be spread over many properties.

Some individual properties are piled, probably the site was cheap or deep piles are not required and a system called 'short bored piles' can be used. This system is specifically designed for use on domestic building, where there are clay subsoils or where the proposed building is close to trees.

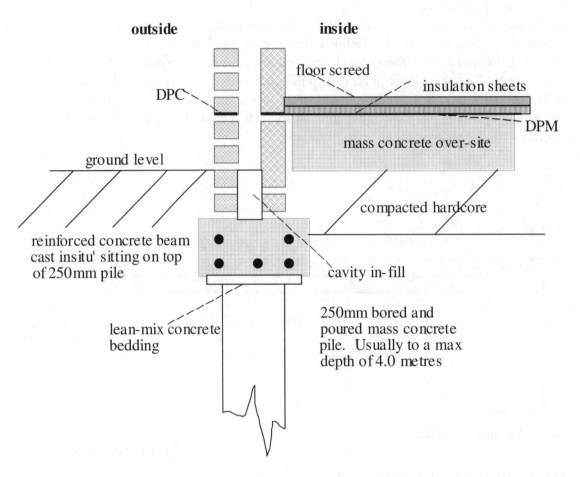

outside   **inside**

floor screed

DPC

insulation sheets

DPM

ground level

mass concrete over-site

reinforced concrete beam
cast insitu' sitting on top
of 250mm pile

compacted hardcore

cavity in-fill

lean-mix concrete
bedding

250mm bored and
poured mass concrete
pile. Usually to a max
depth of 4.0 metres

How are 'piles' constructed?

Generally they are constructed by boring holes into the ground and then pouring mass concrete into the holes. The holes are bored using a tractor or lorry mounted auger or drill, some of these vehicles have on-board pumps to force the concrete down the bores. On larger properties or where the piles have got to go into the ground further than 4.0 metres, they use percussion piles; these are steel lined piles that are hammered into the ground.

How do they work?

The pile is driven into the ground until it reaches firm subsoil, or the bottom of the pit that may have been filled. Once it reaches firm ground it can act as a support for the ring strip foundation that will be constructed on top of the piles.

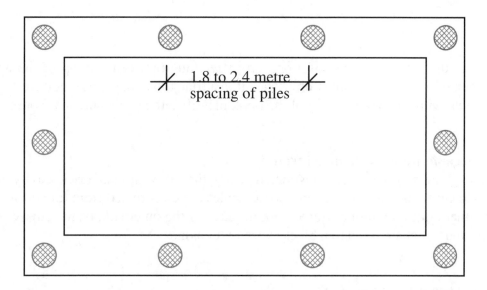

The diagram above shows a plan of a foundation giving a typical layout of piles and a strip beam above. It should be noted that if the builder says that you require a special foundation it is normal that a structural engineer will have to be instructed to design it. This type of foundation has to meet with building control requirements, so it is probably beyond the mental capacity of the average 'cowboy builder, furthermore specialist firms normally do the construction of this type of foundation.

What faults should you look for in foundation construction?
The main problem with 'cowboy builders' is they try to save money by using the incorrect depth to the concrete foundation, when they are out of the way dig down the side of the concrete to expose the bottom and measure its depth. If it is incorrect complain and get the fault rectified.

It should be remembered that if the project were large enough to require planning permission the building control inspector would if necessary do this check on your behalf, so tell them of your suspicions. They should have inspected the trench prior to the concrete being poured but they are not normally present to see the concrete enter the trench, this is the only way of ensuring that regulations are adhered to.

Another favourite trick is to dig the trench shallow, not down to the sub-soil, this means that they will have less soil to take away from the site.

It is also important that the topsoil is not mixed with the sub-soil, as when the ground around the building is eventually landscaped you will not want clay, gravel or rock in amongst the garden topsoil.

If the subsoil is very near the surface it is important that the builder digs deeper, to a minimum depth to the top of the foundation as shown in the diagram at the beginning of this section. This is to prevent the concrete being exposed when the landscaping takes place and also to prevent frost damage to the foundation. Because of its rough texture water could sit in the surface and when it freezes the concrete could split with the expansion.

In very hot weather the foundations, when being constructed, must be covered with a tarpaulin, this to prevent the surface drying out too quickly, and causing the surface of the concrete to crack, this is known as 'plastic cracking'. If this occurs it is a serious fault and such work should not be accepted.

If the foundation is small and the builder is mixing the concrete on site ensure the correct mix is being used, it should be a (1:3:6) mix the breakdown of this mix is stated in the section on concrete.

Gable

This is name given to the wall at the end of a property stretching between the top of the upstairs windows and the apex of the roof. On most properties it is a triangular shape, but they are found in various shapes. The drawing at the beginning of the book identifies the gable end on a house.

What materials are gable walls constructed from?

On domestic dwelling, most gables are constructed using the conventional brick cavity format described earlier. However for aesthetic reasons some gables are constructed from timber or plastic cladding. This is either built on a timber framework in place of the outer skin of the cavity wall or fixed on timber 'grounds' that are fixed to a block-work outer skin.

What problem areas should you look for?

There are some key points to look for in gable construction, they are:

- Do the bricks and mortar match the rest of the brickwork below the level of the eaves? Sometimes, because the gables are built at a later stage the bricks are from a different batch and the shade varies or the sand used to make the mortar is from a different gravel pit and when the mortar dries it is a different shade. This does not necessarily mean the brickwork is faulty, but it is a sign of sloppy workmanship.

- Check that the brick bonding is of a reasonable standard and that the cut bricks ('rake cut') rising up the slope of the roof are cut accurately and that the pointing around them has equal joints to match the rest of the gable. Bad tradesmen often use mortar to make up differences where bricks are not cut accurately.

- If timber framing and cladding are used there must be a water barrier placed on the frame prior to the boards being fixed. This is usually achieved by using either building paper, a paper impregnated with bitumen, or by using under-slaters' felt. Polythene should not be used as it may allow timber to sweat and cause rotting problems. Timber used should be pressure treated with preservative except where cedar cladding is used, cedar has natural preserving oils of its own.

- Ensure that where the scaffolding was supported in the joints of the brickwork, that the edges of the bricks have not been damaged and that the holes left has been pointed with mortar correctly.

- Any lead flashing that adjoins the gable must be installed correctly to comply with current regulations as described in the section on lead flashing.

Gas supply.

Who controls and administers gas connections?

Since privatisation of the gas supply industry this may vary from region to region, but the first point of call can still be British Gas, most of the other supply companies have to use the existing supply system to deliver the gas to your home. If there is a gas main in the road near your property the charge is normally calculated per metre from the main to the supply meter box to be installed on an external wall of the property. Any pipe-work within the property is the responsibility of the property owner and is normally installed by a plumber, to the gas supplier's regulations.

The supply pipe and meter box are normally provided by the gas supplier as part of the installation package. However, the box installation is generally the responsibility of the property owner. Sometimes the property owner, rather than paying the supplier to do it place the supply pipe in a trench. The gas supplier will make the connection to the main and the meter.

All gas installations must comply with the Gas Safety (installation and use) regulations 1994 legislation, and with the Building regulations section J.

What are the basic rules that affect gas service installations?

These rules are applicable to all new gas service installations or those where major alterations will result in the current installation being relocated:

- Underground service pipes must be at least 380mm deep, supplied by the Gas Company. A polythene marker strip must be laid in the trench above the pipe to prevent damage during future excavations. Service pipes must never pass beneath a foundation.

- Where the supply pipe rises above the ground below the meter box it must be securely clipped to the wall.

- The meter box will contain the main control valve and the usage meter. The position is normally agreed with the gas supplier, near to the front of the property, (not behind gates or fences). The boxes are supplied by the gas company and require a hole in the outer leaf of the cavity wall 450 x 530mm, this positioned at least 5 courses of brickwork above the DPC, this may vary with each supply company.

- The gas meter box and supply pipe should if possible enter the building on its nearest side to the main.

- The service pipe that connects the meter with the household appliances must pass through the wall by the shortest possible route. It can pass through the cavity but must not travel within it. A duct must be used to pass the supply pipe through the wall. Its ends must be sealed with mastic.

- When gas supply pipes are located in floors or walls, they must be protected using a duct or sleeve, the ends of which are sealed once the system has been commissioned. The most direct route between meter box and appliance is normally taken, and pipes within wall must rise and fall vertically.

- Internal gas supply pipes are normally made from copper, much the same as the rest of a property's plumbing, occasionally steel is used with threaded joints and bends. There must be no kinks or damage to the pipe used.

- Any new gas installation or one that has received major alterations must be commissioned, tested and then certified by the supplying gas company before use.

- A competent, experienced and qualified engineer must install all gas installations, there is no alternative to this. (See section on boiler maintenance).

Glass and glazing.

Glass is manufactured from a mixture of soda, lime and silica, which is essentially sand. Glazing is the application of glass to openings within the fabric of a building. Glass provides a means of weatherproofing a door or window, while allowing the passage of light.

Are there different types of glass?
The following is a list of most of the different types used:

- **Clear float glass**   Use in windows and doors, available in various thicknesses (see glazing regulations).

- **Frosted or Translucent glass**   Glass that has one surface patterned, affording privacy This type of glass can have other material added to restrict vision even further. Available in different thicknesses but usually 4 to 6mm.

- **Toughened or safety Glass**   Float glass that has been subjected to high temperature treatment, when it breaks it shatters into small grain like pieces.

- **Laminated glass**   Sheets of glass bonded together with a layer of clear plastic. This is to ensure that in the event of the glass breaking, that it does not fall from the place in which it is fixed, much the same as a car windscreen.

- **Wire glass**   You will remember this from your school days, the glass that looks like clear graph paper in the doors. It holds together on impact and provides some fire protection. Most wired glass is known as Georgian polished wire glass, and is 6-8mm thick, with 12mm wire squares. This is not commonly used on domestic properties, however some flats and apartments may have it in the front doors, where they open into a communal hallway.

- **Fireproof glass**   Seldom used for domestic dwellings. Sometimes used in a glazed door leading from a garage to dwelling or a glazed door in a flat that connects with communal areas. This does not have wire reinforcing and looks like normal glass. It may appear tinted; a common brand is 'Pyrite'. ('Pyrex' in cookware)

Are there specific glass types for different areas of dwelling?
There are regulations affecting the use of glass, covered in The Building Regulations document N, there are some simple rules to follow;

- All doors should be glazed with safety glass, normally toughened.

- If a door has small panes of glass (below 0.5 square metres), 4mm float glass can be used, but if possible 6mm should be used.

- Any window areas below 800mm from the floor must be glazed with safety glass. Non-safety glass must have a protective barrier.

- Single glazing above 800mm may be of 4mm-float glass; panes in excess of 1 square metre should be of 6mm glass.

- Glazed roof areas should be of laminated glass, so that in the event of breakage, glass cannot fall on people below. Laminated glass for domestic purposes comes in 4.8mm and 6.4mm thicknesses. Toughened glass can be used on a roof, but when it breaks it makes an awful mess.

These rules are applicable to any new or replacement glass.

How is a piece of glass measured?

One of the main causes for glass cracking is bad measurement. Glass must never be tight in a glazing rebate, because it expands at a different rate to the material it is secured to. In cold weather this can cause glass to crack. If glass is tight against the rebate this also prevents the putty from sealing all around the glass.

There must be a space between the glass and the rebate, ideally a minimum clearance of 2mm.

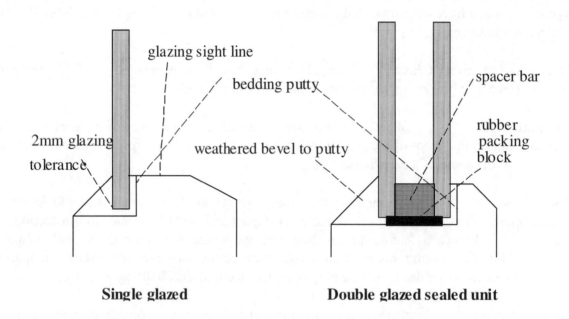

Single glazed　　　　　　　　**Double glazed sealed unit**

This glass measuring technique applies to sealed unit glazing as well, the difference here is that the sealed unit is held in place using rubber-packing blocks.

How is glass fitted?

When glass is secured using putty rather than glazing beads, it should be held against the bedding putty using brass or copper glazing sprigs, these are small pins or triangular shaped clips. If Glazing beads are used they should be secured using plated steel pins; this method of glazing still uses bedding putty. The putty must be bevelled so that the top of the bevel is in line with the back of the rebate, or so that it covers the sealed unit spacer bar (see diagram above).

Are there different types of glazing compound used?

Wet glazing in timber frames is done using linseed oil putty manufactured to BS544. Prior to the putty being applied the rebate must be cleaned and primed, and it should be painted within 14 days of glazing. Putty is available in various colours to match stained timber.

Wet glazed metal windows are seldom used today, and have been replaced with aluminium windows with integral rubber glazing seals. If your property has metal windows with glass that is secured with putty, in the event of a pane having to be re-glazed, it must be done using the correct method:

- The old glass must be carefully removed.

- The old putty or glazing compound must be removed entirely exposing the steel rebate.

- Rusty areas must be treated with an appropriate treatment. Failure to do this can result in the glass breaking due to the rust expanding against the glass.

- The new piece of glass must have a glazing tolerance of 2 to 3mm; metal windows can expand more than timber.

- Bedding putty is placed into the rebate and the glass is pushed into place, clips are normally used to hold the glass in place until the putty has set.

- The putty has a bevel applied as in a timber window.

- Beads are sometimes used to hold the glass in place, if this is so, bedding putty is still placed around the glass to weatherproof it.

Common faults to be aware of.
The usual problems associated with glazing are specification faults and unskilled workmanship; these have been covered on the preceding pages. The list below highlights further points to watch for, and gives tips to identify the problem:

- If a glazier has to chisel out the rebate beyond the old putty, ask why. This is usually a sign that the glass has been cut too large, and that once the glass fits the rebate, it will be secured. This will give no glazing tolerance and after a period the glass could break. Do not let this happen.

- Sealed unit spacer bars showing well beyond the glazing sight line; Either caused by the sealed units being made too small, or the rebates were not intended to house sealed units. This is a fault because,

  (i)   It looks unsightly and ,
  (ii) The sealed unit can break down because sunlight can effect the polysolphides used to hold sealed units together.

  Complain and insist the fault be corrected.

- Glass that has a crack starting from under the putty or glazing bead; This is an expansion crack caused by either a rusty glazing sprig or a piece of glass that has been cut too large. If the frame has rot, this can cause this fault, check before re-glazing.

- Rain blowing between the glazing rebate and the glass; This is caused by two faults,

  (i)   The rebate was not primed prior to glazing, and the putty has not keyed to the rebate, or
  (ii) There is insufficient bedding putty around the glass (see drawing at beginning of section).

Guttering

What is guttering, and what is its purpose?

It is the shallow trough fitted just below the eaves on a roof. Its purpose is to collect rainwater from the roof and to direct it to the storm water drain.

Are there different types of gutters?

Yes there are, and they can be found in many locations around the roof. Most properties have just those on the eaves, but older properties which have been added to over the years, may have difficult areas on a roof to locate a standard gutter. In these instances 'box gutters' are built, as a means of collecting the rainwater. Where two roofs intersect, a valley will be built; this is another form of gutter.

Are gutters made from different materials?

Most new properties will have guttering fitted that is made from uPVC (plastic), this is used because of its low maintenance and it is very easy to install. Older properties may have cast iron gutters; these require regular maintenance, without which they will rot.

Sometimes plastic gutters are not used because they would not be able to cope with the quantity of rainwater. They could sag or the joints are forced apart. There are alternative ways to overcome this problem. Cast aluminium gutters are available in large sizes, their advantage being that while they are strong they are also light. Cast aluminium gutters are available in many different architectural designs. Guttering is also available in stainless or galvanised steel, but these are very expensive and are normally used for commercial properties.

When a roof has a valley or intersection where conventional gutters cannot be used, box gutters are built. A plywood channel that is lined with lead sheet forms these. This is a very skilled operation and should be carried out by a plumber.

Common faults.

- If guttering is not fitted properly or not functioning in the correct way, it can cause greater expense because of the further damage caused to surrounding masonry, roof areas and land:

- Plastic guttering is very durable, but if it is not installed correctly, it won't function correctly. It must be supported with the correct clips or steel support brackets at a minimum of every 1200mm. Failure to do this could result in the gutter sagging, and the weight of the water pulling the joints apart.

- Down-pipe clips should be placed at intervals of 1500mm or less.

- The point at which the 'swan-neck' bend leaves the gutter outlet spigot must always have a support bracket directly below the bend. At the bottom where the down-pipe enters the drain the clip is just above the 'swan-neck'.

- If a roof covers a large area it may require an outlet either end with two separate soakaways, this will make the gutter work more efficiently.

- Gutters require very little fall, if there is a back-fall, overflowing may occur in heavy downpours.

- Old cast iron gutters may be jointed using putty and after several years the joints may begin to leak. When this occurs it does not necessarily mean that the gutter will have to be replaced, cast iron gutters will last for many years if maintained properly. There is a simple procedure to remedy this problem provided that the gutter is still sound. The gutter needs to be cleaned, hosed out and dismantled. The gutter bolts that hold it together will be rusty and rather than attempting to free them it is easier to tighten them, forcing them to break. They are very cheap and are best replaced.

  Once the gutter is dismantled, all the joints should be thoroughly cleaned and dried. It is then re-assembled placing gutter jointing mastic between the joints before the bolts are positioned and tightened.

  The under-Slaters' felt should extend slightly beyond the end of the tiles; this should be placed in the gutter, to direct any water that blows under the tiles into the gutter. All eaves gutters should have this detail at the bottom. (See also roofs)

- Ensure that the down-pipe enters the storm water system and not the foul sewer, this is an offence if it occurs.

- If the gutter has begun to leak it is likely that the soakaway is not working efficiently. To test a soakaway, place a garden hose into the down-pipe and turn on the tap, after several minutes the water may flow over the top of the gutter. Turn the water off, and watch what happens, if the water level is very slow to drop in the pipe, it is likely that the soakaway needs replacing (see section on drains).

- Always check that you have soakaways or mains storm drains. There may be storm drain covers near the down-pipe if in doubt check the deeds. Failure to check this and you will empty the local reservoir!

Hard-core or 'hoggin'

What is hardcore or 'hoggin'?

It is the aggregate that is used as a base for roads, paths, ground floor in-fill, driveways and over-site in-fill. In most instances it is sand-based consisting of a mixture of sharp-sand and non-graded stone, usually in its natural state, excavated from the ground.

What is its purpose when used for building

Before building takes place any topsoil should be removed, in some instances the topsoil will be several cm deep. Building work is generally designed around the existing ground level so, even though the topsoil has been removed, the DPC will still have to be positioned two brick courses above the original ground level.

Mass slab concrete is generally laid to a 150mm thickness, on top of a compacted hard-core over-site, covering the sub-soil up to the required depth (see diagram). The purpose of the hard-core is to give the concrete a firm and stable base, if the concrete were laid on topsoil this could dry and shrink leaving a void between the concrete and the soil, the concrete could then settle and crack.

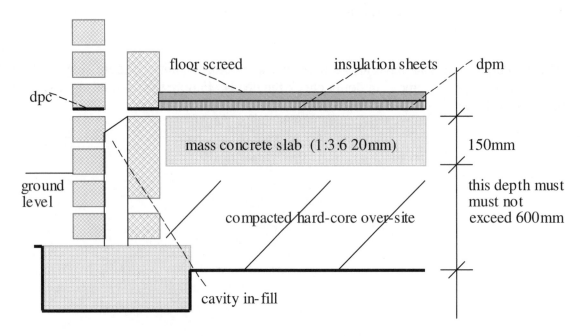

Section showing location of hard-core or 'hoggin'

When hard-core or 'hoggin' is placed under roads, driveways or paths it serves the same purpose, that is to act as a firm and stable base for the construction that is to be placed over it.

Are there different types of hard-core or 'hoggin' available?

There are different types available, the type of hard-core will be determined by where in the country the building project is taking place, as the geological nature of the surrounding countryside will determine what type it is. As an example in Norfolk and Suffolk the naturally available hard-core is sand mixed with flints, whereas in Wales it would probably be a slate or shale based hard-core.

Reclaimed materials can also be used; typical examples are crushed concrete, bricks and metalled road surface.

Are different types used for specific jobs?

There are no specific types of hard-core for each job but some types do a better job than others do. Crushed concrete is better for creating a base for roads because it compacts very tightly whereas sand and flint based hard-core is excellent for dwelling over-sites because the sand binds the flint together and fills any voids easily, thus providing a very stable base for the concrete slab.

What faults should you look for when inspecting hard-core?

Even though the process of using hard-core is reasonably straight forward there is a need to inspect the work thoroughly, as this is another area of building where the 'cowboy builder' will try their luck in an attempt to save money. There are some key areas to be watched for:

- Hard-core must not be contaminated with organic matter, this means roots, grass turf, tree limbs or other plant material. This is because it will eventually rot and leave voids allowing the support to fail, and the concrete slab to fracture.

- It is acceptable to use damaged bricks or large natural stone as hard-core, however without sand to bind it together and fill the smaller gaps a great deal more concrete will be required as it will run in to the gaps as it is 'tamped' into place. It is far more cost effective to use a sand or crushed stone based product.

- Once the hard-core is in place it must be correctly compacted, whatever the purpose. It is generally compacted on an over-site with a 'whacker', a vibrating machine that has a heavy steel plate that glides across the hard-core levelling and compacting it as it is moved across the over-site. Paths, drives and roads are usually compacted with a vibrating roller, this machine needs more room and is not suitable for over-sites.

- When the hard-core has been compacted it is very important that the space left between the top of the hard-core and the top of the brick below the DPC is an even measurement of 150mm. It should be checked in various positions across the whole over-site (see diagram at beginning of section). Any variation should be corrected, as thin concrete is liable to crack, excess concrete is an unnecessary expense.

Heating boiler maintenance

Who do you ask to service your boiler?

This is normally the job of a specialist-heating engineer, however some plumbers are experienced and qualified to service boilers.

Do they have to be specially qualified?

The answer is yes; there are different qualifications for different types of boiler. A certificate is required for solid fuels such as coal and oil, and a separate qualification applies to gas boilers. There are various certification schemes in operation, but the most commonly used schemes are CORGI for gas engineers and OFTEC for oil and solid fuel boiler engineers.

These are regularly updated and improved to ensure that members are kept informed of advances in boiler technology, they also run regular refresher courses for their members.

When your boiler is serviced, what should the engineer be doing?

There are very important items that have to be checked when a boiler is serviced. They also have to be carried out in the correct order:

- All ventilation points in the room where the boiler is located must be checked for efficiency and obstructions.

- Any joints where the boiler flue connects with the building chimney must be checked for soundness. If any doubt exists this is carried out using a smoke test. All cracked fire cement should be replaced.

- Blocking the chimney pot and dropping a lighted smoke pellet into the flue carries out a smoke test. If the flue is sound no smoke will escape, if it has a fault the coloured smoke will be visible and the fault can be identified.

- When a boiler service is being carried out the heat exchange or firebox should be cleaned, these can be encased with ash, soot and other deposits from combustion of fuel.

- The fuel supply pipes must be checked for leaks and/or damage.

- The fuel filter on the oil tank should be checked for contamination, most are of a paper disposable type, and should be renewed every year.

- Once all of these checks have been made the boiler can be re-started, and then checked for efficient combustion using special equipment. This test is compulsory, and must be undertaken by qualified specialists.

- All the seals and insulation should be checked on the boiler casing.

- Finally, all the associated electrical components for the boiler should be checked for correct functioning.

Insulation

What is insulation?

Usually a lightweight material used to insulate areas and/or services within a building. They are generally made from polystyrene, fibreglass or mineral based products. Electrical services have insulation in the form of plastic coatings over wiring. A good overall description of insulation is a material that is an inefficient conductor of heat or electricity. Generally less dense materials are good insulators. The air in a cavity wall is an insulator, as air is a poor conductor of heat.

What is its purpose?

The main purpose of insulation is to contain energy in areas for which it is intended. Electrical installations for obvious reasons have to be insulated to prevent electric shock, so ideally a material is required that is non-conducting. Materials used for insulation of electrical components must have a very high resistance to the flow of electricity; the best materials for this are plastic, PVC or rubber.

Domestic plumbing installations are insulated to prevent heat loss on the hot water side of the system and to prevent damage by frost on the cold supply, whereas the insulation on the fabric of the house is to conserve energy from heat loss. These are examples of thermal insulation:

Thermal insulation should prevent heat loss from one of the following:

Conduction   transfer of heat by touch,

Convection   transfer of heat by current, and

Radiation   transfer of heat in 'wave' form, e.g. infrared light.

Either conduction or convection through a vacuum cannot transfer heat, radiated heat can. Shiny surfaces reflect much of the radiated heat, reducing such transfer, this is why vacuum flasks have silvery linings! Thus, thin aluminium foil can be used as a coating on plasterboard when building walls, and reflective metal on roofs minimises the heating effect of the sun and special coatings can be sprayed on glass to improve its insulation properties or 'U' value.

Air offers about 15,000 times as much resistance to heat flow as a good thermal conductor such as silver does, and about 30 times as much as glass. Typical insulating materials, therefore, are usually made of non-metallic materials and are filled with small air pockets. They include cork, felt, cotton blankets, rock or glass fibre wool, and diatomaceous earth e.g. 'Vermiculite'. Asbestos was once widely used for insulation, but it has been found to be a health hazard and has, therefore, been banned in new construction in the UK, and many other countries.

In building materials, air pockets provide additional insulation in hollow glass bricks, double-glazed windows (consisting of two or three sealed glass panes with a thin air space between them). Insulating properties become poorer if the air space becomes large enough to allow thermal convection, or if moisture seeps in and then acts as a conductor. As an analogy, the air trapped between the fibres and one's body creates the insulating property of dry clothing. This ability to insulate is significantly reduced by moisture: damp clothes feel colder.

Home-heating and air-conditioning costs can be reduced by good building insulation. The recommended minimum insulation requirements are 75mm for walls and about 150 to 230mm for a roof space, and a 50mm insulated ground floor.

Some local authorities offer grants to cover some of the costs of bringing your property into line with these minimum recommendations, (available to existing properties, not for new build or for your planned extension).

Where should insulation be used?

Electrical installations:

All electrical installations have to be insulated; there are no exceptions to this rule. Further precautions are taken in that electrical wires are covered with plastic conduit when they are behind plaster for protection, the same principle applies when they are laid underground, in this instance 'Armourguard' cable is used, this also serves as an insulator against mechanical damage, e.g. digging in the garden!

Electrical cables should not be laid in the same conduits or ducts as water pipes, either hot or cold. But if this is unavoidable, the pipes must be insulated to retain their heat, because heat can reduce the insulating properties of most plastics.

Domestic water system:

Hot water distribution pipes are not normally insulated when they run within the living areas of a property, if, however, hot and cold pipes are boxed-in or ducted side-by-side it is advisable to insulate the cold pipe to prevent condensation. If there are pipes that are outside the property or in the roof space (loft or attic), these must be insulated using specially made foam rubber pipe sheathing, failure to do so will result in burst pipes when the frost freezes them, ice expands, and ruptures the pipes.

Walls:

On a new property it is possible to fill the cavity wall to achieve a greater thermal value for the wall, with new build this is often done as the property is built by placing sheet insulation material in the cavity during construction. In existing properties filling the cavity is achieved by injecting insulation material through holes drilled in the joints of the brickwork. In both instances the insulation is either polystyrene foam or rock wool.

If your property is old there probably isn't a cavity so these techniques cannot be used, however older properties tend to have thicker walls constructed from various materials bound together using lime mortar. This extra thickness usually helps them to retain the heat in cold weather and to stay cool in the summer. There are thin polystyrene coatings available on rolls that can be glued to the wall to improve the insulation, and prevent condensation, prior to decoration.

Floors:

This subject can be divided into ground and upper floors, as both are treated in very different ways and the type of materials used in their construction affects both. As a rule upper floors are not thermally insulated but they may be insulated for sound. Ground floors can be constructed in several ways but the two main forms for domestic dwellings are 'hollow ground' and solid concrete slab. 'Hollow ground' means that there is a void under the floor, solid concrete is self explanatory, a large slab of mass concrete supported by the prepared ground below it (see earlier section).

Hollow ground floors are constructed from timber boarding supported on timber joists, in some instances pre-formed concrete beam and in-fill blocks are used. If a timber floor requires insulation it is normally achieved using cut sheet insulation supported on battens just below the top of the joists, or whole sheets are placed on top of the joists prior to the floorboards being laid. If a concrete beam floor needs insulating sheets of rigid polystyrene or similar insulating material are laid in the beam floor prior to the floor screed being laid, the cement based screed is then placed on top of this.

If a conventional slab of mass concrete is used, this can still be insulated, by using the same method as above for the beam floor and placing the cement screed on top of the rigid insulation sheets.

Roof:

The insulation in the roof space or loft area is probably the most important insulation in your home. Heat rises, and therefore needs to be contained within the living areas of a domestic dwelling. Part L of The Building Regulations (appendix 'A') gives precise rules for the amounts of insulation required in a roof space, to give it the necessary U value. Explained simply, any roof space covered with sloping 'walls' must have a minimum depth of 150mm of suitable dense insulation, usually glass fibre wool or sprayed 'rock wool'. The insulation is placed at ceiling level, between the ceiling joists, thus creating a cold roof space. Insulation can be fixed at sloped rafter level, but this takes more time and would therefore cost more.

Is there any faults or bad trade practices to watch for?

As with all the other areas of building already covered by this book, insulation is no exception! The list below highlights the most serious and common faults, how to identify them and how you can correct the fault, especially important if the 'cowboy' has left the 'ranch'!

- When the cavity wall is filled it is important that all areas of the void are filled and that there are no spaces where the sheets are missed or the injected insulation does not reach. If this fault occurs it creates cold spots, or in the instance of injected foam or rock wool can cause any moisture entering the cavity to cross over to the inner skin and cause damp areas, in extreme cases black mould will form on the inside of the wall.

  If this fault has occurred on an injected wall is very hard to detect at the time the work is done. A good prevention is to ensure that the holes are drilled reasonably close together, at regular intervals, around the building as this lessens the chances of voids being left. Where a 'cowboy' outfit is doing the work, a favourite trick is to spread the holes out leaving voids, thus using less insulation material and increasing their profits.

  The chances are that if they are doing this, it is a sure bet that the guarantee that they supply is not worth the paper it is written on! The only way to rectify this fault is to drill more holes and inject the walls in the areas that have shown the problem.

- When you are having new building work done that involves walls with insulated cavities let the builder know that you are aware of the problems that can occur, this should put them on their guard. It may be a good idea to inspect the work daily, looking for gaps between insulating sheets and insuring that sheets are fixed to the block-work inner leaf and not touching the outer brickwork. The sheets are held in place with special clips that fix to the cavity ties.

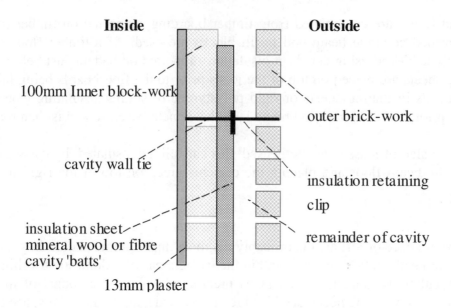

Inside | **Outside**

100mm Inner block-work

outer brick-work

cavity wall tie

insulation retaining
clip

insulation sheet
mineral wool or fibre
cavity 'batts'

remainder of cavity

13mm plaster

Section through a cavity wall showing sheet insulation

- The correct insulating material has been used; this is probably the most common error, mainly through ignorance rather than as a cost cutting measure. Some common errors are:

  (i)   Not using foil backed plasterboard on the ceiling of a bay window or any other location where space limits the amount of insulation material.

  (ii)   Where a specially coated material is used, it must be placed the correct way round, for example (foil coated polystyrene used in a floor that contains under floor heating must be placed foil side upwards so as to reflect the heat back into the room).

  (iii)   Ensuring that where necessary insulation complies with building regulations for fire precautions.

  (iv)   Materials that are specially designed for building insulating must always be used, a good example of what not to use would be packing bubble film as a loft insulation as this is not fire resistant and it could trap moisture and cause rotting problems.

  (v)   Making sure that insulation material is not contaminated before using it, with insects, vermin or moisture.

- The correct amount of insulation has been used; this is explained carefully in building regulation data books available at your local authority building control department.

Improvements that can be made to increase the insulation of a property.

Sound insulation:
Sound can be described as either airborne or impact, the source of the sound will ascertain which it is. Airborne sound is will cause the structure of a building to vibrate as the waves of sound strike it, and impact sound is caused by direct contact of the building's structure. Once either of these has occurred the sound created can be transmitted to other parts of the building, or to an adjacent one.

Sound insulation properties are built in to a property design to muffle noise, or at least, to keep it at a level that does not spoil the enjoyment of a property for its owners. Section E of The Building Regulations covers the use of sound insulation, and clearly states that it is a compulsory requirement to ensure that there is sufficient sound insulation to reduce, both air borne and contact sound. This is applicable to sound travelling through the roof, exterior walls, and glazed areas, from one room to another and from adjacent properties.

Key points applicable to sound insulation:

- A cavity wall for sound insulation purposes must meet the minimum requirement of an outer block or brick skin of 102mm, a cavity of 50mm and an inner block skin of 100mm coated with 13mm of plaster.

- A solid wall dividing semi-detached properties must have a minimum thickness of 215mm; this is applicable to both bricks and lightweight concrete blocks.

- On domestic properties sound insulation is not normally placed in floors, but a layer of glass fibre wool can be laid on top of the plasterboard, between the joists, prior to the floorboards being fixed. A good idea if you have noisy children!

- Timber stud partition walls are also not normally insulated to prevent sound passage, because they are normally constructed approximately 125mm thick and this gives sufficient sound insulation to comply with Building Regulations. Insulation can be placed between the two layers of plasterboard to improve the sound deadening quality. Glass Fibre wool can be used for this as well. A good idea where the stud-wall is enclosing a bathroom.

Draught proofing;
This is the prevention of cold air being able to enter a building. When this occurs, heat energy produced within a building escapes through defective areas of the building's fabric, and increases the cost of heating the building. There are key areas of a building that should receive special attention:

- Around window and doorframes a mastic seal should be applied all around the external edge of the frame where it abuts the brickwork, there are also insulated cavity 'closures' available, to use in place of the lightweight block. (see diagram)

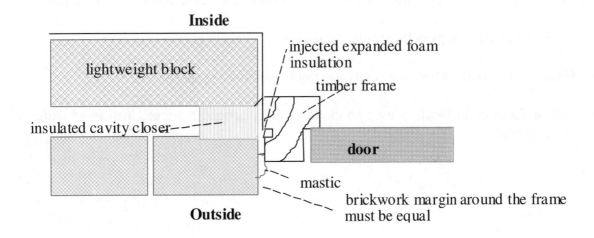

- Skirting board should be fitted tightly to the floor or have a mastic seal applied between it and the floor.

- Loft hatches can have a seal applied to the stop or cleat that the hatch sits on, a catch or barrel bolt securing the hatch shut will compress the seal.

- Where wires and waste pipes enter or leave the fabric of the building is an area of draught prevention that is often overlooked. A pipe or cable that pierces the external fabric of a building must have a seal of mastic applied around it to prevent entry of cold air.

- When the external walls of a dwelling are dry-lined rather than conventional render and plaster, it is possible for air to circulate behind the plasterboard sheets. Where the plaster board sheets abut window and door frames there must be a continuous seal of plaster, not 'dabs', this also applies where air vents are located and where services pass through the walls. (See diagram below).

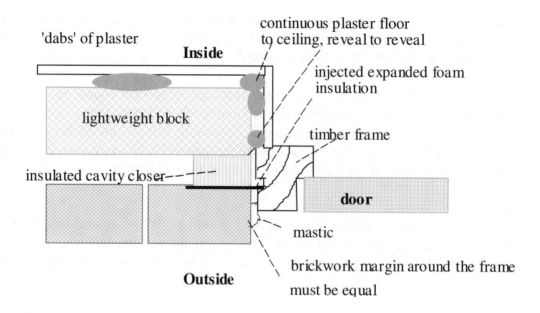

Thermal bridging;
This is probably the main cause of condensation in domestic dwellings, and is very easy to prevent. The main problem area is around window and door frames, and this is clearly a 'cowboy' problem because it is caused by bad building techniques and/or lack of experience. The common causes are:

- Cavities that have gaps in the insulation sheets.

- Under windowsills, where the cavity has not been closed properly.

- Where lightweight block is used to close a cavity around a frame, instead of using insulated closer pieces.

- Steel lintels that have no isolator block inside.

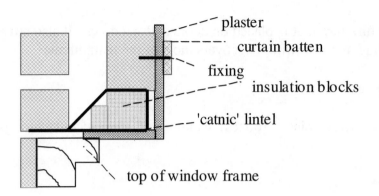

All of these points have been improved by current legislation and are a compulsory part of current Building Regulations. Check that the builder ensures that these faults do not occur, as it is impossible to see these faults once building work has finished.

Ironmongery

What is ironmongery?

It is the name used to describe the furniture that is placed on doors and windows. It also covers any other fittings that are used in building; the following list covers most of the main items;

- Window fasteners, hinges, stays and locks.

- Door hinges, locks, latches, bolts, letter 'plates' (boxes), handles and other security fittings.

- Safety handles and handrails.

- curtain rails

What problems should you look for?

It is obvious to most people when a door or window fitting has not been fitted properly; this will also apply to most of the other items listed above. For those who are not sure the simple test is, if it is loose or it looks odd, in most cases your intuition is correct. All handles, fasteners, bolts, stays and catches should be firmly fixed and their operation should be smooth and easy, doors should close with the slightest of pressure and when shut should not rattle. Security bolts should enter their keeps without force and when in place should remain fast even if the door or window is shaken and forced.

Hand or safety rails must be fitted securely and be able to support sudden loads, for example full adult body weight should pose no problem to a staircase handrail.

Are there any common faults to be looked for

Badly trained tradesmen are often not aware of faults and it is one of the reasons for the writing of this book. There are some common faults that should never occur. They go uncorrected because the 'cowboy builder' convinces the homeowner that the work is correct, these faults are:

- Letter box holes cut out too small so that the flap does not open fully, or the hole is cut rough and liable to cut or graze hands that are passed through it.

- Door handles and locks placed at the wrong height, this makes operation awkward. Positioning locks in line with the middle rail of a door. This is extremely bad as when the hole is cut out to hold the lock the tenon is removed thus weakening the door.

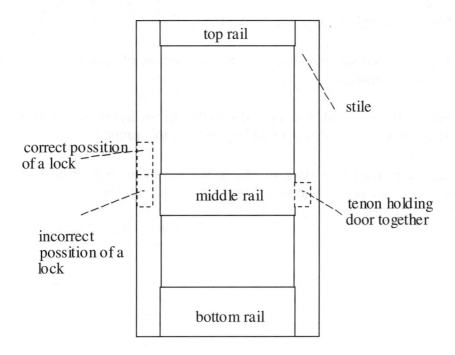

- If safety handles are fitted ensure they are at a sensible height and that they are fixed firmly. Often when they are fitted to walls the incorrect masonry plugs are used or the hole is drilled too large to enable the plastic masonry plug to grip.

- Any screws in a fitting should fit snugly into the hole provided for them. There should be no sharp edges on badly fitted screws; a shiver of metal from a damaged screw head can cause a nasty cut.

Ironmongery items identified

- **Casement stay**   These are fitted on the leading or bottom edge of a window casement, it is the long bar with holes in it that locate on the pins or anchors fitted to the frame. These are available with locks or security screws.

- **Casement fastener**   This is the mechanism that holds the window casement shut, when the casement is side-hung. These are also available with locks or security screws.

- **Storm-proof casement hinge**   These are special hinges that are shaped to fit the rebated edge of a storm-proof window casement, all opening windows should now be storm-proof.

- **Butt hinge**   These are the standard hinges that you will find on any door. Usually steel or brass, but they are also made of nylon or aluminium.

- **Rim lock**   This is a lock that is fitted on the internal face of a door usually coated steel or solid brass. This type of lock is not sufficient for some insurance companies.

- **Mortise lock**   This is a lock that is fitted in the stile of a door, the hole that the lock fits into is called a mortise. This type of lock is very strong, available with several level specifications, and in many different sizes.

- **Rim night latch**   More commonly known as a 'Yale' lock.

- **Barrel bolt**   These are surface mounted to doors as a means of added security, they are made from steel, brass and aluminium.

- **Security mortise bolt**   These are fitted in a mortise in the stile of a door, much the same way as a mortise lock. They are a very good way of adding security to a property.

- **Security chain**   these are fitted to a door to enable the occupant to open a door slightly, allowing inspection of visitors before allowing entry. Available in brass but the chain must have welded steel links.

Joinery

What parts of a building fall under this category?

Joinery describes all the wooden parts of a building, these maybe external or internal. The list below identifies the main items:

- Windows

- Window boards

- Doors and door frames

- Door linings

- Fascia boards

- Timber cladding

- Stair cases and associated components

- Fitted furniture

- Specialist floor boards

- Internal timber cladding

Who makes or supplies joinery?

Standard size joinery can be supplied direct by joinery manufacturers or supplied by them through appointed builder's merchants. Local joinery companies usually make special order or non-standard joinery.

What types of timber are used to manufacture particular types of joinery

Various woods have been observed to have their own unique textures, hues, and fragrances and are used accordingly. Tough and durable Oak, Japanese or English, can be fashioned into bridge girders, fence posts, flooring, panelling and long lasting external joinery. Beech and maple is used for flooring and kitchen work surfaces, whereas Cedar is widely used for external cladding of gable ends of timber framed buildings. 'Green heart' was used widely for barn timbers and wood pegs, called 'treenails' or dowel pegs. Mahoganies are used to make the best joinery, whereas pine, or softwood, (as it is more commonly known) is used for most standard joinery products.

The depletion of hardwood forest reserves since the Middle Ages has made all timber increasingly expensive. This has brought about greater reliance by the construction and manufacturing industries, in modern times, on composite wood products such as plywood, chipboard, and fibreboard (MDF Medium Density Fibreboard). These new materials are stable and do not swell or shrink as readily as natural timber. They do not require long seasoning periods, and they can be waterproofed, fireproofed, and impregnated with protective chemicals. Plywood is particularly valuable to carpenters and joiners because it allows them to cover broad areas of framework in a short time, door panels or similar do not have to be made from glued softwood boards to gain the required widths.

Apart from plywood, composite wood products are not as strong as natural timber. These products cannot be bent or steamed into different shapes, as can plywood, so joinery built from them often appears boxy. Screws and nails cannot fasten them together securely unless plastic or metal inserts, fittings, and connectors are used in the joints.

Many joinery products are a combination of composite and natural timber, for example a door may have a plywood panel in a natural timber frame, whereas a staircase may have plywood risers, secured into the pine 'strings' (see stairs). Composite and natural timber work well together and in many cases give a greater combined strength to the joinery product.

What faults should you look for when inspecting joinery?
Quality is the main issue when inspecting joinery and there are some key points to lookout for:

- All timber sections should be well sanded in the direction of the grain, this means there should be no scratching or other marks running across the grain of the timber. If this fault is present the timber will have to be sanded again prior to staining or varnishing, as any scratches will show through the finish.

- There should be no sharp or splintery edges to the joinery.

- There should not be large knots near the edges of timber sections, as these may fall out in time or when knocked.

- Any external joinery should arrive on site with a protective coating of primer, unless otherwise specified.

- Expensive joinery can be wrapped with polythene while building is taking place; this can be cut away with care when the work is complete.

- Any external joinery must be protected with preservative, ask for proof of treatment or smell the item, if it has been treated is should have a strong aroma of petroleum to it.

- If a window has been supplied with glazing beads check that all the beads are temporally fixed to the frame.

If a builder has quoted for hardwood joinery make sure this is what has been fitted. If it has been primed scrape away some of the primer and check the exposed wood, if you are still in doubt, cut into the protruding 'horn' on the head or sill, this is going to be concealed in the brickwork.

Note:
The words 'cheap' and 'joinery' don't really belong together as there is usually a reason for joinery to be cheap. It is true that there are many joinery manufacturers who are competitive in their pricing while still producing a quality product, however the price will normally affect the quality of the product.

The following points should be considered when decisions are being made on the purchase or acceptance of joinery products:

- Are the products 'seconds', if so for what reason. Have they been stacked wrongly causing them to miss-shape or warp, is the jointing sub-standard, are there stains on them that will not come out, or is there a design defect? Always ask for an explanation as to why they are cheap, it could be as simple as the end of the design production run.

- How long do you want external joinery to last for? More expensive hardwood joinery will last up to three times longer than that made from softwood.

- What performance qualities do you expect from the joinery products? The price of a window or doorframe can affect the storm proofing and preserving it may have been subjected too.

- Lastly, some joinery products are supplied with a warranty; it may be worth considering the extra cost for peace of mind.

Kitchens and kitchen units

This is probably the biggest area of home improvement and therefore attracts high numbers of 'cowboys' into the industry; it should also be noted that it is probably the most expensive investment you will make on your home apart from the mortgage. The cost can amount to several thousand pounds which makes it so important that this book makes you aware of the problems that can arise and guides you through the basic fitting procedure and the quality of the work that you should be able to expect.

Who should install a kitchen?

Whether the kitchen is part of a new building or a renovation project it should be installed by a suitably experienced trades person, generally this is the job of a carpenter. The installation will also involve other trade areas including plumbing, electrical, ceramic tiling and, if the project is a major one, possibly a bricklayer.

Where do you find these trades persons?

Some carpenters specialising in kitchen installations do other associated work as well. Often the plumbing and electrical alterations will only involve slight adjustments or moving. Many carpenters are competent ceramic tilers as well. If your kitchen is from a large DIY store, they may have an approved list of recommended contractors. Often the best way to go about a kitchen installation is to employ all the different trades independently and instruct the main trades' person, the carpenter, to plan the timing of the other trades.

If someone says that they can do all the work associated with the kitchen fitting, get some sort of reference or preferably view some of their previous work and ask the customer if they are happy with their kitchen.

How do you know if your kitchen units are being installed correctly?

There is a well tried and tested method for installing kitchen units and most carpenters will use this method, it is as follows:

- The floor should be checked for level and if there are any variations the highest point in the floor should be taken as the starting place.

- From this point the height of the base units should be marked on the wall, this is generally between 850mm and 900mm, this will vary dramatically if the kitchen is being installed for someone who is wheelchair bound or very tall.

- With a spirit level and long straight edge this height should be marked around the room to be used as a guide to position the units, this will ensure that all the tops of the units are level. Most units now come with adjustable feet on them; this will enable the fitter to overcome any variations in the floor level. It must be remembered that the Work-top thickness is generally 40mm and this will have to be allowed for above the height of the units, thus the overall height from floor to top of the Work-top would be 850mm + 40mm = 890mm. (Cheaper worktops are as a rule only 30mm thick).

- The next stage is to draw a line around the room to use as a guide to install the wall units. The height of the units needs to be marked on the wall and then the same method of drawing the line is used as in stage 3, generally this is between 500 and 610mm above the level of the Work top. This distance is determined by the type and size of ceramic wall tiles used, if the tiles are expensive or the pattern is not suitable to allow cutting, the distances need to allow for this.

  Explained further, a standard tile is 150mm square, so if the space between the wall units and Work-top was 610mm this would allow for 4 rows of tiles and give a small allowance for the joints, each joint requiring around 2mm. If the units had been installed correctly there would be no need to cut the tiles to fit the space, whole tiles look much better than having one row of cut tiles at the bottom because the space left did not account for the tile size. There are various sizes of tiles available ranging from 50mm boarder tiles up to 300mm high, the bigger the tile the more expensive it will be so if cutting can be avoided it will keep the cost of the job down. As a rule the larger the tile the thicker it will be and the more difficult to cut, this could mean that more will be broken and become unusable, further increasing the cost of the job. So, good planning allowing for the size of the tiles will be very cost effective, not a trait of a 'cowboy builder'! Once all of these factors have been taken into account, a temporary batten is fixed around the wall at this height to sit the wall units on and make installation easier, this ensures that all the bottoms of the units are level.

- It is normal practice to line up the doors vertically, this means that doors on the base units will line up with wall units above, creating defined lines and giving a professional look to the finished job. A good kitchen designer will leave spaces for appliances and still keep the line of the units; they will also have considered the height of the main user of the kitchen as this is an important factor when positioning wall units.

- Any plumbing or electrical modifications and service installations should be completed before the carpenter starts to install the units, only tap connections or electrical socket faces and other final fix items should be left until after the units are fitted.

What are the common faults to look for?

It is true to say that there are many good kitchen supply and fitting companies who operate with many happy customers but there are lots of unscrupulous builders out there who exist because it is human nature to take the cheapest quote. It should be noted that there are some companies that are cheap and give an excellent service, this is usually achieved through volume sales and a proven quality control procedure. If you are not sure ask to see examples of their work.

Most faults could be prevented, even by the 'cowboy builder' if they planned the job better, but it is true to say that most of the faults are caused by people doing the work without the proper training or experience.

This book has already identified areas of pre-planning as well as the techniques that are important to ensure that the kitchen is installed correctly, so follow the guidelines given and thoroughly inspect the work being done, if there is a possible problem or fault complain.

The list below highlights the most frequent faults and gives instructions on how the faults should be corrected:

- **Doors on units that don't line up properly**
Probably the most common fault generally caused by either lack of knowledge or care. This problem is easily corrected by using the screws that are located on the hinge anchor plate located on the kitchen unit not the door. These screws if loosened allow the plate to move up or down by approximately 5 to 8 mm, this is for adjusting the height of the doors. There is usually one more screw on the hinge itself, adjacent to the plate described above; this usually has a smaller head. If this screw is turned in either direction it will tip the opening edge of the door up or down by approximately 8 to 12mm, this adjustment allows for the paralleling and evening out of the gaps between doors of adjacent units. It may be necessary to slacken off the screw holding the hinge to the anchor plate to allow this adjustment to take place. Once the adjustment is correct the screw should be re-tightened. There is no reason for leaving new kitchen units in this way, the problem can occur with time and usage but not in the time between fitting and completion. If you think it isn't correct, or doesn't look right, complain!

- **Wall units that appear to be loose or move when the doors are opened**
Most kitchen units are secured to the wall using hooked anchor brackets at the top back corners, a plate is secured to the wall to which an adjustable hook on the unit fits. There is an adjuster screw on the bottom of the bracket fixed to the unit that is used to correct the level, once this is complete the screw on the face of the bracket is used to pull the plate and bracket together and secure the unit to the wall.

    If there are several units placed side by side they need to be fixed together. This is done by using either short screws (25mm max. due to each side of the units being 15mm thick) or using the special 'pan head' fixing bolts that are pushed through a hole top and bottom of the front edge of each side of a unit. (These are always supplied with kitchen units and their use is advisable for base units as well). This procedure nips the two units together to prevent movement when the doors are opened and closed. Once the tiling and grouting is done between the base and wall units they will not move.

    If rows of tiles are not fitted between the base and wall units, corner brackets can be fitted at the bottom rear corners of the wall units to prevent them from moving. These are not usually needed as the design of the top fixings is such that this movement should not take place if the units have been fitted correctly.

- **Base unit doors that move and do not align when weight is applied to the work-top above**
This fault is caused by lazy building practices and there is no excuse for it. All kitchen base units have fixing brackets around the top edge, this means along the back, both sides and the front. The holes in these brackets face upwards, they are there to secure the worktop to the units. There is another important role for these brackets to play. When all the fixings are used they tie all of the units together making it more rigid and preventing the worktop from moving, thus making final adjustments on the doors more successful.
Note: If the fixings were not needed the manufacturer would not have put them there, they want to save on costs too!

- **Washing machine or other plumbed appliances that do not fit flush with the fronts of the doors of the units**

This fault is caused by bad planning or lack of experience, some builders are not even aware of the technique used to overcome this problem. It is caused by the pipes for the water supply and waste water being placed in the void for the machine, these protrude from the wall at the back of the space by approximately 65 to 100mm, thus pushing the appliance beyond the line of the unit doors.

This problem is easily resolved by placing the pipes in the adjacent unit and drilling holes in the side of the unit for the service pipes to pass through. Washing machines or dishwashers should be located near the sink to reduce the amount of pipe work required and to enable the use of the draining area of the sink. If your appliances don't fit flush complain and get the problem corrected, after all it is supposed to be a fitted kitchen!

- **Badly fitting joints in work-tops**

If joints are not finished to a satisfactory standard on worktops the results can be very expensive as it will inevitably mean replacing them. Most kitchen worktops are made from plastic laminate e.g. (Formica) covered chipboard, which has a 'post formed' front edge to it. The 'Formica' layer is glued to the chipboard and under normal usage will last for many years. If, however, the bare ends of worktop are subjected to continuous wet conditions, the laminate will detach from the chipboard base.

Because of the shape of the front edge, jointing of the worktop in the corners of rooms is made difficult without the use of a specially shaped jointing strip. These are available in various colours and finishes to match the many different worktops. They are also made to match the different shapes of front edges. Each jointing strip is generally made so that it can be used in either a left or right hand situation; it is shaped at both ends.

When the two pieces of work top are fitted there should be a 3mm gap between them. This is to allow the centre of the joining strip to fit snugly between them. Once it has been determined that there is no resistance against the strip fitting between the two work-tops, the strip can then be fitted permanently. Sufficient silicone sealant should be applied to the gap between the two worktops so that when the strip is pushed into the gap, a small amount of excess sealant squeezes out. If necessary the strip can be held in place using masking tape. Check that the securing screw is used at the front underside, to keep the shaped section of the strip in place. The last job is to clean off all the excess sealant before it sets.

There are better quality joint strips available that have screw holes in the centre spacing allowing the strip to be fitted to one of the work-tops, when it is placed against the other work-top it holds it in place. Silicone must still be used to seal the strip to the worktop.

If you are inspecting work already completed you can open the door of the unit and look underneath the worktop for signs of excess sealant, if there is none then the chances are it has not been done. Complain straight away as the sealant is what keeps the strip in place, if there is no sealant water could enter and cause the laminate to detach from the chipboard base. The sealant also helps to seal the chipboard edge where the worktop has been cut to length.

- **Bare or badly finished ends to work-tops**

  This fault is a clear sign that you have a 'cowboy' on the premises, at the very least you should have heard a faint rattling of the spurs as he was wandering aimlessly around your home. However, joking aside, this is a serious fault if not corrected, and can incur major costs creating the need to replace worktops prematurely.

  Anywhere a plastic laminated covered worktop has an end that is visible or that has been cut to size it is imperative that the end is finished in the correct manner. If the worktop has been cut to length with a hand saw it should be planed smooth and, if necessary, the corner should be shaped to prevent injury. The edge when planned smooth should be square or at 90 degrees to the surface.

  Worktops are supplied with a strip of plastic laminate to cover bare ends; it is normally approximately 5mm wider than the thickness of the worktop (if the worktop is 40mm thick the laminate strip will be approximately 45mm wide). The first stage is to cut the laminate strip to length allowing 10mm extra for lining up purposes. Contact adhesive should then be applied to both the laminate strip and the edge of the Worktop (see side of can for adhesive usage instructions as it varies from one manufacturer to another), this is then left for the recommended curing time.

  When the glue has cured the two are pressed firmly together and then left for the specified drying time. Once the two are fixed firmly together the raised edges are planned and smoothed to make the end of the work surface safe, there should be no sharp edges, gaps between the laminate and board or loose areas of laminate. As a guide if the end of the worktop looks and feels right to the touch then it probably is, you can safely say that you don't have a 'cowboy' on your ranch!

- **Kitchen sink**

  Two types are used: an in-set sink which is fitted into a hole cut through the work-surface or, a 'post-formed' sink, which is moulded to the same shape as the front edge of the work-top. Which ever used they usually suffer from the same problem, lack of sealant. Where a sink or draining surface adjoins a worktop it must be sealed properly, using high modulus silicone sealant. The bead of silicone should be no more than 8mm wide, neatly applied with a smooth, level finish. If it looks untidy it will probably leak. Some in-set sinks are supplied with a rubber seal, make sure it has been used and that it has been nipped at all points around the sink's edge.

Important note:

Many of the techniques and methods used to fit kitchen units are also applicable to fitting other fitted furniture.

Lead or Zinc flashing

What is a flashing?

It is the black or silvery grey coloured material seen around the chimney where it adjoins the roof, down the pitch of a roof that abuts a wall, around pipes passing through roof tiles, and as a roof coating for bay windows. These are just some of the instances where flashing can be seen.

Why is lead or zinc flashing used?

Flashing is placed on a building to weatherproof it, often in locations where different levels intersect and slopes and angles come together, it is this that creates the need for a flexible, strong and long-lasting material. The materials used for flashing buildings are chosen because of their unique properties, to stretch, mould and be hammered to fit almost any shape while retaining their waterproof qualities.

Who fixes a flashing?

Usually they are fixed by a plumber, but some roofing contractors a very competent at lead flashing and are able to do the pointing as well; a plumber will not normally do the latter.

What is the purpose of flashing?

Their purpose is to weatherproof the area in which they are located, for example where a lower roof, say a garage abuts the end wall of a house. The tiles that cover the garage roof will not seal themselves to the wall of the house, a fillet of mortar is used to fill the gap between the wall and tiles, and this is then covered with flashing to weatherproof it

The flashing is fixed to the wall of the house by placing it in the joints of the brickwork above the sloped roof of the garage. The joints in the brickwork around the area in which the intersection takes place should have been left not pointed for this reason. If they had been pointed as the wall was built it would mean that someone would have to remove the pointing with a grinder, an unnecessary waste of time!

Flashing is inserted approximately 20 to 25mm into the horizontal joints of the brickwork, it is held in place by small wedges made out of the of-cuts that are removed from the role when the steps are cut, these are tapped gently into the joint until the hold. The section of flashing that is fixed to the abutting wall must have a minimum of 65mm coverage before any cuts are made for locating purposes.

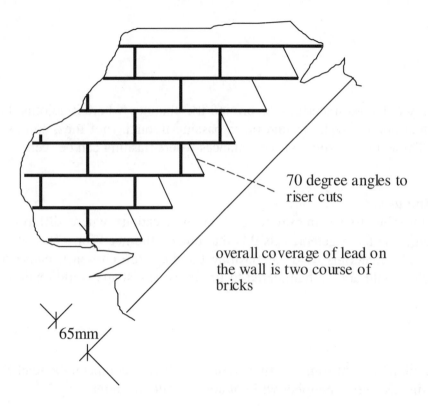

70 degree angles to riser cuts

overall coverage of lead on the wall is two course of bricks

65mm

The flashing is then beaten onto the tiles to mould it to the shape thus forming a tight seal to prevent water and snow blowing underneath, once the lead flashing is securely in place the joints in the brickwork are pointed. Correctly installed flashing on a sloped roof will step up the wall two courses at a time and cover the tile it sits on by at least 100mm, or to the tile's lowest point.

Are there different grades of flashing material?
As a general rule most flashing on a domestic property is subjected to very similar weathering wherever it is located on the building. Flashing materials vary, but most are non-ferrous flexible metal such as lead or zinc. Lead is graded by 'code' numbering, most flashing being either code 4 or 5.

What faults should you look for when checking a flashing
There are some simple checks that can be made to ensure the lead flashing has been installed correctly:

- Is it fixed and pointed securely?

- Does it step up the roof in the correct manner, both in equal steps and by the correct amount of courses at a time?

- Is the flashing clean and free from mortar wash or stains?

- Does it look neat and weatherproof correctly at the top and bottom of the run of flashing, where the ridge of the garage roof is located against the wall the lead must cover the wall by at least 150mm at all points. At the bottom the lead must extend beyond the tiles by the same distance so that rain can run down the wall well past the end of the garage roof.

If any one of these points is not adhered to complain and get it corrected.

Masonry

How do you identify the masonry of the house?

This is how the construction trade describes the main fabric of a house, flat, bungalow etc.; it covers the areas of brickwork, flint and natural stone walls that are used on the main structures of a building. It may be a combination of materials bonded together with mortar. Usually if natural stone is used, bricks are used to give upright and true corners, window and door reveals and used to create defined lines to the buildings design.

Are there any common faults that you should look for?

One of the main complaints with building especially on new property is that of bad masonry. This is often caused by the fact that on speculative house building (this means when property is built for a general market i.e., new housing developments), every part of the project is controlled by strict budgets and time scales. Many developers have to finance the building work, so they have a need to complete and sell the properties quickly to repay the organisation financing the project, this in itself can adversely affect quality.

This finance cash flow situation can create the further problem of poor payments to the bricklayers, which then makes them hurry the work to earn a reasonable living, most bricklayers are paid by the amount of bricks they lay in a day. Crazy things like laying bricks in the rain, frost and snow occur, thus creating white stained mortar from frost damage, cement stained bricks and masonry from rain causing the mortar to run. Brickwork should never be worked on in cold freezing conditions because the water in the mortar freezes and weakens the joints of the masonry.

Bad training and lack of experience more often than not create faults with masonry. Unbelievably the most common cause is the fact that the building contractor just doesn't care, the sale value is more important than customer satisfaction! Many of the other common faults with masonry are covered in the section on brickwork earlier in the book.

When repair work is done on existing or old walls there is a particular need to be aware of problems that can occur, as this is an area of building where experience is very important.

When a wall is repaired there are several factors that must be planned for, they are:

- What type of mortar is used in the existing walls, is it old style (white) lime mortar or the modern mixture of sand and cement?

- Has the existing mortar faded with time or weathered in such away that the new mortar will need to be coloured to enable a better match between old and new?

- If the bricks or stone masonry are not reusable can you get a suitable alternative?

- What type of pointing technique has been used, is it possible to match it?

- If the brickwork or masonry is old the courses may not be level there also may be no recognisable bonding to the brickwork. The new brickwork must line up, match with this and not be levelled to a spirit level as it will look odd and the repair will stand out, and look incongruous.

These are all areas that, if overlooked, will create problems with the finished job. If you suspect there may be a problem ask the builder for comments, their reply should reassure you, if it does not, get a second opinion!

What bad practices should you look for?

There is no set guide to bad practices that occur with masonry, however here are some favourites of the 'cowboy builder';

- Mortar can be dyed to match its colour to the existing; this is achieved using special mortar colouring. It is possible to make cement based mortar the same colour as lime mortar using a colorant. There have been cases where 'cowboys' have used soot, crushed blackboard chalk and even emulsion paint to colour mortar! None of these is permissible and under no circumstances should be accepted!

- If there is a need to replace a single brick or piece of masonry it is important that the same material goes back into the space. Some unscrupulous builders will attempt to use coloured mortar to repair the wall, shaping it to match the surrounding masonry, this should not be allowed.

- When a wall is involved in a collision or similar it is often the mortar joints that crack from the impact and many people assume that re-pointing of these cracks will be a sufficient repair. This is not the case and an unscrupulous builder will often attempt to do a quick repair of this type.

  All of the bricks surrounded by the cracked mortar should be removed and laid on fresh mortar, this will ensure that the wall is returned to its former strength.

- If walls are being constructed in cold weather and an overnight frost is anticipated, ensure that all work completed is covered with old sacking or thin carpet, this will give some protection from the frost, this can also be done to give protection from rainfall, perhaps with polythene sheeting. Frost inhibitor can be added to the mortar when it is mixed but it is no guarantee of total protection from frost damage, better to do both!

Can any thing be done to correct faults with masonry?

There are not many cases where a bad repair or faulty masonry cannot be rectified, provided the correct technique and skills are used. The following illustrates some common faults and the work necessary to overcome them:

- Dirty grey deposits running down a wall, generally caused by rain washing freshly laid mortar out of the joints. This can usually be removed by one of three methods.

  1. Careful brushing of the surface with a wire or hard bristled brush, special care must be taken not to damage the surface of the bricks, stone or other masonry.
  2. Masonry cleaning fluid can be obtained from a builders merchant, care must be taken with health and safety as these products are acid based and can cause serious skin damage. Instructions are given on the products packaging.
  3. If the builder is still on site give him the job. He created it not the weather; he should have protected the wall before he left it!

- If you suspect frost damage the simple check is to press a screwdriver into the mortar, if it enters into the joint easily there is a problem. When frost has penetrated, the mortar will dry like a honeycomb and crumble very easily. There is no cure for this problem, the damaged area must be removed and replaced.

- The pointing is falling out and has a general bad appearance. When re-pointing is done on masonry it is imperative that all the old is removed so that the new mortar has a good key to prevent it falling out. All loose pointing must be removed, brushing well prior to the new mortar being applied to the joints. If the pointing on new brickwork looks untidy get the builder to rectify it; there is no excuse for this type of fault!

  If the masonry is in a vulnerable position such as near a path or road, a special solution can be added to the mortar to make it more durable. If the masonry is very dry and dusty, wetting the wall slightly prior to re-pointing will give the new mortar a better key to prevent it falling out.

- Damaged corners and edges on bricks in an existing wall are not really a problem provided the wall is of a cavity construction or it is a garden wall. If the building is old, constructed without cavity, a damaged brick could allow water to penetrate the wall; it should be removed and correctly replaced.

  If there are damaged bricks in a new building do not except them, tell the builder to remove them. They do not cause a structural problem but you are paying for a new building so ensure that is what you get. After all you would not accept a new car with a dent in the door!

Are you correctly identifying the fault?

Most faults are obvious and have been covered above however there is one fault that is not caused by 'cowboy' building but by a natural chemical reaction between the materials that have been used. I have already described the effects of frost on masonry, stating that a mortar's strength is severely affected. After frost, the mortar will appear white, however frost does not normally turn bricks white.

Some bricks are made from clay with a high content of natural salt in them and when they come into contact with water and wet mortar the salts bleed through to the surface of the brick. In some instances this can look unsightly especially if the colours of the mortar and bricks enhance the white of the salts, it should however be noted that this is a natural occurrence and will have no effect on the building, or its soundness. Given time the stark effect of the white will fade and in some cases disappear altogether. Masonry cleaner can be used but it may not remove all of the salts.

If you do not like this effect, examine older buildings in the locality, if the bricks show no signs of the problem, specify this type of brick to be used on your building. Sometimes the salts are in the aggregate used to make the mortar, and they do not affect certain bricks.

If you believe that there is a problem with the masonry of your property and cannot identify it get a second opinion from a structural surveyor or a reputable builder who specialises in renovation work as they will have more experience of masonry faults.

Mastic and silicone sealant

What are mastics and silicone?

Mastic is a resin obtained from the mastic tree, (Pistacia lentiscus). Used as a binding material and as an ingredient of varnishes and lacquers, it is also an ingredient of building adhesive called asphalt mastic. In the UK mastic has been adopted as the common name for materials used to seal many different combinations of building materials together.

Silicone is also a name adopted by the construction industry. Silicones are organic compounds developed during World War II. They have the physical properties of oils, resins, or rubber, and are extremely useful because they are more stable when exposed to heat and oxygen than ordinary organic compounds. Silicone resins and rubbers are polymers of organic molecules. Silicone resins are used as heat-resistant insulators. Silicone rubbers are used as insulators and for other purposes for which rubber is needed at high temperatures. Where building is concerned silicone is the material used to create a waterproof seal between different materials.

Who fits or applies mastic and silicone sealant?

If there are contractors fitting replacement windows to your home they will normally complete the mastic seals around the windows as they are fixed. Most window installers are carpenters, so mastic and silicone application is considered to be part of their job. There are companies that specialise in the application of mastic and silicone seals. Where there are lots to be done it might be worth contacting one of these firms. They can be found in the 'Yellow Pages'.

In many instances mastic and silicone needs attention when decorating takes place, so it will fall to the painter to remove the old and replace it, most painters are very competent at this, some are so good that you would never know that mastic has been used.

Are there different types for particular jobs?

There are many different jobs in construction that involve the use of mastic or silicone sealant, many of which are for a specific job. Only a 'cowboy' would use any type for all building jobs! The list below identifies different situations and the sealant that should be used:

- **Sealing around wooden window and doorframes** This can be done with acrylic frame sealant, butyl mastic or low modulus silicone. These are available in various colours. Butyl mastic is generally grey and is used on painted frames. One important factor to remember is that silicone must not be painted over, as paint will not stick to the surface of silicone.

- **Sealing around plastic windows and doorframes** This should always be done by using low modulus silicone sealant. Other types of sealant are not suitable because when the windows are washed they will dull and discolour; silicone doesn't suffer from this problem as much.

- **Vertical expansion joints in brickwork** Where a wall is over 12metres in length, expansion joints are placed in the wall every 12m or less to prevent cracks appearing. This is because a wall of this length will expand and contract considerably with changes in temperature. The joint will normally be between 12 and 20mm; the void is first filled with impregnated fibreboard, to support the mastic. The joint is then sealed using either butyl mastic or low modulus silicone.

- **Sealing around bathroom sanitary ware and kitchen sinks and work-tops**
  In situations where there is frequent water splashing a fully setting seal is required. It needs to be flexible and must give a good waterproof seal. To achieve this, high modulus silicone sealant is used. This has a skin setting time of 20 to 40 minutes and is fully cured in 24 hours, setting to a consistency very similar to rubber. It is very tough, withstands most household detergents and gives an excellent hygienic seal around sanitary ware to plastered walls or tiles.
  Note: No water or moisture must come in contact with silicone over the 24-hour curing period. If it does the seal will fail.

- **Lead flashing** The traditional way to fix lead flashing to brickwork is to groove out the joints and push the lead into the gap, wedge in place and then point-up to the lead. There are now mastics available that allow lead to be fixed into a thin slot in the brickwork achieved using a thin masonry grinder, the lead is pushed into the slot and the joint sealed with mastic. These products are normally 'butyl' as opposed to 'silicone' based. (see section on flashing)

- **Gutter joints and asphalt roofs** Most guttering systems have integral rubber seals at each joint, flat asphalt roofs are normally bonded at the joints of each sheet of felt with hot asphalt. However, both can develop leaks. To prevent costly replacement, mastics are available to solve the problem. The same product is used for each; it is normally butyl based, black and very sticky, almost like wet tar. It should not be used by untrained or inexperienced hands because when used incorrectly it is very difficult to clean off. Some aluminium gutter systems are jointed with this from new, as they do not have integral seals as part of their system.

- **Large gaps around waste pipes and frames** Conventionally any gaps would have been filled with sand and cement mortar, nowadays it is often done using polyurethane expanding foam. This is available from the same suppliers of mastics and silicone. It is supplied in aerosol cans and can expand up to 30 times its original packaged size. Once the hole or gap has been filled the foam is left to set, usually about 1 hour. It can then be trimmed, sanded or cut to size. The surface can then be covered with mastic, painted or, if it is not visible, left in its natural state. The advantages of this product, if used properly, are that it prevents drafts, it is very easy to use, it provides for expansion and it is very much quicker than the conventional method. It also improves the insulation properties.

What faults should you look for?

The most common fault with mastic and silicone is the way in which it has been applied, if it is not applied neatly it will look awful and this will be obvious to almost anyone however little knowledge they have of construction techniques.

Frame sealant around windows or doorframes is where the biggest disasters are commonly found. It is not unusual to find sealant with gaps, different widths and heights, colours or even the wrong type of sealant being used. You should not except any of these faults. There is no excuse for them. They are caused by bad training technique or just carelessness.

The key points for correct sealant around window and doorframes are:

- Brickwork or masonry must be clean and dry before the mastic is applied, free from dust, oil, loose brick or pointing.

- The temperature must not be below 6 Celsius as the sealant will not cure quickly enough, and in extreme cases not at all.

- If the frames are wooden and are going to be stained always use a darker coloured mastic, if there is any unevenness it will be less noticeable with a dark mastic than with a light one.

- The mastic or silicone should not be touched once it has been in place for more than two minutes as it will have started to cure and the surface will drag and look rippled, this looks awful!

Nails

What are nails?
Rod like metal fasteners pointed and often headed or grooved. They are hammered to join or anchor materials, primarily wood and other building materials. They are essential in woodworking and building construction. They are available in lengths of less than 1.3 mm to more than 150 mm. The thinnest being the pin-like insulation-board nail, the thickest about 6mm designed for specific purposes, they range from plain box nails to fluted masonry nails and dual-head nails. Flat heads make most nails extractable, the finishing nail and casing nail, however, are virtually headless. Short, headed nails for shallow impact are usually called tacks.

Why are nails used?
They provide a cheap and effective means of securing building materials to one another. Prior to nails being used in construction timber dowels where often used, this was both time consuming and limited to the strength of timber the dowel was made from.

Nails have been used for construction for several hundred years; from early blacksmith handmade cut nails to modern hardened masonry nails. There is now a nail manufactured for just about every use in construction, some are even produced for use in explosive nail guns which will fire a nail through timber into reinforced concrete.

What type of nail should be used?
There are specific nails for many of the jobs in construction. The list below identifies the most common jobs and the type of nail used, if the wrong type of nail is used it could result in failure of the fixing, and damage to the construction.

- **Natural softwood (pine) floor boards tongued and grooved**
  Mild steel 'cut nails' these are also sometimes known as 'cut clasp' nails.

- **Skirting boards fixed to plastered lightweight block walls**
  Mild steel 'cut nails', or large 'oval brad' nails can also be used. Cut nails tend to give a large hole when punched below the surface; this is all right if the skirting board is going to be painted. However if the wood is going to be stained 'oval brad' nails are best as when punched below the surface the wood folds around the nail almost covering it.

- **Chipboard flooring sheets**
  'Lost head' nails or 50mm mild steel annular ring wire nails, the important factor here is that the nails used must not be able to pull through the sheets with wear and tear, thus rendering the floor loose and able to move. The 'lost head' and flat head to the annular ring wire nail prevent this from happening.

- **Door linings fixed to lightweight block walls**
  'Cut nails' should be used but only if the door lining fits snugly into the opening without the use of packing pieces. It is much better to use screws and masonry plugs as these allow for adjustments if required when the doors are fitted to the door lining.

- **Architrave fixed to door linings**
  35 to 50mm 'oval brads or lost heads'. In situations where the architrave is going to be stained 40 to 50mm panel pins can be used, these have a head that is easier to conceal with filler.

- **Door stop fixed to door linings**
  A 12mm doorstop should be fixed using 45 to 50mm 'lost heads' or 'oval brads'.

- **Timber Stud-work**
  This is normally fixed together using 100mm round head wire nails, provided that it is being built out of the standard 50 x 75mm or 50 x 100mm sawn timber, generally used for internal partition walls.

- **Window and door glazing beads**
  Galvanised or 'sheradised' panel pins, the coating on the nail prevents corrosion and possible expansion of the metal that could cause the glass to crack.

- **Picture or 'dado rail' fixed to lightweight plastered walls**
  Small 'cut nails' or 'lost heads'.

- **Plasterboard fixed to stud work or ceiling joists**
  Large headed galvanised plasterboard nails 30 to 50mm long. The large diameter of the nail head prevents the nail from pulling through the plasterboard.

- **Tile battens fixed to rafters**
  Galvanised 75 to 100mm 'wire' nails.

- **Fascia board to the bottom of rafter**
  75 to 100mm 'lost head' or 'oval brad' nails.

- **Storm bracing to pre-made roof trusses**
  Wire nails of sufficient length to hold the storm bracing to the roof trusses, usually the nails are 75 to 100mm wire round head.

- **Mineral coated roofing felt**
  Usually on shed roofs or out-houses, felt is fixed using bitumen paint and galvanised felt nails between 13 and 25mm. These nails have large heads like plasterboard nails, but are usually shorter.

- **Corrugated steel roofing sheets**
  These are fitted using galvanised 'springhead' nails; a nail with a square shank, which is twisted for better grip once it, enters the timber. The head is like an upside-down saucer; this is so it acts as a shield against rain.

- **Plastic or 'polycarbonate' roofing sheets**
  This type of roofing material is fixed using cone head drive nails and rubber seals, these nails are galvanised and have a round twisted shank. Some roofing systems that use these sheets have integral fixings and require no nails.

- **Roof tiles**

  Generally not every tile is nailed down on a roof; the average nailed content is every 4th to 6th tile. They are fixed using galvanised or copper clout nails 40 to 60mm in length; this is only a guide as the thickness and shape of the tile govern the length of nail.

- **Roof slates**

  Normally these are made from Welsh natural slate or man-made material, but whichever is used; the fixings are the same. They are fixed using copper or lead slate strips that are fixed to the roof timbers with copper clout nails.

How do you know if the correct length of nails is being used?

As a general guide the length of a nail fixing timber to timber should be two to three times the thickness of the timber it is fixing. For example architrave 19mm thick should be fixed to the door lining with 50mm 'oval brad' nails and 12mm glazing bead should be fixed with 35 to 40mm galvanised panel pins.

When nails are used to secure timber to lightweight concrete block walls, the nail should be three to four times the length of thickness of the timber it is fixing. For example 25mm thick skirting board should be fixed with 75 to 100mm cut nails.

How do you identify a fault with a nailed fixing?

There are several faults that occur with nails and the fixings achieved with them. All are avoidable and is generally due to lack of skill, technique, and training or simply the wrong type of nail being used.

The following list identifies most of the common faults, their cause and where correction is possible, how the work should be done:

- **loose floor boards**

  This is generally caused by one of four factors:

  (i)   Nails used are not long enough, (the calculation for the length of the nails is given in the previous section)

  (ii)   Not enough nails in each board, there should be a minimum of two nails at every second floor joist as the boards pass across the floor

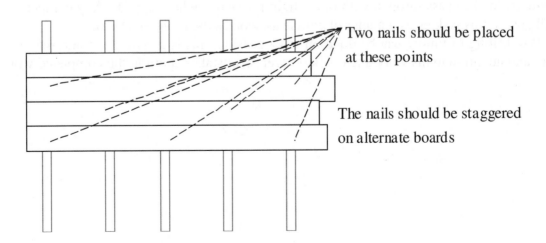

Two nails should be placed at these points

The nails should be staggered on alternate boards

(iii)   The wrong type of nails have been used, they should be mild steel 'cut nails', **(Note);** If there is under-floor heating many builders prefer to use brass screws, this is to allow easy access to the under-floor heating pipes.

A mild steel 'cut nail'

(iv)   Uneven floor joists can cause floorboards to work loose.

All of these problems can be rectified by either changing the length, quantity or type of nail used. In the instance of (d), if the unevenness is severe the joist may have to be planed or packed, but this may involve the removal of all the floorboards, just to gain access to its entire length.

- **Skirting-.or floor- boards that are split around the area where the nails are situated**
  This problem is generally caused by one of two problems:

  (i)   The nails are too close to the end of the piece of skirting board, or
  (ii)   The gauge of nails used is too great for the thickness of timber that they are passing through; (nails are measured by both length and their thickness).

If the skirting board is to be painted, it will probably be all right to fill the split with good quality wood filler, on the other hand if the skirting board is going to be stained or varnished, there is no alternative but to change the board. If the board is going to be left in place you must ensure that it is secured to the wall, if it is not another nail will have to be placed where it is loose.

If the problem of splitting is associated with floorboards there is no alternative to changing the boards, this is because nails in floorboards can only be placed where the floor joists are and further nails placed in these areas will only split the board even more.

It should be noted that some timber would split even if the correct nails were used. The only way to ensure that this problem doesn't occur is to pre-drill the timber with a hole sufficient to allow the nail to pass through with only slight resistance when tapped. Any competent builder will ensure this is done as a matter of course as soon as the problem arises.

Pre-drilling of timber can be done on any occasion, this is a sign of a tradesman who gives care and attention to his work and dislikes careless mistakes spoiling the completed work.

- **Mitre joints that have opened up leaving a gap on architrave round the door frame**
  This problem is caused by one of two faults, they are:

  (i)   Insufficient nailing along the length of the architrave, or
  (ii)   No nails through the sides of the architrave at the joint.

position of nail
through mitre joint

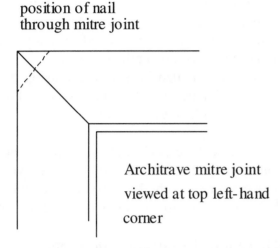

Architrave mitre joint
viewed at top left-hand
corner

Architrave should be nailed to the door lining at approximately 150 to 200mm intervals, generally with 50mm 'oval brad' nails. Greater spacing of the nails will inevitably allow the architrave to work loose and possibly allow the mitre joint to open. If this is the situation the timber should be repositioned and more nails placed centrally between those already positioned, this will result in over-nailing but it is pointless to take existing nails out to space them correctly! It should be noted that if the architrave is going to be stained, it may have to be replaced, as lots of nail holes will look unsightly.

If the problem is just an open mitre joint, it can be rectified very easily. A nail should be hammered into the corner as the diagram above shows the nail should enter from the top so that it will not be seen. Because it is at right angles to the joint it will keep the two halves of the joint together. This should be done every time not just when the mitre joint opens up.

Both of these problems are a clear sign of a badly trained carpenter, and are typical traits of the cowboy variety!

- **Rust stains on external woodwork**
  Using nails that have no protective coating on them causes it. This is probably one of the most annoying 'cowboy' caused faults because to prevent it from occurring takes no extra time what so ever and costs very little.

Where nails are to be used externally or where there is moisture in the surrounding atmosphere, they should be specially coated to prevent rusting. There are several types available; the most commonly used are 'galvanised' and 'sheradised'. Galvanised nails are usually bright silver in colour; 'sheradised' are dark grey or charcoal in colour, both are very similar in price.

If the problem is spotted soon enough it may be possible to rectify it. This should be done as follows:

(i)   Don't try to pull the nail out if it is a small headed type such as 'lost head' or 'oval brad'. Instead, punch it through the timber it is securing, repeating this on all the nails, and then remove the timber. If the nails in question are 'wire nails', they have a substantial head and are reasonably easy to remove with a claw hammer, pincers, or a good quality nail bar. Always ensure that there is a piece of scrap wood under the tool used to protect the timber when you lever against it.

(ii)   Once all nails have been removed the timber should be sanded to remove all of the rust, as the slightest particle left on the timber could continue to stain.

(iii)   The timber should now be repositioned and nailed back in place using the correct nails. Once in the correct position any old nail holes should be filled and the timber should be stained or painted as soon as possible to give it protection.

Note: when nails or screws are inserted into oak there is a natural chemical reaction that takes place creating a blue stain around the nail or screw. There is no way of preventing this from happening and after some time the colour mellows. Using brass fixings can help but they have a tendency to break off while they are being worked into the oak due to its hard nature.

- **Bent over or badly placed nails hammered hard into the surface of the timber**
  Here we enter the realms of the 'Wild West' because this is undoubtedly the work of 'Butch Cassidy', with the 'Sundance Kid' holding the bag of nails for him. This is an unforgivable trait of a 'cowboy builder'. Good builders would be ashamed to leave a nail in this way.
  This fault is normally caused by one of four reasons:

  (i)   Using a hammer with a dirty or damaged head,
  (ii)   Lack of concentration when aiming for the nail,
  (iii)   No real care or interest in the job, or
  (iv)   Bad training.

Any nail left in this way should be removed and replaced, you should insist that the builder, if they are still on site, correct the fault immediately. If the timber has been badly bruised by the nail when it was hammered into the surface, you should insist that the timber is repaired or replaced.

Note: There is an effective way of removing a bruise from a piece of timber, this can prevent removal of the damaged timber. This is done as follows:

(i)   First carefully remove the nail, thus preventing further damage,
(ii)   Find an electric clothes iron and switch it on to its highest setting,
(iii)   Get a piece of cotton cloth and wet it, place this over the bruise and then place the hot iron over the cloth, the steam created should remove the bruise. Hold it in place for thirty seconds and then remove to see if the bruise has been drawn out, if not repeat until the bruise has gone.
(iv)   Once the bruise has been successfully removed, sand the area and re-treat the surface prior to replacing the nail correctly.

This is a trade skill used by cabinet makers that works well on any timber, not a skill known by your average 'cowboy builder'!

Openings in walls.

A common alteration to domestic properties is the installation of an additional doorway or the knocking of two rooms into one. Often this will require making an opening in the structural fabric of the property; it is for this reason that a lintel or beam will need to be installed above the opening. Its purpose is to support and absorb any loading imposed by the weight of the structure above the doorway or opening.

What are beams and lintels made of?

In older property beams above windows, doors and openings are likely to be large pieces of oak; sometimes a feature is made of the beam by leaving the sides visible. Some properties will have had their beams above openings 'cast in situ', this means that the beam, made from concrete, will have been cast into the wall at the time the brickwork reached the top of the opening. Shuttering would have been constructed above the opening, to support the concrete and reinforcing rods while the concrete sets. Often when an opening is through an internal wall the above loading will be supported using a rolled steel joist or 'H' section steel girder as they are sometimes called. The bigger the span of the opening the deeper the steel girder used, a building regulation table will give the required size of beam for the opening.

Most external openings in new buildings are supported using pressed steel lintels often called 'Catnic' lintels. These are manufactured in standard sizes to suit almost every possible opening. They are designed to give a good key to the plaster used internally and are not visible from the outside, apart from a small amount showing just in front of the head of the window. See drawing below.

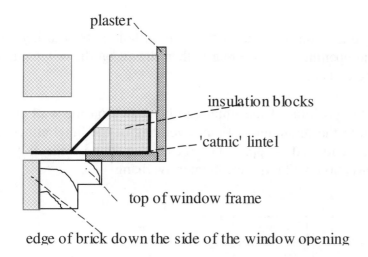

The diagram shows the pressed steel lintel supporting both leaves of the cavity wall. The centre sloping area acts as a DPC directing moisture within the cavity above the window out through the face brickwork.

Does every opening require a lintel?

When an opening or doorway has a decorative archway, the brickwork forming the arch will create the strength required to support the wall above. There are various types of arch; all are constructed using the same basic principles and rules. The brick or natural stone arch is supported by a timber former or 'centre' as it is sometimes called, while the mortar sets. A carpenter will make this for the bricklayer so that it matches the internal face of the proposed archway. All joints between the bricks making up the archway will spring from the centre point of the arch, see drawing L: 1. Some arches may have up to three centre or springing points. For the arch to be sufficiently strong, the joints must relate to the springing points. An arch will transfer all the loading above; down either side where it connects to the wall.

How do you know if a lintel is required?

Any opening that has brick or block-work above requires a lintel of some sort. The dimensions of the opening and the loading above determine the size of beam required. If the wall being altered is an internal 'stud' partition, this will not require a lintel because it is not a load-bearing wall. To find out if a wall is load-bearing, lift the floorboards on the floor above the wall to establish which way the floor joists run. If they are at right angles to the wall, it is likely to be a load-bearing wall. If, however, the floor joists run parallel with the wall, this indicates that the wall is not load-bearing. If you are unhappy with the situation and the builder is not being very co-operative when you ask questions, this is probably a good time to get a second professional opinion, the local authority building control department will only be too willing to help.

How should a lintel or beam be installed into an existing wall?

An opening is not just knocked through the wall; there is a set procedure that must be adopted when a lintel is to be installed.

- The opening should be carefully drawn on one side of the wall. A hole is then drilled through the wall at the centre point of the opening. The opening is then drawn on the other side of the wall, using the centre point as a reference.

- Once the above has been done the position of the lintel can be drawn on the wall above the opening, paying special attention to the minimum 150mm overhang of the lintel either side of the opening. The minimum size mentioned is appropriate for new or sound walls only. Older walls or walls of composite construction, will require a greater overhang.

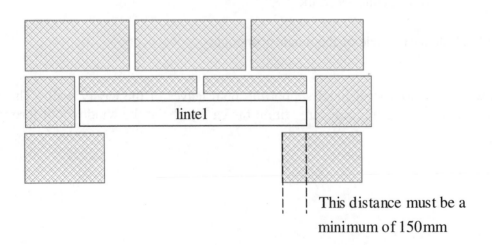

This distance must be a
minimum of 150mm

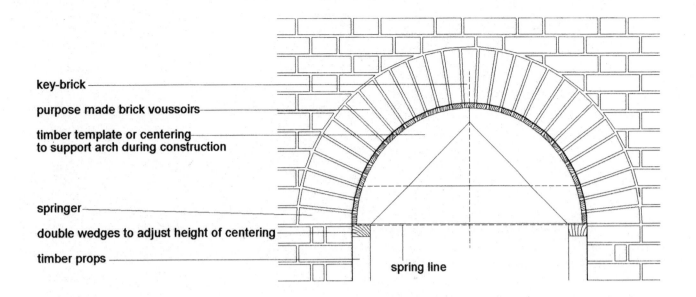

key-brick

purpose made brick voussoirs

timber template or centering
to support arch during construction

springer

double wedges to adjust height of centering

timber props

spring line

L:1 Semi-circular Brick Arch

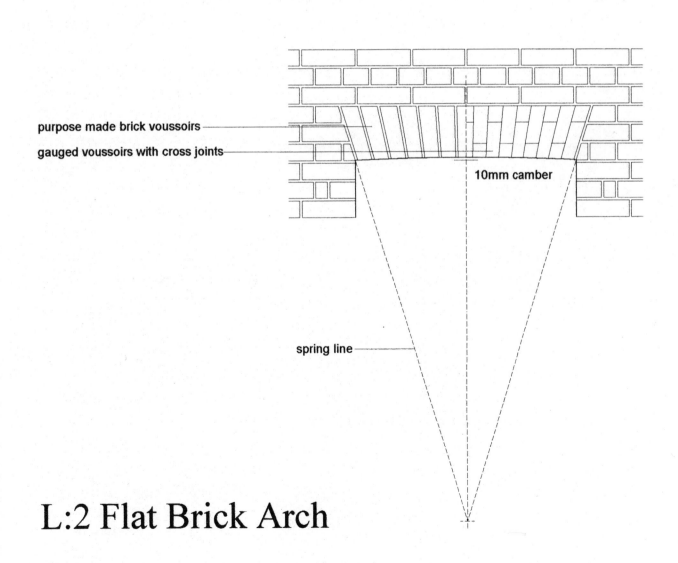

purpose made brick voussoirs

gauged voussoirs with cross joints

10mm camber

spring line

L:2 Flat Brick Arch

- While the temptation is to remove the whole lot, the correct procedure to follow is to remove only sufficient to allow the lintel to be positioned and bedded in place, if necessary on engineering bricks, and left for a couple of days to 'go off'. Where any levelling of the lintel is required, this should be done with slate other dense sheet material.

- Once this has been done, the rest of the opening can be removed, paying particular attention to the upright edges of the opening, thus preventing weakness.

- Once the opening has been fully removed any loose bricks should be re-bedded; all the making good should be done, such as plastering or re-pointing if the wall is bare brickwork.

What problems should you watch for?

On a new property the lintels and beams over openings will have been inspected as part of the building control process, so there should not be any problems! If there are severe cracks appearing above windows and doors on the external walls, this is a clear sign that the support is failing, get it checked.

These are the main points to check for when inspecting opening support structures:

- Brick or stone archways have mortar joints of even thickness; to achieve this the top brick is usually wedge shaped to allow the joints to spring from the centre point.

- When a timber arch centre or former is being used, check that it is symmetric and that it has been positioned centrally and level. There is nothing more obvious than an arch that is out of centre or not level. This is often not visible while the supports are in place.

- The underside of an opening is level.

- If it is an opening on an existing wall, make sure it is constructed in the correct order.

- Even though the brickwork, when a hole is made, appears to be strong and holding together, it must have a beam or lintel installed.

- When the opening is being made through a cavity wall ensure that a lintel supports both leaves of the wall.

- When a beam or lintel is being added to an external wall, check that there is provision for a damp-proof course above the lintel.

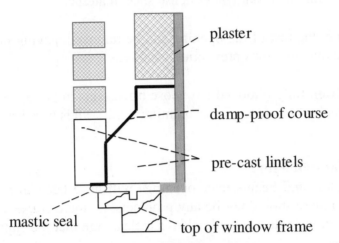

Diagram shows opening supported using concrete pre-cast lintel showing the position of the damp-proof course

- If a doorway is being installed in an external wall, planning permission may be required.

- External openings must be aesthetically acceptable.

Painting

Paint.

Paint provides a relatively quick and effective means of decorating a building, but more importantly it provides a way in which building materials can be shielded against the effects of weather.

Are there different types of paint?

There are many different types of paint for various different parts of a building, but for the purposes of this book we will look at the wider description of these paints.

- **Water-based paint**   Commonly known as emulsion, available in many different formats but normally with a vinyl silk or matt finish. The vinyl and eggshell type finishes are generally tougher and suitable as washable surfaces. Emulsion is probably the main finish applied to internal walls new properties.

    There are many new water based paint products available, suitable for both interior and exterior decoration. These can be used for painting timber frames and cladding, traditionally painted with oil-based paints. There are also acrylic paints, usually masonry paint, but more and more timber finishes are acrylic based.

- **Oil based paint**   As a rule these paints are used for the priming, base or undercoating and top or finish coating of timber products. There are also masonry oil based paints available, usually for use in extreme conditions such as cellars and other exposed situations. Oil based top coat paints are available with many different finishes such as eggshell, gloss, satin, matt, enamel to mention just a few. It should be remembered that all finishing paints are only as good as the primmer and undercoat that is beneath them

- **Wood stain and preservative**   Finishes that can be applied to timber building components, both internally and externally. Water or spirit (petroleum) based, their particular use varies with each manufacturer. The main advantages that these products have over conventional painting methods are:

    (i)   They allow the grain of the timber to remain as a feature.
    (ii)   They permit the wood to breathe naturally, allowing water to escape from the timber, preventing rot from developing.
    (iii)   They are and quicker to apply.

There is a large range of colours available, and various products designed for particular types of timber. Some of these timber preservative/stains, if applied correctly to the manufacturers' specifications have life expectancy times that far exceed those of conventional paints.

Some of the manufacturers of these specialist stains are also producing porous breathable paint finishes, usually acrylic based with incredible durability and ease of application. As with the specialist stains and preservatives, these paints are only effective when applied correctly and the correct preparation procedures are followed.

What are the component materials of building paints?
It is not possible to explain this in great detail, as each product will vary. The aim of this book is to explain briefly the component parts of paint products to give you a better understanding.

Paint is a mixture of three components:

(i) **Pigment** Which gives colour to the paint.
(ii) **Thinner or solvent** This is allows the paint the to be spread evenly over a given area.
(iii) **Binder or adhesive** These bind the components both together and to the surface to which the paint is applied.

What are the basic application rules?
There are paints available for application to every building material. All work successfully provided that the manufacturer guidelines are followed correctly. Most painting fails, not because the paint was faulty, but because the incorrect primer or undercoat was used.

Most paints rely on a process of layers being built-up on the surface to create a protective barrier to the building material. This procedure is basically the same for new or re-painting of existing parts of the building. All bare previously unpainted surfaces require primmer to create a key for the consecutive coats. This rule must be applied if re-painting, correct preparation takes the surface back to the untreated surface of the building material.

The normal paint or stain application procedure is:

• **Firstly the application of primer** This is normally applied to all unpainted surfaces, whether metal, wood, plaster, plastic or any other building material. The role of primer is to create a key or adhesion for the undercoat, some primers have grain filling and sealing properties that is not a characteristic of undercoats. Some treated metals such as galvanised steel and raw aluminium require that an 'etching' primmer be used. This is a special primmer that uses a chemical reaction to key itself to the surface of the metal. When softwood timber is painted for the first time all the knots must be coated with 'knotting', this is to seal the knots and prevent them from bleeding resin through the surface of the paint.

Steel that has not been treated for corrosion will require painting with anti-corrosion primer, such as 'red oxide' or one of the other proprietary products available. Some resinous hardwoods if they are to be painted must have aluminium oxide paint used as a primer.

• **Secondly the application of the undercoat** The role of the undercoat is to create smooth surface ready for the finishing coats of paint. If necessary several coats can and should be applied to achieve this. Failure to ensure good standards will result in a poor finish when the topcoat is applied. Undercoats should not be applied until all defects have been corrected; the primer will usually show these more clearly. It is imperative that the undercoat is allowed to dry thoroughly prior to the topcoat being applied, this will vary with each manufacturer, but must be adhered to.

- **Finally the application of the top or finishing coats**   Most primers and undercoats are slightly porous to enable the following coats to adhere to them. It is for this reason that the finishing coats must be applied at the earliest convenience. This is because these have additional properties that enable the paint to protect the material below. The finishing coat may require one or more layers to achieve sufficient coverage; thin application is a false economy, because the paint will fail much quicker.

   There are many micro-porous paints available which, when dry, allow the timber or other material to breathe, when moisture is behind the paint. It is imperative that the correct primers and undercoats are used for these paints, use of standard paints will cause the finishing layer to fail, and it will also render the usual manufactures' guarantees with these types of paint void.

Preparation of the materials to be painted.

Most failures in painting are as a result of poor preparation prior to painting. The preparation of a surface is as important as the choice of paint to be used. The preparation will ensure that the surface is smooth and stable but more importantly as the preparation is being carried out it allows the painter to check that the surface is clean and dry. The correct procedure is:

- Any new timber must have a moisture content below 16%, this means that the timber should be fully seasoned (see section on timber).

- When existing timber building fixtures are to be re-painted it is imperative that the timber is dry; wet or damp timber does not give a good base for paints. Timber can be checked with a moisture meter, but this is probably over cautious.

- All surfaces, prior to painting must be sanded, brushed clean and any dirt must be removed. Any oil based foreign substances must be removed using a suitable solvent or spirit, especially on metal surfaces.

- Knots must be treated with knotting prior to primer being applied, when existing timber is being prepared and knots are exposed, as a precaution knotting should be applied also.

- Any small holes or deep grain should be filled after the primer has been applied.

- Existing surfaces prepared for painting must be smooth, have all loose flaky paint removed, and have any rust or rot treated and any bare areas coated with primer.

- Existing surfaces are in poor condition with lots of loose paint, will require complete removal of the old paint, usually with a heat paint remover e.g.: blow-lamp. Once this is complete the surface should be treated as if it were a new unpainted surface.

- When painting involves the application of several coats, each layer must be permitted to dry fully. Each time the previous coat must be lightly smoothed with abrasive paper, to remove any foreign objects and to create a key for the next coat.

- No painting should be carried out if the temperature is below 6 degrees centigrade, and for best results exterior painting should be carried out during the spring, summer or early autumn. If there is a chance of night frost, external painting should not be carried out.

Building surfaces that may require special treatment.

Cement based boards   These are sometimes used for soffit boards or for heat protection, they are grey in colour and the surface is very dusty. These must be sealed with the manufactures' recommended primer prior to painting. Please note that painting a board that has been installed as a fire barrier may reduce its fire retardant properties. Also it is normal not to paint this type of board when it is used as soffit closure.

Plaster and plasterboard   If painted with modern emulsion paint no special treatment is required. However, if a plaster with a heavy lime content is used, a alkaline resistant primer can be applied to the wall or board, this will make easier application of emulsion or other standard paint.

Plastic and uPVC products   Although this not usually painted, it is possible to paint them. There are various specialist primers available, which once applied will permit the use of standard paints to achieve the desired colour. Some shiny plastics will not give a good key for standard paints and it may be necessary to sand the surface lightly.

Some uPVC windows after a time become dull and discoloured and many people are tempted to paint them. It is much easier to use special uPVC cleaner, which if used properly (according to manufacturers' instructions) will return the windows to their former glory. After all, plastic windows were designed to reduce maintenance responsibilities for homeowners.

Ceramic tiles   There are paints available specifically designed to paint ceramic tiles or glass. The process involves using special acrylic primer, which creates a tough key for the topcoat. For best results the tiles must be cleaned thoroughly, removing all traces of grease and other substances that will stop the paints from sticking. For an even more professional finish, the grout should be raked out prior to painting and re-grouted a few days later - after the tile paint has dried. No one will ever know that the tiles have been painted.

From personal experience the best way to use tile paint is on cheap trade white tiles. If laid flat on battens the paint can be applied without the fear of the paint running, and cheap tiles can be turned into very expensive looking hand painted tiles. If allowed to dry for about a week the tiles can be successfully cut, shaped and grouted with no effect to the surface.

Common faults that can occur with paints and painting.

This is definitely an area of construction where the 'spurs' rattle and many homeowners accept the problems - it appears without question, perhaps because the faults often don't show until the 'cowboy' has made his escape. The main reason that many homeowners fail to question 'painters', is that they are not sure of the correct techniques or what the trade standards should be. The following points should enable you to check existing paint-work on a property or to inspect painting as it is being completed:

- **Bubbles under the surface of the paint**   The trade should call this 'blistering'. It is usually caused by the paint being applied on wet timber or by the use of non-seasoned timber, which has resin bleeding to the surface. Also caused by the lack of knotting to knots and resinous areas in timber. This is a very common fault and is clearly the sign of a 'cowboy'. There is only one way to cure this problem and that is by the complete removal of all the paint to the affected areas and not to re-apply the paint until the surface is dry and appropriately treated. This problem can occur on metal surfaces as well, usually resulting in rust. The same procedure is used to correct the problem, but the rust must be treated with a corrosion treatment prior to the new paint being applied.

- **Paint that is peeling and flaking**   Again this is a fault caused by a 'cowboy' and no excuses should be accepted for this occurring. Unfortunately it will probably not occur until after payment has been made and the 'cowboy' is long gone. This fault is caused by lack of adhesion of the paint to the surface of the timber or other building material. Common causes are lack of sufficient cleaning prior to painting, poor or no sanding of the surface prior to painting, but the most common cause is again moisture. The only cure is to remove all the affected paint-work and to prepare the surfaces properly before any further paint is applied.

- **Paint that has uneven colour and streaky stains**   This is the result of a chemical reaction between paints and is known by the trade as 'bleeding'. Applying incompatible paints over one another normally causes it, a good example would be applying cellulose paint over oil-based paint, and the cellulose would soften the latter. The only successful remedy is the removal of all the affected paint and using the correct combination when re-painting.

- **Paint that has a surface that is misty or goose-pimply**   This is usually a fault found on varnishes or high-gloss finishes, affecting metal surfaces more than timber or masonry. This is a common fault caused by bad practice and inexperience, again damp and cold weather is a contributory cause. This fault is more commonly known as 'blooming'. The cure for this fault is 'flatting' or heavy sanding of the affected area and re-painting when the weather is suitable.

- **Paint that is cracking or 'egg-shelling'**   This is sometimes called crazing and is caused by the different layers of paint expanding at different rates. A common fault of 'one-coat' paints that have been applied over regular oil-based paint. The only cure is to remove all the affected paint and to replace it with layers of paint that are compatible.

- **Finishing coats that are translucent, the undercoat or previous paints are visible**
  This is a typical 'cowboy' inspired fault, where the finishing coat of paint has poor coverage and allows the undercoats to show through. This is known in the trade as 'grinning', and is normally caused by excessive thinning of the finishing coat(s) of paint or too much spreading out of the paint when it is applied. Rushing the job can also cause this. Correction is achieved by applying more coats of paint, correctly thinned, applied in the recommended manner.

What should the life expectancy of exterior painting be?
This will vary with each product, and regular cleaning of the surface treated, but as a guide the reasonable life periods for paints and stains correctly applied are:

Oil-based paint	Should last for three to five years.
Micro-porous paints	These should last longer due to the fact that they have the ability to expand and breath. Should last for five to seven years.
Stains with sheen finish	Three to five years.
Masonry paint	This will depend on the soundness of the walls, but normal life expectancy is around five to eight years.

Varnish This will depend on the timber it is applied to, hardwoods move less than softwood and therefore are less demanding on the elasticity of the varnish. It should last on softwood two to three years, hardwood three to five.

Yacht varnishes are the most durable, water-based varnishes are not advisable in areas with severe weather conditions.

Life expectancies quoted here are guidelines only, and regular inspection is recommended. It should be noted that some reputable manufacturers market paint whose life expectancies are considerable longer.

Partition or internal walls

What are partition walls?

They are the walls used primarily to divide floor space; they can be lightweight concrete, timber stud or plasterboard composite. It should be noted that many construction companies use the plasterboard composite walling systems for speed, these are assembled in much the same way as conventional timber stud and plasterboard walls.

When most properties are built now the external shell is completed to weatherproof the building, this will include any load-bearing walls within the structure. Once this has been completed the plaster board ceilings are installed on the underside of the 1st floor joists (only if a house) and the ceiling rafters on the bottom of the roof trusses. The ceilings are installed at this stage because it is easier than trying to fit and manoeuvre large sheets of plaster board into small rooms. The ceiling to the whole floor is boarded as one big room, the dividing walls are erected later.

The next stage will be to create the rooms by dividing the remainder area up and installing the dividing walls. It is common practice in houses to build ground floor partition walls using lightweight concrete blocks and to use timber stud and plaster board partitioning for first floor walls. Timber 'stud-work' can be used for ground floor walls provided that the wall is not required to support the floor above. It is also possible to use lightweight concrete blocks for first floor walls, but if they are not directly above the ground floor wall a suitable support for the wall needs to be provided, usually a steel beam or lintel.

Other roles of an internal wall:

- To provide a durable structure for fixtures and fittings.

- To create a fire barrier.

- To provide a sound base for skirting boards, architrave, etc.

- It provides for the installation of services such as electric.

- Creates a barrier against sound travel.

- They allow for variation of interior decoration.

Can any other materials be used to construct partition wall in a domestic dwelling?

There are several other materials that can be used to build internal walls the list below identifies the most widely used:

- Dense glass blocks,   **Note** when glass blocks are laid there is no bonding pattern, they are laid on mortar directly above one another. Steel rods should be placed in the mortar joints to tie the wall together, this is often not done and the walls collapse.

- Decorative brickwork.

- 'Paramount' walling system--this is a pre-made wall consisting of two outer leaves of 10 or 12mm plaster board with an internal spacer or cavity filler made of cardboard 'egg box' or honeycomb. This walling system is available in different sizes to enable the building of walls of different thickness. This system of walling is widely used by many of the larger house developers.

- Timber frames with glass panelling.

- Powder coated or stove enamelled extruded aluminium framework with in-fill panelling of glass, uPVC, or 'Perspex'.

There are many other materials that can be used to construct partition walls, most of which can be used to comply with today's stringent building regulations. The aim of this book is to look in detail at the three most commonly used systems, timber stud, lightweight block and pre-manufactured walling system.

How do you identify which walling systems your home has

This is not as difficult as it may at first appear, most internal partition walls are easily inspected to determine their type of construction. The list below shows the walls most commonly used and the way in which to identify their construction:

- **Lightweight concrete blocks or bricks, rendered and plastered**
  Tapping the wall with your knuckles can simply identify this; it should give a dull thud. This type of wall is approximately 125mm (5 inches) in thickness (the depth of the door lining).

- **Timber stud-work clad with plaster board**
  When tapped this type of wall should sound hollow, tapping across the wall the sound should vary in pitch as you tap the areas where the vertical studs are situated. This type of wall is approximately 100mm (4 inches) in thickness.

- **Pre-formed walling system**
  This type of wall is treated much the same as a timber stud wall and is identified in much the same way. The main difference with this type of wall system is that they are much thinner normally around 75mm. It is delivered in large sheet sizes of 1220mm x 2440mm (4 feet x 8 feet), this is to make it very quick to install. The vertical studs are placed at the corners, ends and where each sheet of the walling system meets.

Is there any insulation for sound or thermal values in partition walls?

It is not general practice to insulate internal timber stud walls for either of these reasons and is usually done as a preference of the customer or architect by builders, however there are instances when insulation is necessary for sound.

If a bathroom wall is adjacent to a bedroom it is general considered wise to insulate the cavity in the partition wall with fibreglass or sheet polystyrene; this is done to deaden the sound of water running into the bath or the toilet flushing. If the home has young children or teenagers it may well be advisable to insulate the walls of their bedrooms for sound deadening, for the sake of the parents sanity! It is good building practice to insulate any partition as it provides for the future users and insulation is inexpensive.

If a pre-fabricated walling system is being used such as 'Paramount' it is not possible to put insulation into the void where the honeycomb spacer is. It is common practice to double up the system placing two layers side by side to create the sound deadening required, this can prove to be expensive so it is normally only done on bathroom walls or where the system is used for flats and apartments.

Sometimes it may be necessary to create a fire break wall, perhaps the stud partition wall is near a stair well. In an instance like this it is necessary to create a firebreak that can contain the fire to allow escape for a period of between 1/2 to 1 hour (local building control can confirm this requirement). This is achieved by placing two layers of plasterboard on the partition wall faces, this is normally only required if there are solid fuel fires in the rooms on the first floor. This technique is sometimes used as a means of cheap sound deadening.

What are the advantages and disadvantages of each system of internal walls?
There are very distinct advantages and disadvantages to each of the main three systems used; this section looks at each system individually.

Lightweight concrete blocks or bricks, rendered and plastered:

The main advantages of this system are:

(i)   It is very strong.
(ii)   It is very easy to fix things to a block wall, such as shelves or pictures. The sound insulation values are good and improve if a thicker block is used.
(iii)   More affective as a fire barrier.

The main disadvantages of this system are:

(i)   It takes much longer to construct than stud-work or pre-fabricated systems.
(ii)   It costs more to construct.
(iii)   The drying out time prior to decorating is much longer.
(iv)   Cracks can occur with drying and shrinkage.

Timber stud-work clad with plasterboard:

The main advantages of this system are:

(i)   It is reasonable quick to install.
(ii)   It is much easier to fix door linings to timber studs than it is to block-work.
(iii)   A stud partition wall cuts down on the amount of wet trade work on a building project (no sand and cement render to mix).
(iv)   Very few shrinkage- or drying-cracks occur.

The main disadvantages of this system are:

(i)   It is not as tough and durable as a block wall.
(ii)   Without provision sound insulation is poor.
(iii)   Special fixing devices are required to fix things to timber stud partitioning, unless provisions are made to place the studs where items are going to be placed or fixed (it is possible to secure screws to timber studs).

Pre-formed walling system

The main advantages of this system are:

    (i)   It is very quick to install.
    (ii)   Drying time prior to decorating is shorter.
    (iii)   If it is installed correctly it gives very flat quality surfaces to walls.
    (iv)   Very little shrinkage or drying cracks occur.

The main disadvantages of this system are:

    (i)   It is very easy to dent and if a hard collision takes place penetration of the outer board can take place.
    (ii)   Sound insulation is poor.
    (iii)   Special fixing devices are required to fix things to timber stud partitioning, unless provisions are made to place the studs where items are going to be placed or fixed (it is possible to secure screws to timber studs).
    (iv)   Some people consider it to be an inferior system that devalues the quality of a home.

What faults are there to be looked for?

When looking for faults it is best to look at each partitioning system individually, as each type of partition wall suffers from its own unique faults;

Lightweight concrete blocks or bricks, rendered and plastered:

The best way to check this walling system is as the work takes place, you will need to check for these key points:

- Prior to plastering taking place ensure that the wall is either fixed to the outer wall using a metal profile or that it is toothed into the outer wall block-work (this mean that the blocks of the two walls interlock where the meet). If this is not done it may be possible to push the wall over.

- Ensure that the block-work is accurate where door linings are going to be fixed, this will save lots of time and money when the carpenter comes along and fits the door lining.

- All the electrical conduits are buried sufficiently so as not to obstruct the plastering.

- That the surface of the wall is level and in-line.

- The wall is upright.

- That the finished plasterwork is flat, smooth, and that there are no cracks or obvious defects.

These points can however be checked on a new property or where the work is completed in your absence:

- The corners, both external and internal are reasonably square and upright.

- There are no vertical cracks where the internal walls intersect with the external walls; this is a sign of bad interlocking of the walls.

- The plaster surface is smooth, level and that there are no obvious defects.

Timber stud-work clad with plasterboard:
This again is best inspected as the work is being done, but there are also some checks that can be made when the work is complete or if you are inspecting a new home;

As the wall is being built;

- That the timber studs are securely fixed to the main structure of the building, at the floor, external walls and ceiling.

- That the walls are being positioned upright and in the correct place.

- There are sufficient vertical and horizontal studs to support the wall boards, the vertical studs should be at maximum 450mm centres and the horizontal studs should at a minimum divide the height of the wall in two (assuming the wall is a standard 2285mm height).

- When the wallboards are fixed that sufficient nails are being used, the board should be nailed to the studs at approximately 250 to 300mm centres.

- If required insulation is placed in the wall before the wallboards are applied.

- The joints between the wallboards are reasonably level, this will make the plaster skin easier to apply.

- That the electrical wires are placed within the stud-work and that any socket and light switch 'cans' are neatly fitted.

These points can be checked on a completed wall:

- When you push firmly on the wall there should be only slight movement in the wall surface, if it is more than 5mm this is a clear sign of insufficient stud-work (the studs are placed to far apart).

- There should be no steps or bumps where the sheets join; in fact you should not be able to determine where the joints are.

- There should be no cracks because the joints must be taped prior to applying the plaster skin, much the same as described in the section on 'dry lining'.

- There should be no gaps between the wall and the skirting board, if there is it is a sign that either the wall is not straight at the bottom or that the skirting board is insufficiently nailed to the wall. If the skirting board is going to be painted it may be possible to fill small gaps with decorators 'chalk' or gunned filler, but this is clearly bad building to rely on filler rather than doing the job properly.

Pre-formed walling system;
This system has checks that can be made either as it is being built or after it is completed for example in a newly finished home.

Checks that can be made as construction takes place:

- The anchor battens that are fitted on the floor and ceiling are firmly secured, they should be anchored approximately every 450mm, greater spacing of the fixings will not be adequate.

- There should be another fixing batten anchored to the external wall at the point where the pre-formed wall abuts it.
  Note: these fixing battens fit between the outer layers of plasterboard of the walling system, the diagram below shows this, it is the same arrangement where the batten is fixed to a load bearing wall.

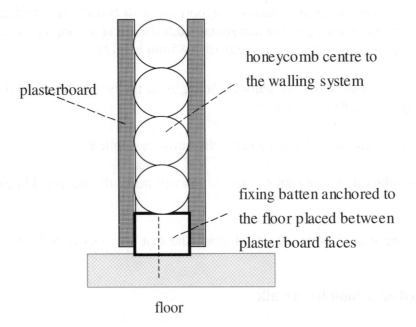

plasterboard

honeycomb centre to
the walling system

fixing batten anchored to
the floor placed between
plaster board faces

floor

- When two sections of the walling system are joined together there must be a batten placed vertically between them to prevent the wall moving at the joints. This vertical batten is anchored top and bottom. (See drawing below)

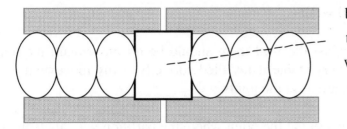

batten placed between
the two sections of the
walling system

Section through the wall looking down

- Any joints between the sections must be taped prior to the jointing compound being applied. (This system of walling does not have a plaster skin).

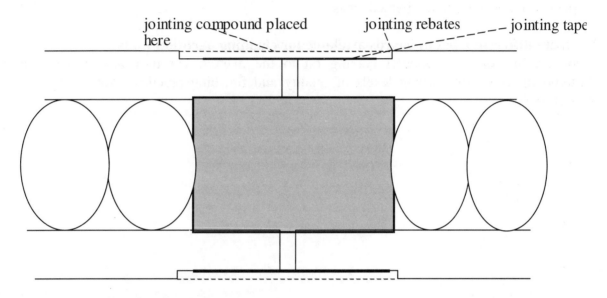

jointing compound placed here   jointing rebates   — jointing tape

an enlarged section through the wall boards showing the rebate on the
edge of the wall sections to alow for jointing compound
this is viewed looking from the top of a wall looking downwards

- There must be sufficient battens where any door linings are going to be fixed, they are placed in the same location as the anchor battens and usually the same size sections of timber are used.

- The joints should not be visible after the jointing has been done; this is after the sanding of the wall is complete.

Points to be checked on a completed wall:

- When firm pressure is placed against the wall there should be no movement, the honeycomb centre to these walls make them very stable if installed correctly. Any movement is a sign of bad anchorage or lack of vertical battens at the joints.

- The same exercise should be carried out at the point where the partition wall abuts the structural walls; there should be no movement.

- There should be no bumps or unevenness in the surface of the wall.

- The joints between the sections of wall should not be seen.

- There should be no cracks where the joints are, if there are this is a clear indication that there is poor tape coverage on the jointed areas.

Are there different types of boards available for cladding partition walls?

There are lots of new products coming on to the market, but they are all very similar to plasterboard, there are varying levels of quality and finishing practices Note; (see section on plasterboard).

Plans and Drawings.

Drawings associated with building work, however big or small the project should be clear and easy to understand. Most builders and architects will ensure that the drawings fall into three categories to ensure clarity, and to avoid confusion. Normally site plans are one group, floor, elevation and sections are another, with assembly and component drawings the third group. It is not normal to find a mixture of these drawings on one sheet, except occasionally for small projects.

What are the rules, standards and guidelines?

- **Site or location plans** These are used to show mains services, roads and paths, property boundaries and 'site setting-out' positions for the buildings. Another important piece of information that is shown on all site plans is the site levels for buildings, drains and roads. These will relate to a local datum level usually found on a church or permanent building in the locality. No site plan should be drawn to a scale any less than 1:2500.

- **Elevation drawings** The role of these drawings is to explain the external aspect from all sides of a proposed building. It will show the style of masonry, windows and doors, roof and any other features that will be applicable for planning purposes. These should be drawn to a scale no less than 1:100.

- **Floor plans** These denote or identify room dimensions; position of doorways and windows, location of services entering the building and services within the building such as electrics and plumbing. Drawn to the scale of 1:100 or larger.

- **Section drawings** These are drawings that identify particular areas of a building. They can be expressed horizontally or vertically through a building's structure to highlight special construction details or structural construction techniques. They should be drawn to a scale no smaller than 1:50.

- **Assembly drawings** These are to assist builders with the assembly of parts of a building, usually joinery or carpentry areas of a building. They are detailed drawings rather like those that you find in a 'flat pack' furniture kit, giving accurate dimension and joint details. These drawings must be drawn to scale of between 1:5 to 1:20.

- **Component drawings** These drawings are normally produced to give detailed drawings of fixture and fittings that will form part of a building. They provide all the information required by a contractor to produce the component part(s) of a building. The scale of the drawing will depend on the component(s), but a window or doorframe will be drawn at a different scale from a specialist staircase. The scale will range between 1:1 (actual size) and 1:100.

Where more than one drawing is used to explain construction, each must be numbered and relate to a job or project reference. All the drawings must be clearly dimensioned, labelled, titled and where applicable cross-referenced so that they all relate. If design changes or structural amendments are made the new drawings must be dated when changes take place.

Plasterboard

What is plasterboard?

Put simply it is gypsum plaster of a uniform thickness sandwiched between two sheets of thin 'Mill board' (similar to cardboard). The outer layers of board keep the gypsum plaster stable, without this plaster has no strength. Plasterboard is strong in compression but weak in tension.

Are there different types of plasterboard?

There are different types of plasterboard, they are manufactured to comply with BS1230: Pt.1, each has its own particular use, the list below identifies those used for domestic building:

- **Wall-board**   This is the standard plasterboard, it has one face off-white in colour for taping, direct decoration and jointing, the other face is grey coloured, this side for finishing plaster or dry lining 'dabs'. It is normally used for partition walls and ceilings. It is available in 9.5, 12.5 and 15mm thickness, with sheet sizes of 900mm x 1800mm or 1200 x 2440, special sheet lengths of up to 3000mm can be manufactured, normally for commercial applications.

- **Moisture resistant**   This is a special wallboard for use in kitchens and bathrooms; it generally has a pale green colour similar to water-resistant chipboard. The surface is specially developed for the application of ceramic tiles. Available in thickness of 9.5 and 12.5mm, sheet sizes as for standard wallboards.

- **Ceiling or base-board**   This is a special board for use on ceilings that are to have finishing plaster applied, this is available in 9.5mm thickness, sheet size normally of 900mm x 1800mm.

- **Fire resistant wallboard** This is available in two thicknesses, 12.5 which gives a 1/2-hour fire check and 15mm which gives an hour fire check. This means that they will give a sufficient barrier to a fire for the times stated. Sheet sizes are as standard wallboards.

- **Plank-boarding**   This is used for cladding structural steel and timber to give it fire protection. It is also used to increase sound insulation in partition walls.

- **Foil coated**   This is used for ceilings in areas such as bay windows and porches, where there are small roof voids that have very little space for insulation. The foil is on one face of the plasterboard; this is placed facing the void or roof space, to reflect heat back into the room. Available in standard sheet sizes.

- **Contour board**   A special board for cladding curved walls and ceilings, it is only available in 6mm thickness, with a sheet size of 1200mm x 2440mm.

Faults that can occur with plasterboard.

- It must always be stored in a dry place.

- It must be stacked flat and level with good supports.

- Cracked or bent sheets of plasterboard should not be used.

- Always ensure that the correct type of board is being used.

- Is the board being nailed the correct way round? There is a face and back to any sheet of plasterboard.

Plastering and rendering

What is plastering and rendering?
This describes the finishing process applied to the internal walls and ceilings of a dwelling. Earlier in the book dry lining was explained; this is known by the construction industry as a 'dry' finished wall. A traditional plastered wall is known by the building trade as a 'wet' finished wall. The purpose of this process is to give the wall a flat; level and durable finish to enable decoration treatments such as emulsion paint and wallpaper to be easily applied.

Are there different types of wet plastering techniques used?
One of three methods to finish interior walls with wet plastering is used:

- **Sand and cement base coat covered with finishing plaster**   This has always been the traditional method for finishing interior walls. This method uses a 10 to 12mm layer of sand and cement render, which once dry is covered, with a 2 to 3mm coat of finishing plaster.

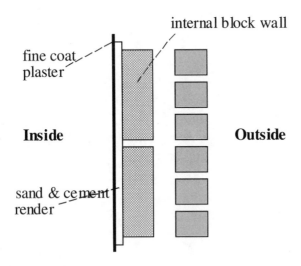

- **A 'two-stage' plaster finished wall**   This is the widely used method for finishing concrete block and brick walls on modern domestic building. It consists of a first layer of 'bonding' or 'Browning' plaster and a second thin layer of finishing plaster.

- **Fine coat plastering on plasterboard partition walls and ceiling boards**   This is a common method of finishing stud-work partition walls and plasterboard ceilings, it is still widely used as a finish on partition walls because it is a very effective and durable way of finishing them. It is simply a thin 2mm layer of finishing plaster applied to the boards, the objective is to level all the boards and give an even finish to the wall.

Are there different type of plaster?

The plaster used for building purposes is Gypsum plaster. It is made from raw gypsum that has been crushed to a fine powder which is then heated to remove the water from it, this is known as dehydration. This process produces Plaster of Paris or Class 'A' BS1191, however, Plaster of Paris is known for its quick setting properties, and is not suitable for building purposes.

To make plaster suitable for use in construction, retarding materials are added to slow the curing process down. Lightweight aggregate is added to produce lightweight plasters. Finishing plaster is a combination of Class 'A' plaster of Paris mixed with a retarding substance, which gives a product, known as Class 'B' finishing plaster Part 1, to BS1191.

The above mixture can be mixed with lightweight aggregates to give premixed or rendering plaster, part 2, to BS1191. 'Perlite' is added to make 'part 1' 'browning' plaster or type 'a1', and vermiculite is added to make 'part 1' 'bonding' plaster or type 'a3'. Both of these lightweight plasters are used as undercoat plaster when the 'two-stage' system of plaster finish is used on walls.

What preparations have to be done to walls prior to plastering?

Plastered walls are very strong and durable provided that some basic rules are followed:

- The walls must be brushed down with a stiff broom, prior to applying the base coat. This is to remove any dust and loose material, to ensure a good 'key'.

- Any external corners to the walls are usually fitted with special galvanised steel or aluminium corner beads. These are special 90 degree angle pieces fixed to the wall from floor to ceiling, giving the corner a smooth rounded finish These serve several purposes;

    (i)   They strengthen the corner against impact damage once the plaster is completed,
    (ii)   They act as a vertical straight edge that the plasterer can work to, ensuring that the wall is 'upright'
    (iii)   They also act as a horizontal guide, using a straight edge to ensure the wall is even in its length, from angle bead to door lining or other fixed point,
    (iv)   They save time, before these were invented external corners took longer to complete,

- All electrical and plumbing 'chases' (cut-outs in the walls where services are hidden) must be completed prior to plastering. If they are forgotten and chases have to be completed after plastering, cracks and falling plaster can occur where the plaster is joined.

- Plaster must never be applied to frozen walls; the ambient temperature should really be above 5 degrees Celsius whenever plastering is done. Below this temperature the risk of water particles freezing in the plaster before it has set is too high, and will result in a disaster.

In what sequence does plastering take place?
Whether sand-and-cement or 'two-stage' plastering methods are used, the same order of work is adopted; the only difference between the two methods is the drying and curing times.

- The walls are cleaned and brushed.

- All chasing is completed.

- All angle beads or arch 'formers' are fixed in place. (Arch formers are pre-formed coated, steel, mesh arches, that are fixed in openings to create shaped arches, various shapes and widths are available).

- During summer months, water can be sprayed onto the wall prior to the base coat being applied; this will slow the drying process slightly.

- The undercoat plaster or render is applied in thin layers until the required thickness is obtained, it is placed on the wall using a wooden or plastic float trowel.

- After a short while much of the water will have been sucked out of the base coat by the wall underneath, it is at this stage that a long straightedge is used horizontally across the wall to ensure that the surface is even. This is worked across the wall in a 'sawing' motion to remove any high points in the applied plaster or render.

- The next stage of the drying process is called the 'green' stage. This is the point at which the plaster or render will be surface dry, at this stage the surface is scored or scratched to ensure a good key for finishing plaster.

- Finishing plaster is normally applied the following day, sometimes later, depending on ambient temperature and humidity. It is usually mixed in a large tub or drum, the powder is added to water and mixed until it smooth, the consistency of whipped cream. It is applied using a steel plasterer's trowel, working it until a smooth finish is achieved.

  After drying for a while, a steel trowel is smoothed over the surface once more, using a little sprayed water, and this is called 'polishing the surface'. This final stage gives the finished wall a very smooth and even surface, it also removes any air bubbles that have worked their way to the surface and any other blemishes.

- The final stage is where the plasterer will work around the wall cleaning out all the electrical 'cans', removing excess plaster from door linings and scraping the floor clean. Some plasterers also use an old trowel to recess the plaster at the bottom of the walls, to allow easier fitting of skirting boards.

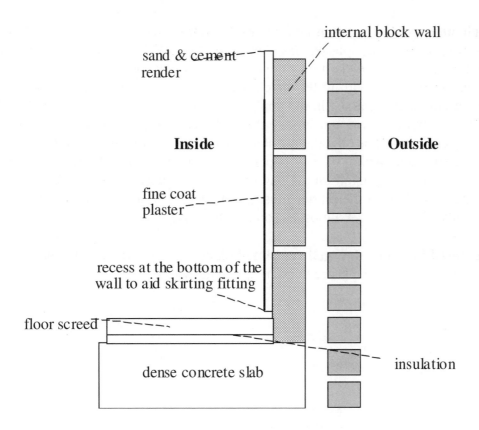

sand & cement render

internal block wall

Inside

Outside

fine coat plaster

recess at the bottom of the wall to aid skirting fitting

floor screed

dense concrete slab

insulation

Common faults to be watched for on finished walls.

Most faults in plasterwork are a result of bad training, lack of experience or 'cowboy' botching. Unfortunately plastering faults are not easily corrected and usually result in the wall having to be re-plastered. The following faults if identified give you just cause to complain and to request the fault to be rectified:

- **Egg shell like cracks on the surface of plaster**   These are caused by the finishing plaster being applied too thickly, as it dries the plaster shrinks and cracks occur. This should be removed and the area re-plastered.

- **Vertical cracks down the corners of rooms**   These are common, and are due to shrinkage. Cement render covered with finishing plaster is more susceptible to this problem, 'two-stage' plastering systems tend not to suffer from this problem. This generally occurs weeks after the plastering is completed, cutting a 'V' shaped groove along the crack line can rectify it. When this is filled with finishing plaster the crack is less likely to reappear. This is a hazard of speculative building methods (the old adage 'Less haste, more speed' might well apply here!), and it is imperative that each stage of a building dries thoroughly before the next stage commences. This is the main reason for lots of builders using dry lining instead of wet plastering, this can be done far quicker and shrinkage problems do not normally occur.

- **Two-coat plaster applied wrongly**   'Browning' plaster, type 'A1' or 'Bonding' plaster, type 'A3' are undercoat plasters used for the 'two-stage' plastering process. They are recognised by the fact that they have large particles, and when dry they look a little like pink polystyrene sheet. These types of plaster must have a topcoat applied, and are not suitable for the direct application of decorating materials. If the base-coat plaster is visible through the topcoat, it means that the finishing plaster has not been applied thickly enough, this must be re-plastered.

- **Walls with rough, uneven plaster and hair-like cracks in the surface**   This is normally caused by one of two reasons, the plaster has started to 'go off' before being applied to the wall, or it was out of date, or old stock; it may not have been stored correctly.

    Once plaster has been mixed with water the curing process begins, the retarding substances added to plaster are only there to assist in the application, plaster starts to 'go off' within 15 to 20 minutes, if the weather is warm and breezy this will occur even sooner. For this reason plaster must be used as soon as it is mixed, once it starts to set it should not be used.

    All building plaster is supplied in bags or paper sacks, with a moisture barrier on the inside. All plaster has a 'use-by' date printed on the bag or tag; this is because its usability decreases with age. If the date has expired the plaster must not be used. Plaster that has past its use-by date by several weeks will start to set almost as soon as it is mixed.

- **Plaster must be stored in a cool, dry well ventilated place**   failure to do this can reduce the curing time or cause the plaster to go lumpy in the sacks.

Plumbing and plumbing systems

What is the plumbing in your home?
It is the network of pipes carrying water into and out of your home. To protect public health, every domestic dwelling must have a supply of safe water for drinking and for the operation of the plumbing fixtures and appliances, and a sanitary drainage system for wastewater disposal (this latter subject is covered in the section on drainage).

To provide the sanitary facilities required, local Government Building Control are responsible for the regulations governing design and installation requirements and the minimum number of fixtures required, based on the size of the property and the number of occupants.

Drainage systems
There are of two basic types sanitary and storm water, these are covered in depth in the section on drainage, the following information is an overview and is for guidance purposes only. Sanitary drainage systems carry bodily and other wastes from the plumbing fixtures and appliances by gravity through a sewer to a sewage treatment facility outside the building. Sanitary drainage piping inside the building must be linked to a system of vent piping, to maintain equal pressures in all sections of the drainage piping. This prevents the siphoning or blowing of water in the traps (U-shaped dips in the piping), which in turn prevents the unpleasant sewer gases, which form as sewage material decomposes, from entering the building.

Storm-water drainage systems carry rainwater from the roof by gravity through a sewer to the mains storm-water drain or to a soak-away. Basement drainage usually needs to be collected in a sealed and vented pit or tank and pumped out of the basement.

Which parts of your home fall under the category of plumbing?
Plumbed fixtures include toilets, sinks, baths, and showers, in addition to these plumbing also incorporates kitchen and utility room needs. Appliances connected to a plumbing system include dishwashers and washing machines, these appliances require both hot and cold water supply as well as drainage.

Heaters using gas, electricity, oil, coal or solar energy can generate hot water. Fixtures today are made of impervious materials such as vitreous china, enamelled cast iron or steel, stainless steel, or plastic. Piping materials include cast iron, steel, brass, copper, stainless steel, aluminium, plastic, vitrified clay (tile), and concrete.

Fresh water supply.
The local Water Company supplies water to your property under pressure. In some areas, water must be obtained from on-site wells or nearby streams or lakes, in which case great care must be taken to ensure that the water is uncontaminated. If mains pressure is insufficient because of the height of the building, it will be necessary to fit a pump to supply a gravity tank in the roof void. Always remember that the homeowner and the local water supply company jointly own the mains stop-tap or water meter, and supply pipe.

Important points to be aware of with the water supply to your property.

- There must be satisfactory cold water supply, of drinking quality to every domestic dwelling.

- A minimum of one tap in a property must be connected to this drinking water supply.

- The water supply system must avoid unnecessary waste, and excessive consumption.

- There must be provisions within the system to prevent contamination of the mains water supply. (anti-return valves on garden taps and appliances)

- The system must be protected against corrosion.

- All pipes must be protected against frost.

- All parts of the system must allow future maintenance.

When a builder designs the plumbing system for a house, they will have to design the system so that it does not work against gravity. Water will always find its own level. To enable the system to operate with gravity, pressure has to be created within the system; this is achieved by placing a storage tank at the highest point of the property, normally in a loft or attic. In some areas the mains pressure is so great that this may not be necessary.

Cold water is supplied to a domestic property in one of two tried and tested methods:

A direct cold water system.

All the cold water within the property is supplied to all the cold water service outlets by mains pressure. There will be a small storage tank (approximately 120-litre capacity) in the loft for supplying the hot water storage cylinder. This system is used in areas of the country where the mains water supply pressure are constant.

Advantages of this system:

- Fresh drinking water is supplied to each cold water outlet.

- Less storage facilities are required in the loft space.

Disadvantages of this system:

- There is only a small reserve of water in the event of a mains supply fault, and this is only available to prevent explosion of the hot water cylinder.

- There can be reduced pressure when there is peak demand of the water supply.

- No cold water reserve in the event of mains failure.

An indirect cold water system.

With this type of system all of the cold water is supplied to service outlets via a large storage tank fixed as high as possible in the loft. There will be a fresh drinking water supply direct from the main for the kitchen sink and basins where teeth are likely to be cleaned.

Advantages of this system:

- There is a large reserve of water should the mains supply be interrupted.

- This type of system lessens the risk of 'back-siphonage', caused by negative mains pressure. As the water pressure fails gravity creates suction down the pipes.

Disadvantages of this system:

- Up to 40% more pipe work may be required compared with a direct system.

- This type of system is not suitable for use in areas of hard water.

Hot water supply system.

This describes the means in which hot water is distributed throughout a domestic dwelling; normally one of three systems is used;

How do you identify what type of water heating and distribution system your home has, or what type of system you should install?

Direct hot water supply system:

This is both a simple and economic way of installing a hot water supply system into a domestic dwelling. Water is heated by a boiler, as it is heated it rises up a pipe into the top of the storage cylinder (copper tank in the airing cupboard). As the hot water is used in the dwelling it exits from the top of the cylinder, usually by a pipe located on the opposite side of the tank. The water is replaced to the system by the water storage tank in the loft; this enters the copper storage tank at the bottom and returns to the boiler. Water level in the loft storage tank is controlled by a floating ball valve.

Key points to help you identify the direct heating system:

- There is only one storage tank in the loft or attic.

- There probably are not water-heated radiators, more likely electric storage heaters.

Advantages of this system:

- Very cheap to install.

- Maintenance is minimal.

Disadvantages of this system:

- This type of system is very prone to 'furring', a high build-up of white deposits within the system, much the same as occurs in your kettle.

- Not suitable where the water is hard.

- A central heating system cannot be incorporated as part of this type of system.

An indirect hot water supply system:

This type of hot water supply is more complicated than the direct system; the layout of the pipe-work is very similar, with the addition of a small header tank to feed the primary side of the system.

There are two circuits to an indirect heating system, the primary and the secondary. The primary circuit acts like an element, its purpose to heat the water in the copper storage cylinder. Water heated by the boiler flows up a pipe which enters the top of the storage cylinder, and flows in a coil within the cylinder, acting as a 'heat exchanger' - hot water in the coil heats the surrounding cold water in the cylinder. It then returns to the boiler to be reheated, thus the cycle begins again.

In some areas (with hard water) anti-furring, or anti-scaling, agents are added to the primary system to prevent the build up of 'fur' or scaly deposits of lime, which would clog the system. The primary system also incorporates water in the heating circuit. This is generally pumped round the property to make the system more efficient and because central heating pipes are horizontal; hot water does not circulate horizontally.

The secondary circuit is the supply side of the system; this distributes the hot water to all the outlets. There is no flow and return in a secondary system. Cold water is introduced at the bottom of the hot water cylinder, replacing hot water drawn off at the top.

Key points to help you identify the indirect heating system:

- There are two storage tanks in the loft, one with a minimum capacity of 230litres for supplying the water to the taps, the other much smaller, around 40litres capacity for supplying and charging the primary side of the system.

- There will probably be water-heated radiators incorporated as part of the system.

Advantages of this system:

- It is not as prone to furring-up; therefore this type of system is suitable for use in areas where the water is hard.

- Central heating systems can be added.

Disadvantages of this system:

- Cost considerably more.

- The anti scaling additive should be replenished regularly, to ensure efficiency.

Mains fed indirect water heating system:

This is a relatively new method of heating water in a domestic dwelling in the UK; it is used extensively in mainland Europe and North America as a cost-effective alternative to traditional methods of heating domestic water. Its main features are that it requires no cold water storage tanks and installation time of the whole system is much shorter.

If a property has this type of system it is normally installed along side electric storage heaters, thus removing the need for a boiler, an immersion heater heats water for domestic use. When an immersion heater is used there is no primary circuit and the system is really a direct system, making it very cheap and quick to install. Conventional water-heated radiators can be installed using this type of system, but this will require the installation of a boiler.

As water is heated it expands; the plumbing system within a dwelling has to be able to cope with the increase of volume. Traditional systems have a vent or expansion pipe that flows back into the cold water storage tank in the loft, any excess water flows back into here. The mains fed system does not have a storage tank, instead there is an expansion vessel incorporated into the system, usually incorporated as part of the hot water storage cylinder. Air is used to cushion the expansion of the water; a rubber or neoprene diaphragm is used to keep the water and air separate. As an extra precaution a thermal release valve is fixed to the top of the hot water storage cylinder and a pressure control valve is fitted to the mains supply pipe.

Key points to help you identify mains fed water-heating system:

- There are no cold water storage tanks.

- The hot water storage cylinder is usually tall, up to 1500mm is not unusual

- There may be a manual pump fixed on the side of the cylinder for re-pressurising the expansion vessel inside the cylinder.

- There may not be a boiler if there are electric storage radiators.

Advantages of this system:

- Very cost effective, quick to install.

- Needs no high storage facility.

- A good system for using in flats and apartments, it is easy to give each property its own independent system.

Disadvantages of this system:

- The system will cease to operate if the mains water supply should fail.

- In areas of hard water use of the immersion heater can create excessive furring.

- This system has to installed by a qualified and experienced plumber, to prevent explosions!

Is there any built-in safety features to plumbing systems?

Both water supply and drainage systems must be carefully designed to prevent serious contamination of the mains water supply and the natural ground water that may be present in the soils surrounding a property. There must also be provision in the drainage system to prevent sewer gas from entering the building.

All water connections to fixtures and appliances must be provided with devices that prevent contaminants from being siphoned or forced back into the water piping, a condition known as 'back-flow' or 'back siphonage'. Thermostats and pressure safety valves must be installed on all water heaters to prevent explosion in the event of malfunctioning controls.

What should you look for when inspecting the plumbing system?

This section looks at the supply side of the domestic plumbing system, and the initial stages of waste plumbing, before it enters the drainage system.

Domestic plumbing is a complex part of building, carried out by highly skilled and experienced people. This section of the book highlights the important areas, and explains the correct procedures and building practices, and helps identify potential problems.

Key points to look for when checking the water supply side of your home's plumbing system:

From mains supply to inside of the property.

- The pipe supplying your property with water must connect to the mains supply pipe at right angles; this is to aid future location if repair to the supply is necessary.

- The mains supply stop valve located outside the property must be at a minimum depth of 750mm, this is to protect it against frost.

- Where the supply pipe enters the property, if it passes underneath the foundation it must be protected with mass concrete.

- Where the pipe passes below the ground floor it is normal practice to use a 75mm plastic drainpipe to protect the supply pipe.

- The water supply pipe can be made from the following materials:

  (i)   Copper to BS2871
  (ii)   Plastic
         Polythene to BS1972 and BS3284
         uPVC to BS3505
  (iii) The local Water Company may accept galvanised steel.

- Materials that are not permitted for use as water supply pipes are:

  (i)   Plain steel (unprotected)
  (ii)   Plain iron (unprotected)
  (iii) Lead, this is prohibited in all areas of the country.

- Once the supply pipe enters the property there must be a stop valve and a drain-down tap directly above it.

Rules to be applied to the supply plumbing of a property.

- The kitchen sink cold tap must be fed direct from the mains supply, it must not be supplied from a storage tank in the loft. This water will be used for cooking and drinking.

- The cold supply to bathroom or en-suite basin must also be fed direct from the mains supply, as these will be used for cleaning teeth. Water from a storage tank will not be fresh and could be contaminated.

- Any water that is heated can be supplied via a storage tank, as this is not intended for human consumption.

- Any outside taps must have an anti back-flow valve fitted, to prevent contamination of the water supply from garden hoses (from back-siphonage).

Supply pipe-work: types of materials that may be used.
Domestic building should be kept simple and most builders adopt this principle when planning new and refurbishment projects. Plumbing can be very complex so it is imperative that where possible simplicity is adhered too. For this reason most builders use four materials for the supply side of domestic plumbing:

- Copper tube, 15mm, 22mm, 28mm and 35mm.

- Copper tube on a reel, this is called 'micro-bore' and is normally used for central heating systems or oil supply pipe for boilers. This requires no special tools for shaping or bending and is very easy to install.

- PVC pipe of various lengths with solvent weld joints.

- Polythene pipe available in 100metre reels, a common type used for domestic plumbing is 'Hep 2o'.

- Cast iron or mild steel pipe is sometimes used for heating systems.

Are there any common problems to watch for when checking the supply pipe-work?
Most plumbers are very competent at their job and very few problems occur, however plumbing repairs can prove very lucrative, especially when you call a plumber out after normal trading hours. It is this that attracts the rogue into the industry! Common faults in new pipe-work:

- Ensure that the pipes are not damaged in any way, i.e. kinked or buckled.

- Where pipes have been shaped to a radius or bend, there must be no crushing of the pipe.

- If PVC or polythene pipes have been used, check that they conform to British Standards, and that the pipe is the correct type.

- All pipe-work is sufficiently clipped back to walls or joists; it must not be loose anywhere.

- If pipes have to pass under floors, holes should be drilled for the pipe to pass through, not notches cut out of the top of joists.

- Any new pipe-work in a roof space or similar cold area is adequately lagged to protect it from frost.

Minimum pipe diameters for each section of the supply system:

Direct cold water supply.

    (i)   Mains water supply pipe or rising main 22mm
    (ii)   Bath supply to cold tap 22mm
    (iii)   All overflow pipes 22mm
    (iv)   Cold feed pipe to the copper storage cylinder 22mm
    (v)   Other basin, WC and sinks 15mm

Indirect cold water supply.

    (i)   Mains water supply pipe or rising main 15mm.
    (ii)   Bath supply to cold tap 22mm
    (iii)   All overflow pipes 22mm
    (iv)   Cold feed pipe to copper storage cylinder 22mm
    (v)   Other basin, WC and sinks 15mm

Direct hot water system.

    (i)   Mains water supply pipe or rising main 15mm.
    (ii)   Pipes between the boiler and storage cylinder 28mm
    (iii)   Cold water supply pipe between the storage tank and hot water cylinder 22mm
    (iv)   All other supply outlet pipes 15mm
    (v)   All overflow pipes 22mm

Indirect hot water system.

    (i)   Mains water supply pipe or rising main 15mm.
    (ii)   Primary circuit pipes (between the boiler and storage cylinder) 28mm
    (iii)   Cold water supply pipe between the storage tank and hot water cylinder 22mm
    (iv)   Vent or expansion pipe from the top of the hot water cylinder 22mm
    (v)   All overflow pipes 22mm
    (vi)   All other supply outlet pipes 15mm
    (vii)   Hot water supply pipe between floors 22mm
    (viii)   From primary circuit to central heating pump 22mm
    (ix)   From central heating pump to radiator circuit 22mm reduced down to15mm at each radiator.

Mains fed indirect system.

(i) Mains water supply pipe or rising main 22mm.

(ii) Primary circuit pipes (between the boiler and storage cylinder) 28mm

(iii) Cold water supply pipe between the rising main and hot water cylinder 22mm

(iv) All overflow pipes 22mm

(v) All other supply outlet pipes 15mm

(vi) Hot water supply pipe between floors 22mm

(vii) From primary circuit to central heating pump 22mm

(viii) From central heating pump to radiator circuit 22mm reduced down to 15mm at each radiator.

Note: All of the above sizes are to be used only as a guide, to enable you to spot obvious mistakes. The technical details for each type of system should be used in the same manner, but more importantly these specifications are to familiarise you with the different systems. All sizes given are the external diameter of the pipe.

Supply pipe-work joints.

Are there different types?

There are different types of joint used; this varies with each type of pipe-work used. The type of pipe and correct joints are listed below:

- **Copper tube** Four methods are used to join pipes:

  (i) Standard compression joint, copper tube is placed in either end of the joint. The port-holes of the joint contain a soft copper compression sealing ring or 'olive', the joint is sealed by tightening the coupling nuts either end of the joint, which squash the sealing ring or olive around the pipe. (Normally used for repairs, not new build).

  (ii) Manipulative compression joint, This works in the same way as the standard compression joint, there is no soft copper sealing ring used, in place of this there is a friction locking seal. The ends of the copper tube have a bead or bell shape formed on them using a swaging tool, when the coupling nuts are tightened the bead is pushed into the joint, pulling the friction seal against the bead. (this method is not used much on domestic building, because it takes longer)

  (iii) Soldered capillary joint, A very simple means of joining copper tube. The joint is a sleeve of copper that fits over the two pieces of copper tube; each end of the joint has an integral internal groove containing solder. When heat is applied to the joint using a blow-lamp, the solder flows around the joint by capillary action, a successful joint will have a silver ring of solder visible at each end. (Used more than any other joint, very reliable and inexpensive).

  (iv) Standard soldered joint, This is a copper sleeve without the integral solder groove, and the solder is applied manually by the plumber. (Very cheap to buy, may leak if the copper tube is damaged or not clean).

- **Copper tube on a reel ('micro bore')**   This is joined using standard compression or soldered capillary joints, these work as described above (may also be jointed using a swaging tool, as above).

- **PVC pipe**   A PVC coupling sleeve is used, a solvent solution must be applied to weld the joint to the pipe. Standard friction joints are not used on water supply pipes.

- **Polythene pipe**   Normally joined using compression joints, with a soft copper compression seal. A copper sleeve is placed inside the polythene pipe to prevent distortion.

- Cast iron or mild steel pipe   Threaded socket joints are used, this is a sleeve that is internally threaded. The ends of the pipes are externally threaded to screw into the sleeve. The thread is sealed using PTFE (poly-tetra-fluoro-ethylene) tape or hemp and jointing paste.

All of the above joints are available in various angles and pipe sizes.

Common faults and the repair details required.

- **Over flow pipes exiting the roof void that drip water**   This is a common fault that is normally caused by one of two problems.

    (i)   A faulty ball valve on the supply pipe to the water storage tank, which is housed in the loft space; this is obviously corrected by fitting a new ball valve.

    (ii)   The problem can also be caused by a breach of the primary circuit within the indirect hot water storage cylinder, this normally only occurs in old storage cylinders. This has the effect of continuously filling the cylinder with water from the primary circuit storage tank housed in the loft space, not as it should be filled by the main storage tank that is housed in the loft. This then will force water back up into the main storage tank in the loft, which is what you, see exiting the overflow pipe. This problem cannot be repaired and will require a new hot water cylinder being fitted.

- **Dripping taps**   Again a common fault normally caused by continually turning the tap off with too much force. Fitting a new washer inside the tap rectifies it. If this problem is not corrected it can result in the seat being damaged within the tap and a new tap having to be fitted. It may be possible to correct the seat with a re-seating tool if only minor damage has occurred.

- **Taps that are difficult to operate**   A very common fault in areas of the country where the water is hard. The build-up of lime scale inside the tap can restrict operation of the tap, and in an extreme case result in total failure of the on/off operation of the tap. Turning the water supply off, dismantling the tap, cleaning out all the moving parts and re-assembling the tap, lubricating the top of the shaft with thick oil can rectify this. While the tap is dismantled it may be worth fitting a new washer; this could save another call-out charge. Only very severe cases will necessitate the replacement of the tap.

Central heating circuits.

Three types of central heating circuit normally are used; they all use the principle of a primary system already discussed;

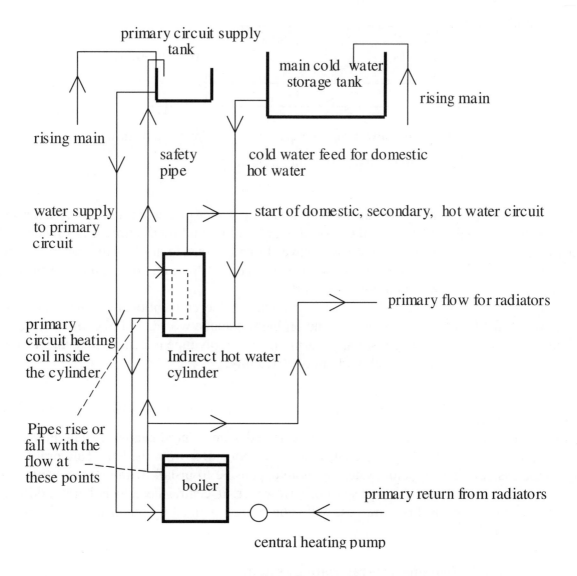

One pipe system;

This method is simple to install, and relatively cheap. As the heading suggests water is circulated around the property in one pipe, starting at the boiler, and returning to the boiler once it has passed through all the radiators with the assistance of the circulating pump. Where a radiator is needed a pipe is branched off and connected to the top of one side of the radiator. Another pipe is connected to the bottom of the opposite side of the radiator, and returns to the supply pipe.

One pipe central heating system

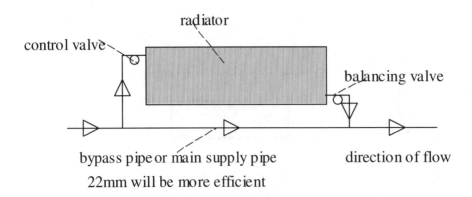

The main disadvantage of this system is that the water passes through the radiator and then on to the next, as it passes through the system is gets colder and by the time it has reached the last radiator in the circuit the temperature will have dropped considerably. This can be allowed for using balancing valves to control the flow of water, so that the radiators at the end of the circuit have a greater rate of flow than those at the start.

If supply pipes to the radiators are connected in the conventional manner, (i.e.: flow and return both at the bottom of the radiator), the problem is made worse, and in extreme cases the last radiators in a circuit may only get slightly warm. If the supply pipe is 22mm in diameter rather than the standard 15mm, the system will work more efficiently.

Two pipe system;

This is the most common method of installing a heated water central heating system into a domestic dwelling; it is very efficient, easy to control and does not suffer from the balancing problems of the single pipe system. This type of system is more expensive to install, with up to twice the quantity of pipe needed over the single pipe system. However, if central heating is being added to your home as an improvement this extra cost will soon be recuperated by the efficiency it has over the one pipe system.

Two pipe central heating system

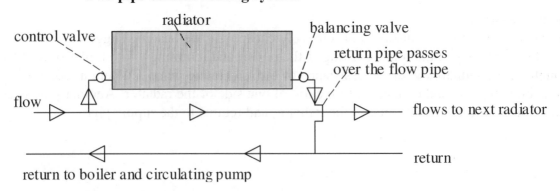

With this system, the circulating pump is placed at the boiler end of the return circuit; the single pipe system has the pump located at the start of the flow circuit. This system is more efficient because each radiator has the water delivered at very similar temperatures by the flow or delivery pipe. The water exiting the radiators is delivered straight back to the boiler and re-heated by the return pipe, not on to the next radiator as with the single pipe system.

Micro-bore heating system:
This system is different from the previous central heating methods; it uses 6 to 12mm soft flexible pipe, wound on a reel. It still uses the primary circuit system as described with the two previous systems, but this is generally a small loop circuit feeding the micro-bore section of the system with hot water. The heating system will be designed so that it is divided into areas or banks of radiators; the primary circuit via a manifold supplies these. The primary circuit and manifold are normally made from 22mm copper tube; the manifolds are sometimes larger.

Once water reaches the manifold it is distributed to the radiators in micro-bore pipes. Each radiator is supplied independently with a flow and return pipe; it is normal practice to place one manifold on each floor of a domestic dwelling. For this type of system to work efficiently a powerful distribution pump is required. Double entry valves are sometimes used on the radiators to enhance the efficiency of the system. Double entry valves are easily identified, flow and return pipes to each radiator enter on one side of the radiator, instead of the conventional alternate sides.

Micro-bore heating system.

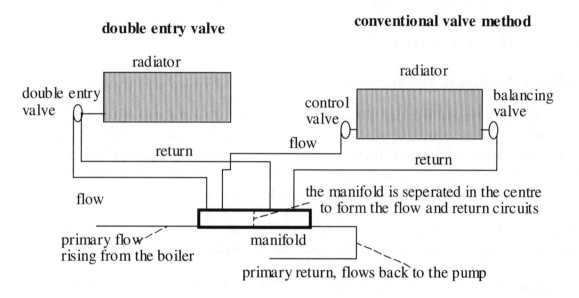

The manifolds for micro-bore systems are manufactured with ports or outlets built-in as part of their structure, all the plumber has to do is make the connections where needed, those not required are blanked-off.

Common faults with central heating systems.
Even though the three systems discussed are very different, they could suffer from the same faults, bad workmanship or problems resulting from unskilled plumbers. The list below identifies these:

- **Noisy, rattling pipes**   Usually caused by insufficient securing of pipes, or where they touch the underside of floorboards. There is no excuse, an attempt to save clips, or time, by cutting notches out of floor joists rather than drilling holes through the joist for the pipes to pass through, is just shoddy workmanship.

- **Water trickling or bubbling noises near the boiler**   This is caused by air trapped in the primary system, probably on a bend or near the circulating pump for the heating. This is very difficult to prevent, normally only corrected by forcing water under pressure through the drain tap near the boiler. Bad levelling of the primary flow circuit, which is reliant on the natural rise of heated water, some times causes it. The primary circuit should have pipes that rise and fall vertically; horizontal pipe-work must be kept to a minimum. Horizontal pipes on the flow side of the primary circuit must rise slightly towards the hot water cylinder; this prevents air pockets forming (see plumbing layout diagram at beginning of section on central heating).

- **Central heating pump that vibrates pipes**   Two faults normally cause this, no rubber mountings securing the pump to the wall or floor to absorb vibrations, or air trapped near the pump. The lack of rubber mountings is rectified by their installation; there is normally a drain tap or bleed valve next to the pump to free trapped air.

- **Radiators that are noisy and not heating correctly**   This is caused by air trapped in the radiator, there is a 'bleed' screw on one of the top corners of radiators. This should be unscrewed until the air escapes, once water runs out instead of air, the bleed screw should be re-tightened. **NB: the water could be very hot**

- **Radiators that are furthest away from the boiler not heating sufficiently**   This is normally a fault of a one-pipe system, but may occur on two pipe systems as well. It is caused by the water cooling before it reaches the furthest radiators. It can be resolved by balancing the radiators, this means restricting the flow of water to the initial radiators, giving the last radiators in the circuit more of the water from the primary flow. This is achieved by partially closing the balancing valves on the initial radiators in a circuit; to restrict the flow of water through them, thereby giving the last radiators in the circuit unrestricted flow. This should give all the radiators a similar temperature. It may take several attempts to achieve a balanced system. This can also be resolved by installing a boiler with a larger out-put, so ensure that the boiler specified is more than capable of heating your size of dwelling.

- **Water running off the rising main pipe**   This occurs when moisture in the atmosphere condenses on the cold feed and is common where the rising main is located within the living area of a dwelling. This is often a problem under sinks and in utility rooms and gives the appearance that the pipe is leaking, it can be resolved by either insulating the pipe or hiding it inside a duct or boxing.

  A reputable builder or plumber will plan for this and make the provisions to prevent it from occurring.

- **Green or black powdery deposits around the joints on the pipe-work of the central heating system**   This is normally a sign of a leak, but may also be caused by moist air reacting with the deposits from the soldering process. When the cause is a leak, the edges of the deposit are normally wet or darker in colour. This is because as the leak occurs the heat within the system dries any water that has escaped, the dark edge will be more obvious on a bad leak, which may show more when the heating is not on, or when the circulating pump is in operation. The green colour is caused by oxidisation of copper and impurities on the copper pipe. The black colour is usually dry anti-scaling solution, a clear sign that there is a leak.

  If the leaking joint is a compression type, then the cure may effected by tightening the coupling nuts. If this doesn't cure the leak the system will have to be drained, the joint separated, the compression rings replaced and the joint reassembled and tightened.

  When the leak is on a soldered capillary joint, the problem is not always as easily cured. If the area around the joint is cleaned with wire wool, it may be possible to apply more solder to the ends of the joint, but this may not be successful. The more successful solution is to drain the system, separate the joint using a blow-lamp, clean the ends of the pipes and solder a new joint in place.

- **Location of the room thermostat**   This is one of the main causes of heating problems in domestic dwellings, and is easily avoided by using common sense and/or experience. If the thermostat is placed in the coldest room, the rest of the house will feel too hot. If it is placed in the warmest room, the rest of the house will feel too cold. When placed in the smallest room, which will heat up quickly, the rest of the house will feel cold. And if it is in the largest room, the other rooms will be too hot.

  The thermostat should be positioned centrally within the property away from draughts and heat source (e.g. chimney-breast, sunlight, & cold.) for it to work effectively and efficiently.

Room thermostats, important points to remember:

(i)   In two storey properties, place the thermostat in the hallway well away from the stairs and draughts.

(ii)   Similarly, do not place the thermostat on the upper floor, heat rises, and the thermostat will stop the boiler at the temperature upstairs, leaving the rooms downstairs cold.

(iii)   A room thermostat should never be placed on an exterior wall of a property.

(iv)   Never place a room thermostat in a position where direct sunlight can strike it, this will heat the thermostat and the wall and give a false reading.

Sanitary fittings explained with key points regarding wastewater disposal:
This is a very complex area of building, so this section highlights the basic points that may be identified by the average homeowner. Each type of sanitary fitting is described with its required waste water plumbing and any regulations or British Standards that apply. Any water supply technical details not discussed previously are also explained, where applicable.

Sinks for use in kitchens and utility rooms:

- These are available in various shapes, sizes and fitting styles, they must be made to British Standards, identified by a stamp.

- They should have a bowl depth of between 180 and 200mm.

- They may be made from stainless steel, enamelled pressed steel, enamelled cast iron or plastic composite materials.

- Metal sinks must comply with BS1244.

- There must be an adequate overflow facility connected to the waste pipe.

- The waste outlet pipe must be a minimum 40mm in diameter, incorporating a 75mm 'seal trap' with an integral cleaning eye. 75mm 'seal trap' means that once the water has drained away there is 75mm of water left in the bend of the trap to prevent smells/gases escaping from the drains and entering the dwelling.

Washing machine and dishwashers:

Many properties have fitted utility rooms and kitchens, it is important that provision is made for fitted appliances requiring water supply and waste disposal.

Supply:
- Washing machines normally require hot and cold water supplies, these should be provided with the correct screw fitting taps, clearly identifying hot (red) and cold (blue).

- The same rules apply to dishwashers, although many require a cold feed only.

- All appliances that use water must have a supply that is delivered at mains pressure, water delivered from loft storage will not have sufficient pressure to operate.

Waste:
- The waste pipe must have a raised section of no less than 500mm, (the pipe into which the waste pipe from the machine is fed). The waste pipe should have a minimum diameter or 40mm, incorporating a 75mm 'seal trap' with integral cleaning eye.

Wash basins:

These are generally made from glass fibre, plastic, stainless steel or ceramic. All should be made to comply with British Standards. Ceramic basins must comply with BS1188.

- Normally fitted at a minimum height of 790mm, on steel cantilever supports.

- If it has a pedestal support this will determine the finished height.

- Bowl depth should be a minimum of 165mm.

- There must be an adequate overflow facility connected to the waste pipe.

- The waste pipe must be a minimum size of 32mm.

- There must be a 38 or 78mm seal bathroom trap with integral cleaning eye.

- A durable plug and chain or alternative bung system should be provided to retain water in the basin.

Baths:

These are available in many shapes, sizes, materials and colours, this book gives guidelines based on the standard models.

- Standard lengths are between 1670 and 1830mm.

- Standard widths are between 700 to 879mm.

- Standard heights are between 420 and 730mm.

- Cast iron baths are manufactured to BS1189.

- Plastic and glass fibre baths are manufactured to BS4305.

- Enamel coated steel baths are manufactured to BS1390.

- All baths must have adjustable feet, to permit levelling and to allow for uneven floor finishes.

- Water supply pipes must be 22mm diameter.

- A durable plug and chain or alternative bung system should be provided to retain water in the bath.

- There must be an adequate overflow facility connected to the waste pipe.

- There must be a 38 or 78mm seal bathroom trap with integral cleaning eye.

Showers:

Showers may be fitted as part of a bath or free-standing, a screen or curtain must be fitted to prevent water running out onto the floor. The rules applicable to free-standing showers:

- Shower trays are generally made of plastic or glass fibre, but may be ceramic.

- A shower tray must have a minimum depth of 180mm.

- Standard dimensions of shower-trays are from 600 to 900mm square.

- Where a shower attachment is fitted adjacent walls should be protected with ceramic tiles.

- Electric showers are supplied with water direct from the mains, this ensures that pressure is maintained.

- Showers fed from the domestic hot water supply will have less pressure so there must be a minimum 'head' of water of 1 metre. This means that the cold water storage tank that feeds the system must be at least 1 metre above the shower head, the greater the 'head' the more efficient the shower will be.

Toilets or WC;

For domestic building, two types of toilet are used, wash down and siphonic. These are used in conjunction with two types of cistern (flushing mechanism), high level chain pull and low level piston. There are various combinations available, but they all work on the same principles.

- A wash-down toilet relies on the water that is flushed down from the cistern to empty the bowl.

- A siphonic toilet uses the suction created by the bend in the exit pipe, as the water is flushed from the cistern, it is drawn out of the bowl by the water correcting its level, this is governed by the shape of the bend. These are prone to blockage.

- All ceramic toilets must comply with BS1254.

- Water supply pipe 15mm.

- Overflow pipe minimum of 22mm.

- When the toilet is flushed there must be a minimum 'water seal' of 50mm, this means that 50mm of water remains above the bend in the toilet bowl to prevent gases/smells entering the room.

- A toilet pan is normally connected to the 100mm soil pipe using a ribbed rubber seal.

- The toilet pan must be screwed to the floor using brass, stainless steel or zinc-plated wood-screws, untreated screws could rust and the expansion of the metal could crack the toilet pan.

Wastewater soil pipe stack systems and associated pipe-work.

This is the large pipe clipped to the rear wall of many properties. It is a central waste pipe that directs the wastewater into the sewer. All the different waste pipes from services within a property feed into this. It will normally be positioned near the rooms it services. This keeps the branch pipes short, making the system work efficiently. They may be located internally, usually hidden inside a plasterboard box down the corner of a room. If the stack is located within the property, it is advisable to lag it with glass fibre wool to deaden the sound of 'soil' running through it.

Important rules that must be applied to soil pipe stacks:

- Branch pipes to kitchen sinks and baths must be 40mm in diameter, and have a minimum 75mm 'seal trap'. The branch pipe must be no longer than 3 metres and the fall in the branch pipe must be between 20 and 90mm. This is obviously determined by the length of the branch pipe, (i.e. 3 metres would have a fall of 90mm, 1 metre would have a fall of 30mm).

- Basins should have a minimum pipe diameter of 32mm, and a minimum 'seal trap' of 75mm. The branch pipe must be no longer than1.8 metres. The fall in the pipe should be between 20 and 100mm.

- Any branch pipes running parallel to the stack must be 50mm in diameter.

- Toilets branch pipes must be 100mm diameter, fitted with airtight seals. The branch pipe must be no longer than 6 metres, and have a fall of 9mm per metre length of pipe. Where the branch connects to the stack pipe, the junction must have a minimum radius of 50mm.

- The soil stack must have a minimum diameter of 100mm.

- Where a stack system enters the ground, bends incorporated to connect it to the sewer must be of a large radius, to allow drain rods to enter the stack in the event of a blockage.

All plastic branch pipes must be adequately clipped to walls, this is because when hot water is emptied from sinks or baths, the heat may soften the plastic and where there are not sufficient clips the pipe may sag. Pipes should be supported with clips every 600mm, 500mm is better still.

When sagging occurs two problems are created, firstly where there is a sag in the waste pipe sediment could collect and eventually block the pipe, secondly and more seriously, when the pipe sags, water may collect and the added weight could force the joints apart and causing leaks.

Quality, service and workmanship.

What should you expect?

Reputable builders should at all times do their best to give you a reasonable standard of workmanship and a good quality of service. They should ensure that all the material used are of a good standard, and as the law states 'fit for the purpose for which they are intended' (see section on contract, applicable legislation).

Do builders have to guarantee their work?

At present there is no law requiring them to do this, a good reason to use a written contract, with this as one of the terms! However some of the materials that they use may be covered by manufacturer's warranty, the problem with this is that the guarantee will be valid for the purchaser, so if the builder cannot be traced, claiming under the terms of a guarantee may prove a problem.

A reputable builder will, when the project is complete, give you all the guarantee paperwork for materials used. In the event of a claim, your first point of contact will be the builder, who should then make the claim on your behalf. Please note, 'Hard' building materials (bricks, blocks, cement, aggregate, &c) usually have no 'express' warranty, they are normally guaranteed to be free of manufacturing fault. Some building products have a warranty period (usually one year), after which the builder or the manufacturer will not be liable for repair or replacement, unless negligence can be proved.

Is there any guaranty schemes in operation?

For small projects the simple answer is no. However if your property is less than ten years old, it may be covered by an NHBC guarantee, some local authority building control departments run a similar scheme. This covers you against major defects on the structure for a ten-year period from the date of completion.

While drains are similarly covered, joinery products, fixtures and fittings, boilers and plumbing are not.

What should you do if you feel that the quality is not of a reasonable standard?

If there is no written contract, this can prove difficult. The best solution is not to pay the builder, and call in Trading Standards. Often communication is the problem and if you speak to them and make them aware of your worries, they will usually correct a problem, or offer an explanation as to why something is not correct.

If you do not get a satisfactory answer to a problem, go and look at a similar property with the relevant detail, and compare the standard or methods, or ask another builder. If you are still convinced of the problem, question the builder again. Remember, knowledge is powerful; it will make it more difficult for the builder to wriggle out of rectifying the problem or fault.

After all, you have bought this book, use it!

Quantity surveyor.

What is a Quantity surveyor?

This is the person who prepares Bills of Quantities (see section), and who measures and prices work completed on building projects. Their role is to control expenditure, and keep the project on budget.

Do you need to employ one for your building project?

This will depend on the size of the building project. If you are replacing windows, altering a kitchen or building a small extension, the services of a quantity surveyor may not be justified. It may be a good idea to employ their services to prepare a bill of quantities from architect's drawings, as this may prevent problems. To retain a quantity surveyor on a small project is unlikely to be cost effective. They are highly trained, and therefore are not cheap.

On a large extension or major building project, using a quantity surveyor could be an advantage, as they will control costs and payments to contractors, ensure that materials are of the correct specification and price, and keep the project within budget. A quantity surveyor will usually give a fixed price for services, and on large projects their cost should be out-weighed by the savings that they make, if they are efficient.

Roofs

Note!

Roofing is a complex area of building. For this reason this section of the book is written to act as a guide to help the homeowner decide if work being done on their home is satisfactory. It is not to be used by the 'DIY builder' as a manual to complete roof repairs themselves!

What are the main roles of a roof structure and covering?

There are many different types of roof structure and covering, all serve the same purpose and have similar performance standards:

- To provide a weatherproof barrier.

- To retain the heat within the building.

- It must be able to support its own weight and withstand all loading placed upon it such as the weight of snow and the force of wind.

- It must be tough and long lasting, to reduce the maintenance and to give maximum performance.

- All roofs must be aesthetically acceptable and comply with the local planning guidelines and requirements.

- Where appropriate it should provide adequate support for a window, for example a 'Velux' roof-light.

- There must be sufficient means of drainage attached, to collect and dispose of rainwater.

- It must provide adequate sound insulation, as specified in Part E of the Building Regulations.

- All areas of the roof must be accessible for maintenance.

- It must possess insulation qualities, as specified in Part L of the Building Regulations.

- The roof, especially the covering material used, must comply with Part B of the Building Regulations, which relates to the spread of fire in particular.

- The list provides an overview of roofs, their function and current regulations that apply. It is designed to answer questions in these areas, so that the builder may then confirm the technical details when the roof is affected by the items in the list.

Are there different types of roof design?

There are many different types of roof commonly used in modern and existing domestic property design. The type of roof used will be determined by other properties in the vicinity, the size of the building, and the location on the property. If you look at the large diagram at the front of the book (M: 1) it shows you most of the common types of roof.

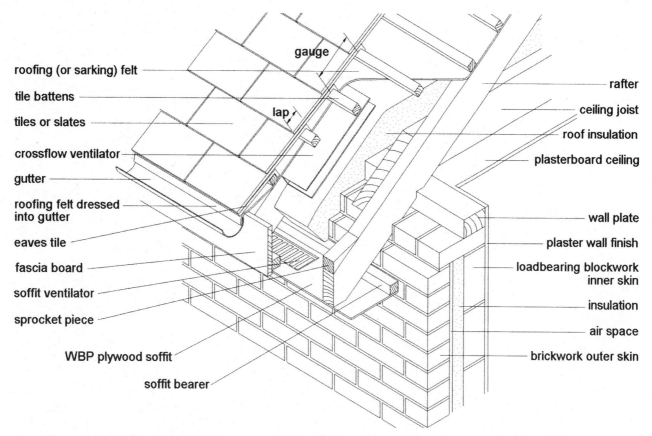

roofing (or sarking) felt

tile battens

tiles or slates

crossflow ventilator

gutter

roofing felt dressed into gutter

eaves tile

fascia board

soffit ventilator

sprocket piece

WBP plywood soffit

soffit bearer

gauge

lap

rafter

ceiling joist

roof insulation

plasterboard ceiling

wall plate

plaster wall finish

loadbearing blockwork inner skin

insulation

air space

brickwork outer skin

R:1 Closed Eaves with Timber Soffit

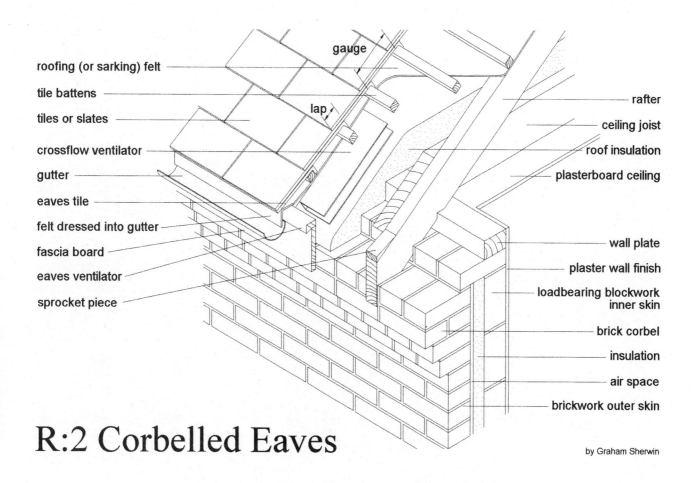

roofing (or sarking) felt

tile battens

tiles or slates

crossflow ventilator

gutter

eaves tile

felt dressed into gutter

fascia board

eaves ventilator

sprocket piece

gauge

lap

rafter

ceiling joist

roof insulation

plasterboard ceiling

wall plate

plaster wall finish

loadbearing blockwork inner skin

brick corbel

insulation

air space

brickwork outer skin

R:2 Corbelled Eaves

by Graham Sherwin

What are the component parts that come together to make a pitched roof?
This section gives a brief description of the main component parts or areas of a pitched roof; you should refer to the large diagram at the front of the book to familiarise yourself as to where they are located.

- **Wall plate**   This is the wooden beam that stretches along the supporting walls of the building. The wall plate is normally located on the inner leaf of a cavity wall (see drawing R: 1 at the beginning of this section). It is normally of stress-graded softwood, and 100 x 75mm in size, and is bedded onto a level layer of mortar.

- **Rafters**   The main support component of a roof, the 'ribs' of the roof. Their role is to support the roof covering, and on a pitched roof, to maintain the roof in its intended shape and slope.

- **'Jack rafters'**   These are the smaller rafters linking the wall plate to the main hip rafter.

- **Purlin**   A substantial piece of timber stretching horizontally across the width of a roof, normally at the mid-point, between the ridge and the wall plate (see diagram M: 1 at the front of the book). Its main purpose is to reduce the span of the rafters. In a gable roof, the purlin is supported at either end, in the internal leaf of the gable end. When the roof is of a 'hip' construction, the purlin is supported on the 'hip'-rafter, located where the hip of the roof starts.

- **Collar or cross-brace**   Used in roofs that are 'cut' on site. Its role is to tie each side of the roof together.

- **Ridge board**   This is the top timber of a pitched roof, the 'spine' to the rafters. This is used on a roof that is constructed on site, not when ready assembled trusses are used.

- **Hip**   The 'external' corner of a roof surface (see M: 1).

- **Valley**   The 'internal' corner on the surface of a roof (see M: 1).

- **Roof or tile battens**   These act as a framework to which the roof covering (tiles or slates) is secured to the roof structure (rafters). They also act as the 'anchor' for the 'under-slaters' felt; the nails pass through the battens and felt into the rafters.

- **Verge**   The name used to describe the last row of tiles along a gable end of a roof. The edge of a roof is raised slightly if slate covered, or is formed by the high point of a tile, directing the surface water away from the edge towards the main area of the roof

- **Gable ends**   The walls reaching vertically to the apex of a roof (see M1).

- **Eaves**   The lower edge of a roof, the last row of tiles, the point where the fascia is attached and the gutter located (see drawing R:2)

- **Fascia board**   The vertical board fitted at the bottom of a roof, it is fixed to the bottom of the rafters (see drawings R: 1 and R: 2), and serves three main functions;

> (i)   It closes the space between the bottoms of the rafters,
> (ii)   It supports the front edge of the soft board if fitted,
> (iii) It provides a suitable anchorage point for the gutter,

  Fascia boards are normally softwood; uPVC fascias are also common.

- **Soffit board**   This closes the eaves when brick corbeled eaves are not used. It normally locates into a groove on the back of the fascia board and is fixed to the wall by means of a batten or bearer. Normally made from 6mm WBP plywood, occasionally uPVC. It is standard practice on new properties to fit ventilator grills in to the soffit to comply with Building Regulations (see section on ventilation).

- **Sprocket piece**   Fitted to the bottom of each rafter, behind the fascia board. Their purpose is to 'kick' the bottom row of tiles up slightly, to direct the water into the gutter (see drawings R: 1 and R: 2). They may be in the form of eaves ventilators.

Rules that apply to the structures of pitched roofs
The structure of the roof comprises of all the components below the level of the felt and battens, down to and including the wall plate.

Site 'cut' roofs:
This, as the title suggests, is cut and assembled on the site. This design of roof can vary; these are the main roofs used in this form:

- Lean-to roof   This is the simplest of all roof-structures. It comprises a pitching wall plate fitted to wall of the building the roof is leaning against, a wall plate fixed to the lower wall of the room that the lean-to roof is to cover, and the sloping rafters of the roof.

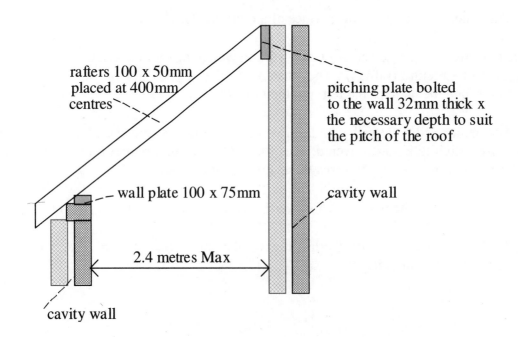

rafters 100 x 50mm placed at 400mm centres

pitching plate bolted to the wall 32mm thick x the necessary depth to suit the pitch of the roof

wall plate 100 x 75mm

cavity wall

2.4 metres Max

cavity wall

- **Couple roof**   The simplest design of a double-sided roof. It comprises a wall plate on both the supporting walls, a central ridge board and rafters either side of the roof.

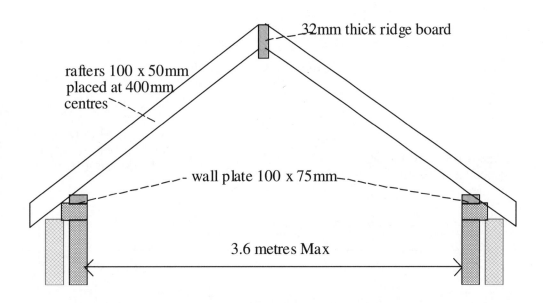

- **A closed couple roof**   Similar to the couple roof, with the addition of a collar or ceiling joists placed on top of the wall plate.

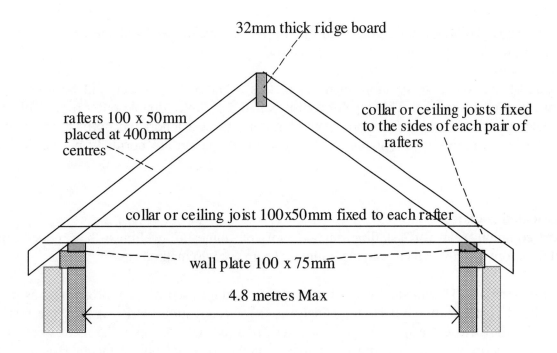

- **A Collar roof**   This type of roof design will allow unsupported spans of up to 5.5 metres, without the use of purlins to reduce the span of the rafters. It is very similar to previously discussed roof designs, simple in construction, the main difference being the location of the collar.

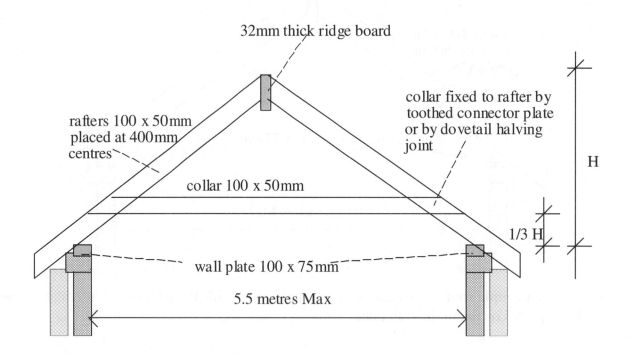

The collar is positioned no higher than one-third the overall height of the roof structure (see diagram), the lower the collar the stronger the roof.

If the span of the roof is to be more than 5.5 metres a 'site cut' roof can still be used, up to a maximum span of 7.5 metres. This type of roof is called a purlin or double rafter roof. This design of roof uses a main frame every fourth pair of rafters, these support the purlins, which in turn support the in-fill rafters (see drawing R: 3). The in-fill rafters are normally placed at 400mm centres.

Pre-fabricated roofs:
The most common means of installing pitched roofs on domestic dwellings; they reduce time on site and therefore are cost effective to the builder. There are two methods used:

- **Roof trusses**   This method of roof structure is seldom used on new properties, as it is not considered cost effective. It is still widely used for renovation work. It uses pre-fabricated triangular roof frames designed to give clear unsupported spans of up to 7.5 metres between the external supporting walls, the timber members of the truss are bolted together using toothed metal timber connector plates or 'joiners dogs'. These main truss frames are generally place at 1.8 metre intervals to support the purlins; in-fill rafters are then placed on top of the purlins at 450mm centres. (See drawing R: 4).

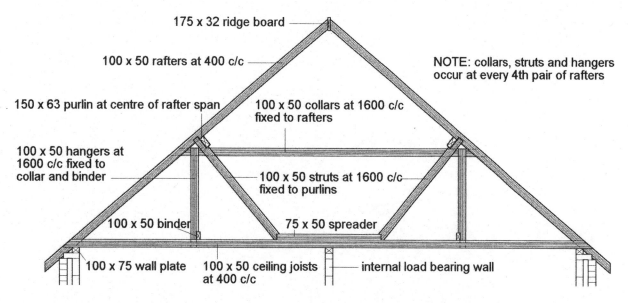

175 x 32 ridge board

100 x 50 rafters at 400 c/c

150 x 63 purlin at centre of rafter span

100 x 50 collars at 1600 c/c fixed to rafters

NOTE: collars, struts and hangers occur at every 4th pair of rafters

100 x 50 hangers at 1600 c/c fixed to collar and binder

100 x 50 struts at 1600 c/c fixed to purlins

100 x 50 binder

75 x 50 spreader

100 x 75 wall plate

100 x 50 ceiling joists at 400 c/c

internal load bearing wall

R:3 Double Rafter or Purlin Roof

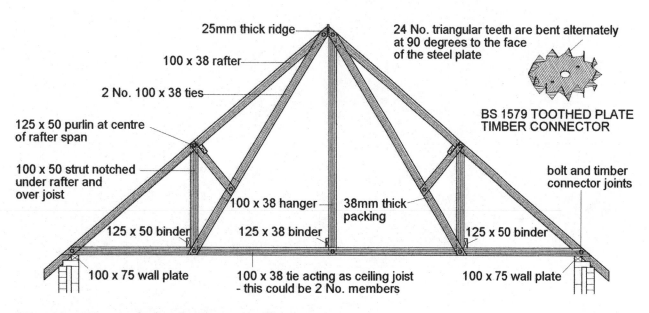

25mm thick ridge

100 x 38 rafter

2 No. 100 x 38 ties

24 No. triangular teeth are bent alternately at 90 degrees to the face of the steel plate

BS 1579 TOOTHED PLATE TIMBER CONNECTOR

125 x 50 purlin at centre of rafter span

100 x 50 strut notched under rafter and over joist

100 x 38 hanger

38mm thick packing

bolt and timber connector joints

125 x 50 binder

125 x 38 binder

125 x 50 binder

100 x 75 wall plate

100 x 38 tie acting as ceiling joist - this could be 2 No. members

100 x 75 wall plate

R:4 Typical Roof Truss

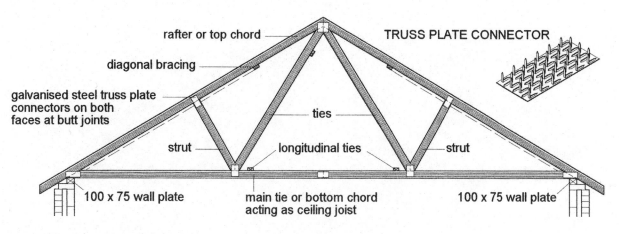

rafter or top chord

diagonal bracing

TRUSS PLATE CONNECTOR

galvanised steel truss plate connectors on both faces at butt joints

ties

strut

longitudinal ties

strut

100 x 75 wall plate

main tie or bottom chord acting as ceiling joist

100 x 75 wall plate

R:5 Typical Trussed Rafter

by Graham Sherwin

- **Trussed rafter roof ('Gang nail truss')**   This is the most common form of roof structure used on domestic property building today. It uses pre-fabricated triangular roof frames designed to give clear unsupported spans of up to 7.5 metres between the external supporting walls, the timber members of the trusses are fixed together using galvanised steel plate connectors or 'Gang nails'. These are a steel plate with lots of spikes on them, and are pressed into the trusses wherever the members are butt-jointed together. They are fixed to both sides of the truss.

This system of roof structure is different from the other types discussed. It uses no ridge board, purlins or in-fill rafters. The trussed rafters can be placed up to 600mm apart, their lateral stability is gained by using 'diagonal' and 'cross' storm bracing. These are pieces of timber approximately 38 x 100mm, nailed across the underside of the truss rafters. The storm bracing or longitudinal bracing as it is sometimes called is placed near the apex and also on the ceiling joist (see diagram R: 5), this runs from gable to gable and is nailed to the top face of the ceiling joist of the truss. The diagonal bracing is placed on the underside of the trusses, stretching from eaves to apex at 45 degrees, and is also nailed to the trusses. Mild steel straps are used to tie the roof structure to the gable end walls of the property; these are placed at 2.0 metre intervals along the slope of the two last trusses at the gable end. Sometimes thicker tile batten is used to increase the lateral stability, it is normal when ordering tile batten to specify batten for trussed rafters; standard roof structures use smaller section tile batten. (See drawing R: 5).

Trussed rafters can be manufactured to suit almost any size, shape or span of building. Specialist companies may be found in Yellow Pages.

Problems to be aware of with the structure of a roof

Provided all the guidelines are followed and shortcuts are not taken, a roof should give many years of maintenance-free service. All timber used for roof structures must be pressure treated. When renovation work takes place all timber including existing, must be treated to prevent rot and fungal attack. When a company makes trussed rafters they will supply a working drawing with them, this will give precise instructions to their installation. When the roof is 'cut' on site it will usually be from an architect's drawing. It is imperative that all sizes and fixing details are followed correctly, failure to do so could result in the roof failing. If the builder has not followed the drawing specification the architect cannot be blamed for the fault. When this occurs, you have to pray that the builder has adequate public liability insurance cover.

Repairs or re-roofing

The most common faults with roof structures occur when re-roofing takes place. When re-roofing occurs, often the old tiles are removed and replaced, older clay tiles tend to warp and distort with age. Old concrete tiles frequently break when they are disturbed. Some older properties may have no under-slaters' felt, adding underlay does not cause the problems, it is the placing of the new tiles on the roof structure that can. The weight of the new tiles may introduce more or less loading on the roof structure, if this occurs, a major material alteration will result, Building Regulation 3(2) provides for this.

There are three stages to complete prior to re-roofing;

- **Compare the planned and existing roof loading**   Allowance must be made for water absorption of the new tiles, Welsh slate will only absorb 0.3% of its dry weight, clay or concrete tiles can absorb up to 11% of their dry weight.

- **A structural inspection of the original roof structure must take place**   It must be ensured that;

  (i)   The roof is able to support the increased load of heavier tiles; or
  (ii)   The structure has enough vertical restraints to prevent 'wind uplift', a fault that can occur when a lighter roof covering is installed or when under-slaters' felt is added to an old roof.

- **To carry out the necessary strengthening alterations**   The type of additional work to a roof can be;

  (i)   Replacement of any defective timber.
  (ii)   Installation of additional vertical restraints.
  (iii)   Replacement or addition of extra nails and other fixings.
  (iv)   The addition of galvanised steel restraint straps to prevent the effects of wind 'uplift'.
  (v)   Installation of extra structural members such as purlins, stronger rafters of in the case of a trussed-rafter roof, extra trusses.

Any property that is undergoing a major re-roof project must be subjected to this assessment process; failure to do so can be disastrous. The average 'cowboy' may not take sufficient precautions or adequate consideration of the structure.

Loft or roof void conversions

Experienced specialist builder's carry out most conversions. However other companies, who are shall we say less concerned when it comes to structural design and defect prevention, carry out some! These are the basic guidelines that should be adhered to or checked for:

- All areas of the new room(s) comply with Building Regulation, including stairs, doorways, floor joists etc. Where necessary alterations will have to be inspected by Building Control.

- If the existing roof uses trussed-rafters, it may not be possible to alter them to incorporate a loft room, they normally have to be removed and a complete new roof built. If the cross bracing and struts are removed from trussed rafters or 'gang nail' trusses, they would collapse.

- Natural light has to be allowed into the rooms, the roof structure must be able to support dormers or roof lights, additional structural members may be required.

- The structure must be adequately insulated for heat and sound to comply with regulations.

- In some areas planning permission may be required, it is best to check.

- When a floor is added to a property and is above 4.5 m from ground level, additional protection against fire to the stairs or provision of an alternative escape route may be required. This doesn't have to be carried out if:

  (i)   The ridge will need raising, or
  (ii)   The conversion floor area is over 50 square metres, or
  (iii) The floor area is divided up into more than two rooms.

It is best to enclose the staircase anyway; it will make the sound and thermal insulation more effective to the new rooms.

Common faults in pitched roof structures when there is a 'cowboy' on the ranch

It could take forever and a day to explain fully in writing all the areas of roof structures that could fall prey to a 'cowboy builder'. The aim of this book is to act as a basic guide and deterrent, therefore this overview of the areas that need watching should be sufficient. Always remember that a 'cowboy' will constantly be trying to avoid spending more money than he needs too, he will like to call it financial efficiency!

- Ensure that all timber used is of the minimum size for the type of roof, or greater.

- Ensure that the main structural timber is stress-graded.

- All new roof timber must be pressure treated, old timbers should be treated in situ.

- Ensure that the builder removes all faulty timber, all diseased or insect infested timber should be burnt.

- Check that coated nails are used.

- If trussed rafters or 'gang nailed' trusses are used, check that they are spaced correctly, that there is sufficient storm bracing and that adequate coated metal ties are used in the right places.

- If the design of roof is one which is cut and assembled on site, see diagram R: 3 for comparison, there may be some variation in the position of some components. The basic principles and sizes should be more or less the same. A cowboy will often try to space the rafters further apart, miss out the purlins or not brace the roof adequately.

Roof coverings

Most domestic properties have a roof covering of tiles, made from clay or cement based products, some tiles are made from plastics. In many areas of the country natural split slate is used, cut to tile size pieces. Whichever is used, they all have under-slaters' felt beneath them as a secondary barrier.

Under-slaters' or 'sarking' felt.

If you have ever watched a roof being constructed, this is the black roll of material placed over the rafters or trusses prior to the tile battens and tiles being fixed in place (see drawing M: 1). It serves three purposes:

- To act as a barrier, preventing snow, rain and wind from entering the roof void.

- It prevents the moisture created by condensation on the underside of the tiles or slates from seeping into the property.

- Prevents water penetration by capillary action between the laps of the tiles is prevented from entering the roof void.

Many older properties do not have underlay felt, there may be reeds instead, some properties even have pitch-coated boards under the tiles. However, during re-roofing, an under-slaters' felt barrier is installed, as this is now a Building Regulation requirement, but more importantly it is a very good way to protect the structure of the roof against rot and fungal diseases cause by damp.

Are there different types of under-slaters' or 'sarking' felt used?

Yes there are, most construction projects use bitumen based felt, however plastic sheeting underlay may be used.

Common types of underlay are:

- Bitumen glass-fibre reinforced felt.

- Bitumen natural fibre reinforced felt.
  Both are supplied as, 1metre wide rolls, 10 or 20m in length, both are manufactured to BS747.

- Plastic sheeting or rolls.
  This type of underlay has several advantages over the bitumen-based products. It is lighter, easier to handle and does not tear as easily as bitumen based underlay. When used in large sheets rather than rolls it requires much less storage space, is considerably cheaper than the other products available, and polythene roof sheeting is normally reinforced with thin cord in a net pattern for added strength.
  It does however present one major problem: Bitumen felt has a surface covering of sand, which absorbs a certain amount of water vapour, this is released into the atmosphere in dryer conditions. Polythene underlay does not have such a covering of sand, and so do not absorb the vapour, especially in warm humid conditions. For this reason it must never be used on a roof with a pitch less than 20 degrees. It is not recommended for use on older timbers, or for re-roofing on older properties, where the timber may have absorbed moisture.

What rules apply to underlay application?

Applying the underlay to a roof is a very straightforward and simple procedure, and if completed correctly will give many years of maintenance-free service. The simple rules are:

- The underlay is applied to the rafters starting at the bottom or eaves, laying it across the roof not from top to bottom. Each row of underlay must overlap the previous by a minimum of 100mm, most under-slaters' felt has a feint white line to act as a guide, both for minimum lap and to keep the rows of felt parallel.

- It must overhang the bottom, so that it reaches well into the gutter. On new or major refurbishment, the gutter may not be in place so an allowance must be made.

- Underlay must be taken right to the edge of the verge, i.e. level with the outer face of the brickwork on the gable.

- Where underlay has to be joined across the width of a roof, it must overlap by a minimum of 100mm.

- The last row of underlay (top of the roof) must pass over the ridge and a short distance down the other side, the last row on the other side of the roof should repeat this action; i.e. ridge has two layers of underlay. If ridge ventilator tiles are to be used neat holes will need to be made through the underlay to allow the air through the vents.

- If there are valleys in the roof, a layer of underlay must be placed down the valley first, from top to bottom. This must be between 600 to 1000mm wide, without any joints in the length. The main rows of underlay are then placed on top of this; this acts a secondary barrier where the two planes of the roof meet.

- Where roof has hipped ends, a layer of underlay must be fixed from top to bottom over the main layers of underlay. This is to create a good overlap on the corner; again the strip must be between 600 to 1000mm wide and run from the top to the bottom without joints.

- Where roof has a lower roof with a ridge that intersects down the slope of the main roof (see drawing M: 1), the underlay must be lapped in the correct manner. The row of underlay near the lower ridge, on the main roof must overlap the ridge of the lower roof; it must not be done the other way round. This means that the lower roof will need to be covered with underlay first.

- Where a roof has a hipped end, the intersection point of ridge and hips requires additional protection. This is achieved by placing a square patch of underlay centrally over the intersection point of the hip; this can be difficult, especially where the roof has a steep pitch. This is because the underlay will have to be folded so that it fits the three sides of the roof snugly. Best achieved using lead or zinc, these are easier to form to the shape, will not tear as it is being shaped and will fit closely to the different sides of the roof, sometimes called a 'junction saddle'.

- The underlay may be held in place prior to the battens being secured using galvanised clout nails. Normally placed along the top edges of the underlay only, this is only a temporary measure to prevent wind from removing the underlay.

- Battens are positioned on the roof according to the length of tile and the length of the roof, this is calculated so that the tiles are spaced equally down the roof. (see tile lap sizes later) They are secured with galvanised or sherardized wire nails. They should be nailed at every rafter or truss. Checks must be made regularly to ensure that the battens are parallel with both ridge and eaves.

Problems that occur with roof underlay

Most problems with roof underlay occur on refurbishment or maintenance projects. New properties are not free of problems but this is not usually an area of new-build that gives cause for concern. Any problems with roof underlay that do occur are probably the same as those on repair or refurbishment projects.

Many roofs have underlay beneath the tiles, which has been in place for many years. After twenty years or so it is inevitable that the roofing felt will need maintenance or replacement. It is common that the bottom row of underlay will deteriorate quicker than the rest, this can be replaced without replacing all underlay on the roof.

The basic principles and guide to replacing the bottom row of underlay are:

- The bottom four rows of tiles need to be removed; it is normal to stack the removed tiles on the roof just above the area being worked on. The nibs on the tiles will hold them safely in stacks, provided the weight is distributed across the width of the roof and over the rafters.

- Once all the required tiles have been removed, the old tile batten can be removed. Provided the battens come off without breaking it may be possible to re-use them, however, by the time a builder has removed all the old nails it may be more cost effective to use new battens.

- Old underlay should be removed, taking care not to damage the row of underlay above.

- Where underlay has deteriorated badly, it is possible that the insulation material in the roof void will be wet or contaminated with debris, this should also be removed and the whole eaves area of the roof void cleaned thoroughly.

- All rafter bottoms should be inspected for rot, if any has occurred, it may be possible to bolt a small piece of rafter to damaged one(s). This should only be done when there are a few faulty rafter ends, provided that the rot does not extend up the rafter beyond the wall plate.

- The fascia and soffit, if fitted, should be checked for rot, and if damaged, should be replaced. Ensure that if they are replaced that the new vented type are used, as this will prevent further rot occurring by allowing air into the roof void (see ventilation and drawing R: 1).

- Insulation should be replaced prior to laying the underlay. It is easier to place the insulation in the low part of the roof from the outside rather than from inside the loft space. Ensure that it is laid in the correct manner (see ventilation and drawings R: 1 and R: 2).

- The new row of underlay should be carefully manoeuvred into place, taking care to ensure that it tucks under the row above by the minimum 100mm, but also check that the builder allows it to hang into the gutter (see drawings R: 1 and R: 2). Ask about the quality of the underlay, Bitumen based are the best. The thicker, the longer it will last. The words 'cheap' and 'underlay felt' may come out of your builder's mouth, ensure that they do not end up on your roof!

- The tile battens should now be nailed back onto the rafters, ensuring that they are evenly spaced to match the tiles on the remainder of the roof, and that galvanised or sherardized nails are used.

- The bottom row of tiles should overhang the inside edge of the gutter by approximately 25 to 30mm but no more than one-third the gutters' width. If the tiles come too far over the gutter, water may splash into the gutter and run over the side.

- The verge, where tiles overhang gable ends should be replaced in the correct manner. The verge tile is bedded on mortar and the face or end must be pointed smooth to match the existing tile ends above. Some builders add 'plasticizer' to the mortar to prevent cracking; this is a good idea, as verge-bedding mortar does have a tendency to crack and is in an exposed position.

- Below the verge tiles there is normally an overhang of approximately 50 to 75mm between the edge of the tiles and the face of the gable brickwork. This is to create a weathering overhang to protect the top of the gable wall. Placing a 6mm cement-based board on top of the wall prior to the tiles being bedded forms the overhang. This must be parallel down the slope and the overhang must be no more than 1/3 the width of the tiles being placed on the roof, to reduce the risk of the tiles tipping while the mortar sets.

- Finally, once the tiles are all back in place, check that they are all in line as you look up the slope of the roof.

Total re-placement of underlay, common faults to watch for:
All of the above points must be followed, and these additional problem areas must be checked for:

- If the battens have to be joined in the length to reach across the span of the roof, ensure that the joints are on alternate rafters (the joints not in a line down the slope of the roof).

- The roof tiles at no time should be walked on, roof ladders or walking boards must be used.

- While the roof has no tiles, the builder will walk about on the roof placing their feet on the tile battens and rafters check that no damage or holes are made in the underlay.

- All the laps of each row must be the minimum 100mm, and all the other rules must also be followed as explained in the earlier section.

- Ensure that good quality underlay is used.

- All flashing material is repositioned properly, and replaced where necessary. This can be costly so check that it is done properly, as described in the section applicable.

Tiles, slates and other roof coverings.

Most domestic property within the UK has some form of durable roof covering, usually clay or concrete tiles. In many areas slates are used, natural split slate or man-made, both are widely used. Many properties have 'flat' roof construction and use mineral felt or glass fibre as the finished roof covering material (see flat roof construction). In some parts of the UK roofs are covered with reeds (thatching), and even more unusual some properties have wooden tiles called 'Cedar Shingles'.

Technology is allowing more and more different materials to be used as roof covering, however this books purpose is to act as a guide and for that reason looks at the widely used methods only in detail.

Tiles.

Tiles are probably the most common roof coverings used on domestic properties, there are two types used.

Single-lap tiles:

These are the traditional shaped tiles seen on most roofs; there are two types:

- Roll tiles, have a raised role or curve, centrally or to one side, some have two rolls. The most commonly used is the 'pantile'. A roll tile is designed for use on a roof with a minimum pitch of 30 degrees. This type of tile is designed to give a lesser loading to a roof structure than imposed by double lap tiles (see later section). Usually this type of tile has a tongue and groove moulded into its sides; to allow the tiles to interlock once laid into position. Some tiles have an interlocking facility all around their edges, these are known as 'single lap interlocking' roll tiles.

  Each tile is weatherproofed and sealed by the roll of the next, forming even rolls across the width of the roof. The tiles are 'handed' so that they lay one way only. The tile is approximately 300mm wide and 420mm long. Tiles overlap the tile or below by a minimum of 75mm. This gives them a 'gauge' distance of 345mm (see later). Roll tiles' normal side lap coverage is 30 to 40mm; this is dependent on the radius of the roll. Tile batten used for single lap tiles is normally 38 x 25mm pressure treated softwood, and is secured with galvanised or 'sheradised' nails.

- Trough tiles, have a central lower area and raised sides, normally these are moulded with a square, straight edged profile, in comparison with the roll tiles rounded profile. They are designed for use on any pitched roof, their advantage over a roll tile is that they can be used on a roof that has a low pitch, as little as 15 degrees. Again, they are interlocking by means of a tongue and groove, and they are single lap fully interlocking tiles. They are handed as the roll tile above, so that each tile weathers the adjacent tile, they can be laid in one direction only.

  Trough tiles are approximately 330mm wide and 420mm long, again the lap of the tiles top and bottom is a minimum of 75mm, giving a gauge distance of 345mm (see later). Trough tiles normally have a side lap of between 30 to 40mm; this again is dependent on the shape of the raised sides to the tiles, because one side of each tile must fully overlap the adjacent to create a weather-tight barrier. They are held in position by using 38 x 25mm pressure treated softwood tile batten. Most manufacturers recommend that at least every other tile be nailed to the battens.

Key rules applicable to single lap tiling:

- Single-lap tiling uses 38 x 25mm treated battens.

- The minimum lap is 75mm.

- The eaves or bottom course must be secured and sealed to prevent effects of weather and entry by birds.

- Every other tile in alternate courses must be nailed; this is really the minimum requirement.

- The margin is the same as the gauge measurement; the calculation for this is the tile length minus the lap distance.

Double lap tiles:

These are flat tiles, sometimes called 'plain' or 'pin' tiles, they appear to lay flat against one another but in fact have a slight curve in their length to enable the tile above and below to bed flat. The main difference they have over single lap tiles is that the whole roof has two layers of tiles covering the surface, this obviously creates a greater weight loading on the roof structure. The pattern in which they are laid is as shown on diagrams R: 1 and R: 2. The pattern or 'bond' of the tiles is such that side or edge joints between adjacent tiles is positioned centrally of the tiles immediately above or below them.

Double lap tiles are supported on the roof structure using tile batten, but because the tiles are double lapped the battens are fixed closer together (the gauge is less, see later). Normally double lap tiles have a gauge or length spacing of 100mm. Because the spacing of the battens is reduced and the tiles are smaller than the roll type a smaller size of batten is used, 38 x 20mm. Double lap tiles are normally nailed every 3rd or 4th row; the rest are held in place by the batten and the weight of surrounding tiles. In an exposed location, where wind could cause problems, every tile may be nailed in place. Because of the installation procedure, and greater quantity of tiles used, double lap tiles take far longer to 'hang'.

When double lap tiles are used for a roof covering, they are available with additional special tiles for the other areas of the roof. They are available manufactured from clay and concrete, this is a brief description of the usual range available:

- **Standard tile**   These tiles used for the bulk of the roof surface. They are normally between 260 and 270mm in length and 160 and 170mm in width, with a thickness of 10 to 15mm; this is obviously increased where the batten nibs or anchors are positioned on the top edge of the tile. They usually have a camber in the length of between 3 to 6mm to prevent them 'riding' one another when they are laid. The nail holes are located in front of the nibs so that they are in line with the tile batten.

- **Tile and a half size**   These are used on the ends of a roof, at the verge or where a roof abuts a wall. They are used on alternate courses to allow the bond to form. If these were not used it would mean than a standard tile would have to be cut in its width to keep the bond, the result being a very unstable tile on the verge of the roof. They are still hung using the same bond as used for the standard tile, and have a slight curve in their length. They are normally 260 to 270 long and 240 to 250mm wide, a natural curve, a result of the curing process may occur in the width of the tile, this must not exceed 3.5mm. These larger tiles sometimes have three nibs to give them greater support; the nail holes are located as in the smaller tile.

- **Top course and eaves tiles**   These are used on the first row nearest the gutter and at the top under the ridge tiles. These tiles have the same width of the standard tile of approximately 160 to 170mm, but they are shorter, 180 to 190mm. Their purpose is to start and terminate the bond of the tiles (see drawings R: 1 and R: 2).

- **Ridge tile**   This is the tile used to seal the ridge or top of the roof (see drawing M: 1). Normally half round in shape, sometimes with a vent incorporated to provide additional ventilation in the roof void. Occasionally angular ridge tiles are used, these are available for limited pitch angles, and do not have the flexibility of the half round type. Ridge tiles are available in various sizes, but as a guide they are normally 300 to 450mm long and 200 to 250mm in diameter, with a thickness between 10 to 19mm.

- **Valley tile**   These are specially shaped curved tiles to fit down the valley of a roof. Additional underlay is still placed on the rafters at this point as explained earlier, but these tiles are designed to fit the bond pattern and the slope of the roof. Their shape allows the tiles to give the two layers of tiles and stepped side joints all the way along the valley as with the main areas of a double lap roof, thus removing the need for lead or zinc. They are manufactured to suit a limited number of pitch angles. Architect should design the property to suit the tiles available.
    The width of these tiles is determined by the pitch of roof they are designed for, they are normally 200 to 250mm long.

- **Hip tile**   Two types of tile are used for the hip of a roof when double lap tiles are used. Regular half round ridge tiles can be used, bed in the same way as the ridge, on cement mortar. When ridge tiles are used a galvanised bracket is screwed to the bottom of the hip rafter to prevent the tiles from sliding of the roof; this anchoring bracket is sometimes called a 'hip iron'.
    The other method is using 'bonnet' or 'saddle' tiles, these are specially shaped tiles which when bedded in position on mortar, give a stepped effect to the hip rather like fish scales. The steps of the tiles match the bond pattern of the roof tiles.

Key rules applicable to double lap tiling:

- Double lap tiling uses 38 x 20mm treated battens.

- The eaves and bottom courses must be secured.

- Every fourth course or row of tiles must be nailed; this is really the minimum requirement.

- The margin is the same as the gauge measurement, the calculation for this is:

$$\frac{\text{The tile length - the lap}}{2}$$

As an example

$$\frac{270\text{mm} - 70}{2}$$

$$=100\text{mm}$$

- The ridge tile must overlap the tile beneath by a minimum of 1/5 the length of the tile.

Names and terms used by builders when tiling is taking place.

- **Lap**   This is the distance by which one tile covers the tile below.

- **Gauge**   The distance between the tile battens.

- **Margin**   The amount of face of the tile showing when in place. The margin is always the same as the gauge.

- **Rake cut**   This is the cut made to the tiles to allow them to fit the angle of a hip or valley.

- **Soaker**   This is a sheet of lead or zinc bent at 90 degrees, placed where a roof abuts a wall. It lies over the tiles and rises up the wall beneath the stepped flashing. It is a secondary barrier for the stepped flashing, and covered by it.

Common faults to watch for when inspecting roof tiling.

You have already been warned that roofing is a very complex and specialised area of construction and that this book is designed as a guide. If you suspect a problem and are not getting a satisfactory reply from the 'builder', go to the local Authority Building Control department, they may be able to help. These are common faults to look for:

- All tile margins should look the same.

- All tiles must fit together tightly. Where tiles are old and are to be re-used this rule may not applicable e.g. conservation area or listed building; old tiles may have warped.

- The laps should be the same on each course and at least the minimum recommended dimension, if you can see nail heads or nail holes, there is a cowboy on the ranch!

- All hip and ridge tiles must be bedded on sufficient mortar, which must be pointed and shaped to a smooth finish.

- If you are present while the tiling is taking place, you will notice the builder mark out the roof battens prior to the tiles being hung. This is to ensure that the tiles are in straight lines down the slope of a roof, this is generally done using a 'chalk-line'. (A piece of string or cord which, when immersed in chalk dust, holds on to the chalk particles. When the line is pulled tight and then 'pinged' it leaves a coloured line on the surface the builder is working on). Failure to use this or a similar procedure could result in the tiles 'snaking' down the roof unevenly.

- The end of the last ridge or hip tile should be filled with mortar and tile slips or inserts are pushed into the mortar to prevent cracking and to give the end an aesthetic Finish.

- If the ridge tiles incorporate ventilators, the bedding mortar must still permit the circulation of air. This means the void beneath the ridge tile must not be filled with mortar.

- The eaves or bottom tile on a roof has traditionally been bedded on mortar, to hold it in place and to prevent birds from entering the roof void. With the advances in plastic technology this is no longer necessary. A plastic mesh is fitted to the top edge of the fascia, which adopts the shape of the tile, some meshes incorporate eaves ventilators. The tiles are nailed to the batten for security. Bedding the tiles on mortar can prevent water from running off the underlay into the gutter.

- When more than one pack of tiles is being used to cover a roof it is important that several packs are opened and mixed together as they are taken up to the roof. This is to prevent patches of colour changes occurring on the roof, it is normal for there to be slight variations in tile colours.

- Any areas of fresh mortar should be covered with damp hessian sacks until dry, this prevents the wind and sunlight drying the mortar out too quickly and should it rain, the mortar will not be washed out of the joints and stain the roof tiles.

- It is possible that a roof will not be completed in one day. If the weather looks threatening and strong winds are forecast, provision should be made to secure the tiles already hung. Where work must be left unfinished - e.g. the weather closes in or it gets dark - the last row of tiles must be nailed. This lessens the risk of the wind blowing under the tiles and lifting them.

Natural slates.

Slate is a very versatile and durable material, ideal for roofs with pitches above 25 degrees. The slate is graded and cut into blocks by the quarry, the blocks are then split down the grain of the block to form roof slates. It is surprisingly easy to split, drill and shape slate, the skill is being able to do it to produce a thin slate with even thickness and a square or rectangular shape. Slates are available in various sizes, thicknesses and grades, the thinner the slate the higher the grade-and price!

Some Quarries have their own factories that produce the roof slates, other quarries sell the blocks of slate to specialists, who produce the finished slates. Most slate roofs have half round ridge tiles, often black or grey to match the slates, but some have angular ridge and hip tiles. Some companies produce slate ridge and valley tiles, but these are very expensive having to be cut out of large blocks and are not widely used. Lead flashing is used for valleys on slate roofs.

Are all the slates on a roof the same size?

Slates are hung on a roof in the same way as double lap tiles, once all the slates are in position all areas of the roof have a double layer of slate. The pattern or bond is shown on R: 1 or R: 2. Each joint lies centrally over the tile below.

Slates are available in various sizes and grades, full details and standards are given in BS680. Whatever standard of slate is used, the slates have to be made in a minimum of two sizes for each range or slating system. This gives the equivalent of a standard slate and slate and a half, as for plain tiles. Some slate manufacturers also cut eaves or top course slates to save the tiler having to cut standard slates. Refer to eaves detail on drawing R: 1.

How are slates fixed to the roof?

Slates are flat, unlike tiles, and do not have a nib. For this reason every slate has to be nailed to a batten. The nail holes are usually at the top or 'head' of the slate, but in longer slates the are located near the middle. This prevents them rattling in strong winds and shattering with the vibration. The slate placed above covers any nail used to fix slates. Nails for securing slates should be 'sheradised' or galvanised; copper nails are the best.

Common faults with slate roofs.

All the faults already listed for tiled roofs are applicable in similar ways, however most faults with slate roofing are found after repairs or replacement underlay is installed. These are the important rules and common faults to watch for;

- If an odd slate is cracked or broken it will not be possible to nail the replacement as this will mean that the whole area near to the damage will have to be removed. This is because slates are nailed at their top and the nail of a damaged slate will not be accessible without removing any slates above it. For one slate this would be very costly and an unnecessary exercise. The replacement will have to be slid into place ensuring that it is a tight fit, butyl mastic can be placed under the slate to prevent it slipping. A thin strip of lead, copper or zinc can be used as a hook to hold the slate in place. These methods are useable on one slate but not if three or more are damaged, removing and re-nailing the whole area around the damaged slates best treats this. You must bear in mind that any slate removal and replacement is time consuming and therefore costly.

- Check that the builder is not just turning the slates round to hide the damaged ends.

- When large areas of a roof are being repaired ensure that all the slates are be secured with the appropriate nails.

- The gauge for slate battens is worked out in a similar manner to double lap tiles;

$$\frac{\text{The slate length from nail hole to the bottom - the lap}}{2}$$

As an example

$$\frac{\text{Slate length of 500mm - 70}}{2} \quad \text{(overall slate length will be approx.' 525mm)}$$

$$= \quad 215\text{mm}$$

Flat roofs.

What is a flat roof?
Even though most of us call them flat roofs, most are in fact anything but flat. A roof with a slope of 10 degrees is considered flat.

Why are flat roofs used instead of a pitched roof?
The main reason for using flat roofs is that they are quick and cheap to build. A flat roof can also be used where a pitched roof would block light entry to a neighbouring property; this is often the case in built-up areas in towns where the properties are terraced.

Why does a flat roof have a slope?
The slope is there to shed rainwater from the roof, the pitch of the slope is determined by the roof finish.

How is the fall or slope created?
This is dependent on the direction of the rafters, there are four methods to create the fall. It should always be remembered that joists should span the building by the shortest distance possible:

- **The joists are positioned to create the fall**   This method is cheap and easy to install, but has the problem of the underside of the rafters sloping as well. The rafters are installed with one end lower/higher than the other. This will mean that the ceiling and fascia will also slope, this can be overcome by fixing the ceiling to battens and sloping the top of the fascia so that the bottom is level.

- **The joists are laid in the opposite direction to the fall**   To create the fall 'furring pieces' are nailed across the joists (long thin wedges). This method gives a level ceiling and an effective means of cross ventilating the roof void (see ventilation).

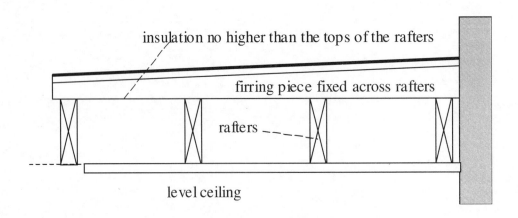

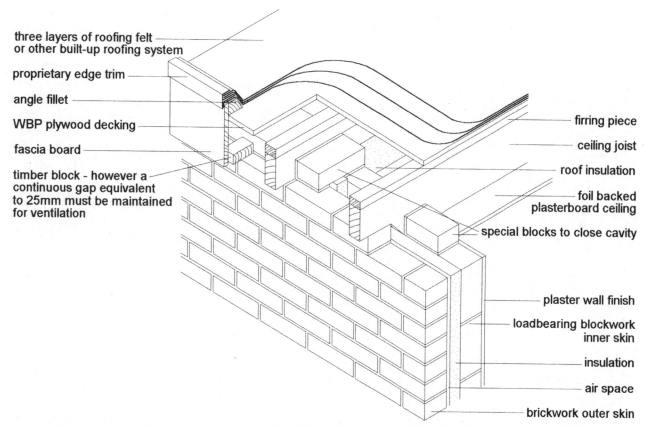

three layers of roofing felt or other built-up roofing system

proprietary edge trim

angle fillet

WBP plywood decking

fascia board

timber block - however a continuous gap equivalent to 25mm must be maintained for ventilation

firring piece

ceiling joist

roof insulation

foil backed plasterboard ceiling

special blocks to close cavity

plaster wall finish

loadbearing blockwork inner skin

insulation

air space

brickwork outer skin

R:6 Upstand Verge to 'Cold' Flat Roof

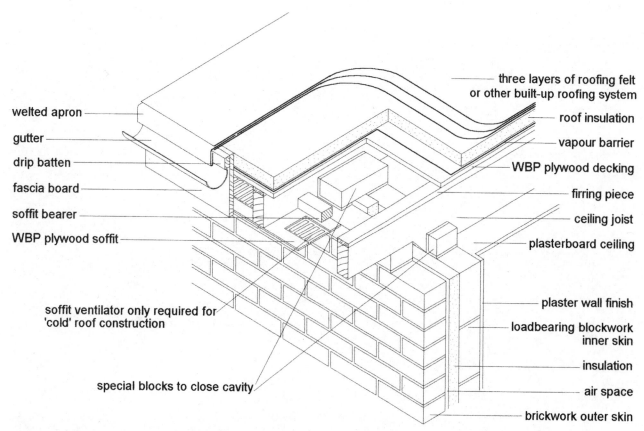

welted apron

gutter

drip batten

fascia board

soffit bearer

WBP plywood soffit

soffit ventilator only required for 'cold' roof construction

special blocks to close cavity

three layers of roofing felt or other built-up roofing system

roof insulation

vapour barrier

WBP plywood decking

firring piece

ceiling joist

plasterboard ceiling

plaster wall finish

loadbearing blockwork inner skin

insulation

air space

brickwork outer skin

R:7 Projected Eaves to 'Warm' Flat Roof

- **Joists that are cut to form the fall**   This is where the rafters are cut to taper. This method is very simple and if two joists are cut from one piece of wood, very cost effective.

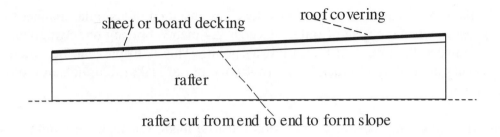

- **Furring pieces are nailed directly to the rafters**   This is probably the most common method used by builders, yet it is the least effective at giving the roof good cross ventilation.

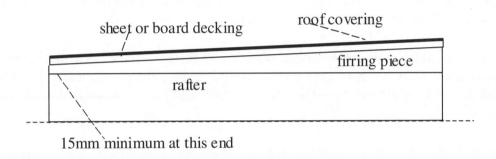

What are the key rules for flat roof structures?

Because flat roofs are simple in structure the rules and regulations are very straightforward, however it is very important that all are complied to, as failure can prove costly. Two designs of roof structures are common. A 'cold' flat roof where the insulation is placed in the roof void (see drawing R: 6), or a 'warm' flat roof where the insulation is placed on top of the decking, leaving the roof void clear for air circulation (see drawing R: 7). It has to be said that the 'warm' design is far better than the 'cold', as there is far less heat loss and better circulation of the air in the roof void. However to save money, the 'cold' design, is more common.

- Smooth coverings such as hot asphalt or glass fibre can have a pitch of 1:80 or more.

- Coverings that are lapped rolls or sheets such as roofing-felt, must have a minimum pitch of 1:60.

- The rafters of a flat roof, because they are laid almost level, are sometimes called joists.

- When furring pieces are laid across the rafters the thin end must be a minimum depth of 50mm. (See slope method (b) above).

- Every effort must be made to ensure that the rafters span the shortest distance of a building.

- The size of the rafters and their spacing is determined by the span of the building and the loading placed upon it, such as snow. Full details are given in Building Regulations document 'A': tables 17 to 22. **Note:** All timber and rafters must be stress-graded timber.

- The rafters of a flat roof, because they are almost level are installed in a similar manner to floor joists. For this reason when the span of rafters exceeds 2.4 metres bracing or herringbone struts must be placed between the rafters at their midway point. This is to prevent the rafters from twisting and causing the ceiling to crack or the roof covering to leak; often the cause of a felt-covered roof failing.

- In some areas where the wind is severe, provision must be made for negative wind pressures, (wind getting under the decking and lifting the roof). This provision can be made by securing the rafters to the wall with galvanised metal anchor straps, which are secured to the wall underneath the plaster. It should be noted that some builders make this provision even if the area is not prone to severe wind, it can help to prevent ceiling cracks.

- Ensure that all timber used for the structure is dry (seasoned, see section on timber). If it is wet, when it dries out it will shrink and the ceiling may crack as a result.

- Ensure that where the rafters sit on the walls, a 50 x 50mm batten is fixed between all the rafters flush with the bottoms of the rafters. This is to secure the ends of the plasterboard sheets to, and reduce the risk of cracking around the edge. This is often not done by unscrupulous and poorly trained builders.

- The cavity in the wall beneath a flat roof must be closed see drawings R: 6 & 7. It must be closed along its entire length in all directions, not just where the rafters are located.

- Ventilation provision must be made at the eaves. The '25mm continuous gap rule' applies (see ventilation). This is one of the main causes of mouldy flat roof ceilings.

- The ventilation provision must have access into the roof void, ensure that the insulation is not covering the holes or grills in the vents.

- The edge to which the gutter is to be fixed must have provision on the fascia-board to direct the rainwater into the gutter. Fixing a drip batten to the top of the fascia-board does this. Failure to do this will place the roof covering very close to the back edge of the gutter, allowing the rainwater to run behind the gutter, a very common fault with flat roofs. (see drawing R: 7)

- When the 'cold' type roof design is used a polythene vapour barrier should be placed on top of the rafters prior to the decking being laid. (ventilation precautions must still be made)

- As an added precaution foil backed plasterboard can be used for the ceiling on a 'cold' roof, this also acts as a vapour barrier.

- If particle (chipboard) or other manufactured boarding is used for the decking it must be a water-resistant type; this is easily identified because it is stained green.

- When the 'warm' designed structure is used a polythene barrier is placed on top of the decking boards prior to the insulation sheets being laid, foil backed plasterboard is not necessary in this instance (see drawing R: 7).

- Prior to application of the roof covering, provision should be made to direct the water into the gutter. A raised angle fillet or water check will need to be fitted down the sides of the roof (see drawing R: 6).

What are the important rules concerning flat roof coverings?

There are various ways in which a flat roof can covered to weatherproof it, built-up layers of roofing felt, single layer roofing felt systems, hot mastic asphalt and several systems that use glass fibre sheets and resin bonding. This book looks at the two systems used most commonly, layered roofing felt and hot mastic asphalt.

Layered felt:

- Ensure that the pitch or fall of the decking is sufficient for the chosen roof covering; (see earlier section on structure).

- Check that the roof decking has no raised areas or hollows that would prevent the water from running off the roof.

- When the layered felt system is used, all the strips of felt have to be bonded together. This can be done using either a cold jointing compound or heated bitumen.

- When felt or mastic asphalt is used, the top layer requires protection from the effects of sunlight and frost. This is done by using mineral felt as the final layer (layered felt system), a thicker felt with a protective coating of fine stone bonded to its surface, usually crushed slate or granite. Traditionally roofing felt or asphalt is protected by bonding a 12 to 15mm layer of stone chipping to the felt with hot bitumen. This can also be carried out now using cold bonding adhesives.

- If the roof covering is to be made up of three layers of roofing felt, there is a set procedure for applying the felt:

  (i)   The first layer must be laid across the roof parallel to the gutter; the subsequent strips are lapped and bonded over the previous strip until the other side is reached (the highest point of the roof).

  (ii)   The next layer is placed at right angles to the first, i.e.: running with the fall. These strips are again lapped and bonded until the other side of the roof is reached.

  (iii) The side aprons that cover the angle fillets or water check battens are now applied. These are normally made from folded mineral coated felt which is nailed and bonded in place and reaches towards the centre of the roof by a minimum of 500mm (see drawing R: 6).

(iv)   The welted apron, also made from folded mineral felt is now fixed along the edge near the gutter, and nailed and bonded so that it reaches towards the middle of the roof deck by approximately 500mm   (see drawing R: 7). Sometimes aluminium or coated steel angles are used instead of felt. It must be checked that whichever method is used it creates a drip to direct the rainwater into the gutter (see drawing R: 7).

(v)   The final stage is the application of the top layer of felt; this is laid in the same direction as the first. It is started near the gutter (see drawing R: 7), each strip bonded and lapping the previous. The final strip is positioned so that it rises up the wall or fits up behind the gutter of an adjoining roof. This top layer seals down using hot bitumen on all the aprons described in part (iv) above.

Note: When lapped felt is used for a flat roof the top layer must always run parallel with the gutter or the lower edge of the roof. The bottom or lowest point of the roof is always the starting point, this is to ensure that the laps in the felt weatherproof the roof adequately.

• Each strip of felt must overlap and be bonded to the previous by a minimum of 50mm.

• Any laps along the sides between the final layer of felt and the side water check aprons must be a minimum of 100mm, the final layer of felt should rise up to the top of the angle fillet (see drawing R: 6).

• All bitumen based roofing felt must be manufactured to BS747. This type of felt is reinforced with a woven base material rather like string.

• At any points where the roof adjoins higher walls provision must be made to assist the felt and flashing to weatherproof the roof;

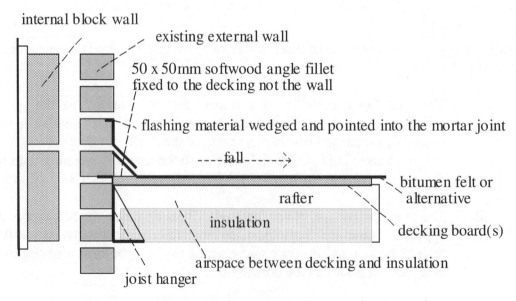

Detail at intersection with wall

- Synthetic and polyester-based felts can be used for flat roofs; these do not have a woven base and can be laid in single or two-layer format. All the lap details and other rules are still applicable, but they will have their own bonding agents and technical data.

- A felt covered roof should never be walked on without use of protective boards. The stones could push through the surface and cause leaks, and when the weather is hot it becomes very soft and easily damaged.

Mastic asphalt.
It is normally done by specialist roofing contractors. The asphalt is heated in large melting pots, poured and spread out evenly across the roof. A special layer of sheathing felt is laid directly on top of the decking to isolate the asphalt from the decking; this is not bonded to the decking. This type of roof covering is not used widely on domestic property because it is more costly than the lapped felt systems. It provides a much better roof covering and lasts longer.

These are the rules and technical points applicable to asphalt covered roofs, these are the obvious areas to check for faults:

- Ensure that the pitch or fall of the decking is sufficient for an asphalt roof covering; (see earlier section on structure).

- Check that the roof decking has no raised areas or hollows that would prevent the water from running off the roof.

- The sheathing or base felt must be of standard BS747 (I), and as with any felt used on flat roofs be laid with minimum laps of 50mm. It must be loose and not secured at any point to allow for expansion.

- The asphalt must be laid to a minimum thickness of 20mm, covered with 12 to 15mm of 10mm stone chipping. (See earlier section).

- With asphalt covered roofs the apron areas around the gutter and sides are sometimes manufactured out of pressed aluminium and bedded into the asphalt, this gives a more professional finish to the edges of the roof.

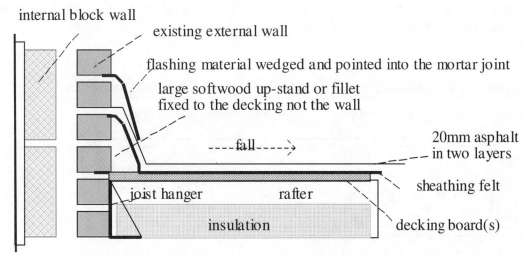

Detail at intersection with wall for a Asphalt covered roof

- Provision must be made to assist the felt and flashing to weatherproof the roof where it abuts walls, see detail above.

- The flashing at abutting walls is just the same as for any other instance, a minimum up-stand or vertical face to the flashing of 150mm (see drawing above). The flashing must be secured into the joints of the wall (see section on flashing).

- All ventilation and insulation details are the same as for the lapped felt system.

Energy issues to consider.

As explained earlier, two methods of insulation are used for flat roofs. A 'cold roof', where the insulation is placed in the roof void between the rafters and a 'warm roof', where the insulation is laid above the decking board(s).

Rules applicable:

A 'cold' flat roof. (See drawing R: 6)

- Some form of vapour barrier must be used, either by using foil-backed plasterboard or by installing a polythene vapour check on top of the rafters prior to the roof decking being laid.

- Soft insulation is normally used such as glass fibre wool, between the rafters above the ceiling boards.

- There must be a minimum air space between the insulation and the underside of the decking boards of 50mm, this space must link with the air vents that are located around the fascia or soffit boards (See R: 6).

A 'warm' flat roof. (See drawing R: 7)

One of two methods can be used to create a 'warm' decked roof:

- Sheets of rigid insulation are placed on top of a heavy-duty waterproof membrane, above a heavy-duty decking board. The insulation sheets must be able to withstand the direct effects of the weather and be capable of supporting concrete slabs or a 30 to 50mm natural stone dressing. This is sometimes called an 'inverted warm deck roof'.

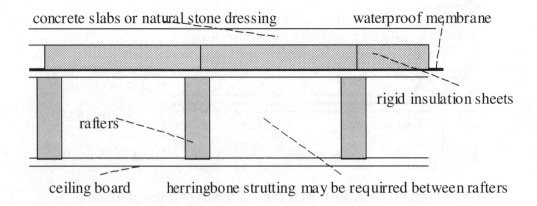

concrete slabs or natural stone dressing   waterproof membrane

rigid insulation sheets

rafters

ceiling board   herringbone strutting may be requirred between rafters

- Sheets of rigid insulation are placed underneath a waterproof covering. A water-resistant sheet material decking, usually water-resistant chipboard or 'sterling board' supports the insulation sheets. The role of the insulation sheets is to keep the temperature constant, above the temperature at which dew will form, and in doing so, preventing condensation forming within the roof void.

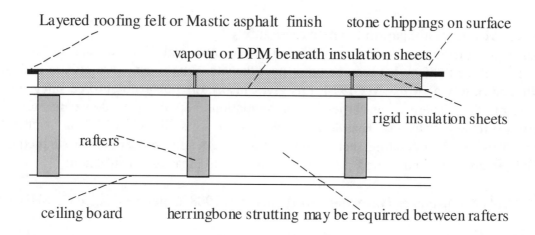

Layered roofing felt or Mastic asphalt finish   stone chippings on surface

vapour or DPM beneath insulation sheets

rigid insulation sheets

rafters

ceiling board   herringbone strutting may be requirred between rafters

Rules applicable:

- No insulation is placed within the roof void.

- 'Warm' roof structures do not require ventilation provisions, installation of ventilation would prevent the 'warm' design from functioning, and the temperature might fall and allow condensation to form.

- Suitable materials for use as rigid insulation are; expanded polystyrene sheets similar to those used in cavities, polyurethane slabs or mineral fibre board sheets that have been manufactured using resin. All of these products are suitable for use as insulation on flat roof structures.

- Because these types of roofs have heavy loading imposed upon them by the covering materials, stronger rafters will be required. It is very important that herringbone struts are fixed between the rafters to prevent movement.

Safety.

Common sense should prevail, but if a 'cowboy builder' is on site, safety is often their last concern, they generally have very little consideration for others nearby, and often take crazy risks to save money.

Do builders have a legal obligation to ensure site safety?

The answer is yes, there are no exceptions, and a builder must at all times ensure the safety of the workforce, himself and others that may be on or near the site. The rules for safety are laid down in **The health and Safety at work Act 1974**; this gives inspectors power to enforce safety measures are practised on site. There is an earlier list of regulations applicable to domestic building, the **Construction (lifting operations) Regulations 1961**; this covers all areas of lifting machinery, the competence of the people operating such equipment and the testing procedure for such equipment. These have been amended and extended to ensure safety in all areas of construction:

- The **Control of Substances Hazardous to Health Act 1988** sometimes called COSHH 1988.

- The **Construction (head protection) Regulations 1989**, safety hard hats.

- The **Management of Health and Safety at Work Regulations 1992**, this was a major overhaul of the 1974 Act.

- The **Construction (design and management) Regulations 1994**, This was aimed at commercial projects, but is applicable to a domestic building project where a main contractor and subcontractors are appointed by a homeowner. These regulations make it necessary for the homeowner to appoint (in writing) a planning supervisor and a principle or main contractor, if you like a list of hierarchy.

The latest legislation is set out in the Construction--Health, Safety and Welfare--Regulations 1996, this is specifically aimed at the well-being of all site personnel, the main objective of this legislation is the ability of management and personnel to be able to assess risk and take the necessary precautions.

These regulations are directed at ten areas of construction:

1. (Doors, gates and entrapment precessions,
2. Emergency lighting provisions,
3. Site planning and organisation,
4. Safeguarding excavations,
5. Scaffolding and all means of access, covering working platform minimum widths, safety, guarding, and inspection procedures.
6. Setting apart of site traffic and personnel,
7. Timbering works (shuttering and shoring)
8. Traffic planning, safe access and escape,
9. Ventilation of all work areas,
10. Welfare facilities, place of work and rest breaks, first aid equipment and trained personnel, heating and food preparation, protective clothing and sanitation.

As you can see, safety is a major consideration for the construction industry, but you must always stay alert, you must never rely on the builder to take the initiative, accidents happen! If you are not sure and the builder is of the same mind, contact the local building control department or visit your local library, you will find the answer at either.

Always remember that a 'cowboy builder' may not act responsibly or be safety conscious. As the homeowner, you may be held liable, if damage or injury occurs to a third party. When the cowboy disappears, your property insurance may have to pay any costs or damages incurred. It is recommended that you ask to see your builders' certificates of (1) Public Liability, and (2) Employers' Liability insurance.

One last point, when it comes to common sense and care for others, 'cowboy builders' are evidence suggesting that evolution can work in reverse!

Site security.
This is probably the most important area of safety with regards to a building site and should be top of the list what ever the size of the project. When painting a house the painter should make safe the area worked - a 'Wet Paint' notice is not enough. A carpenter hanging a door should similarly secure the area worked and the storage area of a project must also be secure.

Any building project should incorporate security measures, but projects of longer duration should make provisions for the following reasons:

- It will provide protection to a by-stander or unwitting intruders.

- It will help to deter vandals.

- It will prevent children playing on the site.

- It will help to deter theft.

- It keeps the building work within a contained area.

There is a legal obligation set out under The Highways Act 1980, which states that any work that is beside a public highway or footpath must have adequate protection by use of fencing. Hoarding or fencing cannot be erected without obtaining a permit from the local authority; this is part of the New Roads and Street Works Act 1991. This act has superseded previous legislation and gives a complete code of practice when building work encroaches on, or is adjacent to, public highways and footpaths. There is provision for each local authority to make reasonable local amendments to the legislation, so that 'hoarding' and fences are not intrusive or unsightly.

What is a hoarding?
It is the name used by the construction industry to describe a temporary close-boarded fence, usually built from timber posts and rails, covered with sheets of 19mm external plywood. The structural elements of a hoarding or fence may be constructed out of scaffolding, covered with plywood or net fencing. They are erected to protect members of the public on a highway or public footpath around a building site.

What are the basic rules applicable to building site fencing or 'hoarding'?

There are strict guidelines for the erection of site security fencing, for both safety and aesthetic reasons:

- Normally erected to a height of 2.2 metres, this is measured from the road or footpath surface to the top of the sheets or fencing.

- If there is a footpath, it must have a minimum width from the roadside edge of the kerb to the face of the fence of 1.2 metres.

- If a temporary footpath has to be constructed while the building work takes place, it must be of sufficient nature to be able to support the weight of pedestrian traffic. There must be ramps at the ends of the walkways where it adjoins existing footpaths or the highway, suitable for wheelchair access. Any temporary walkway should have a guide-rail to the roadside at a minimum height of 900mm, and be filled in to prevent passage beneath the handrail.

- The support structure of the fence or hoarding must be able to withstand reasonable impact damage, wind loading and afford reasonable protection to the general public.

- It must have adequate lighting at night.

- The building site side of the fence or hoarding must provide a minimum working corridor of 1.metre at all points.

Important point of law:

Because of the legislation set out by **The Highways Act 1980** and **New Roads and Street Works Act 1991**, there is an obligation to provide the measures set out. It is the duty of the builder to ensure that these measures and precautions are respected. If the builder fails to carry out these provisions and you as the homeowner are aware of their negligence, you may become vicariously liable for any injury or damage caused by such negligence. You appointed them to do the building work on your property, so ensure that they are adequately insured and that they are making every effort to make the building work reasonably safe, for both the public and authorised people within the site area.

Scaffolding

What are scaffolds?

They are temporary platforms to enable safe working above heights of 1.5metres. Normally constructed from tubular steel or aluminium with softwood timber platforms, This section of the book is written to give you a brief overview of scaffolding, to enable you to watch for obvious mistakes and to ensure that any scaffolding is safe.

All scaffolds must comply with minimum requirements of the **Construction (health, safety, and welfare) Regulations 1996**, further to this all scaffold tubes must comply with BS1139.

Are there different types or styles of scaffolding used?

One of three methods of scaffolding is normally used for domestic dwellings

      (1) Independent
      (2) Putlog
      (3) Mobile

1. Independent scaffolds;

This type of scaffold is self-supporting and is not 'tied' to the building in any way; this is because normally it will encircle the whole building forming a ring around it. Where the scaffold does not encircle the whole building, bracing may be applied at a window or diagonal shore braces used from the surrounding ground. E.g. for a scaffold against one wall or for a semi-detached house.

This type of scaffolding is identified by the fact that it has two rows of standard or vertical supports, one against the wall of the property and the other no more than 1.4 metres away from the building. The scaffold will normally be erected in 'stages' or 'lifts'; these are the stages of working heights as the building progresses. They are normally between 1.3 and 1.5 meters.

Diagonal cross braces are placed on each lift or stage between the two standards; these should have an angle of between 40 and 45 degrees. Once the scaffolding is erected a ladder is laid against the working platform and securely fastened, it should rise above the platform by at least 1.0 metre and should be at a pitch of 75 degrees, (for every 4 rungs climbed, the ladder should lean by 1 rung distance).

This type of scaffold is normally used for renovation and repair work, because it has no effect on the building; it is also used on 'new-build'.

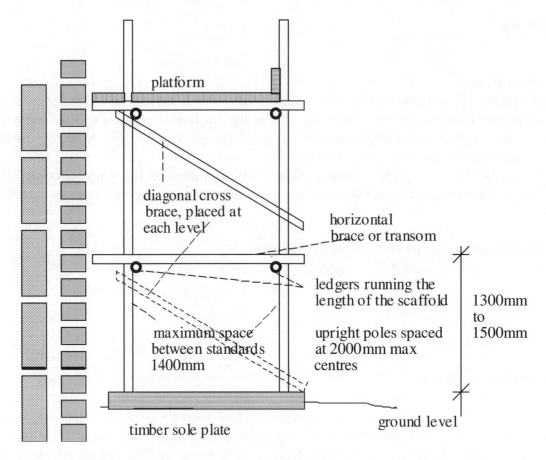

An independent scaffold

2. Putlog or building supported scaffold:

Its outer standards or uprights identify this type of scaffold; none is against the walls of the property. The ledgers or horizontal poles running the length of the building are clamped to the standards; these support the horizontal brace or transom ('putlog'). The other end of the transom is supported in the vertical joints of the brickwork. Occasionally they may be seen in the horizontal joints.

The same rules, measurements and safety features apply to all scaffolding, whatever method is used.

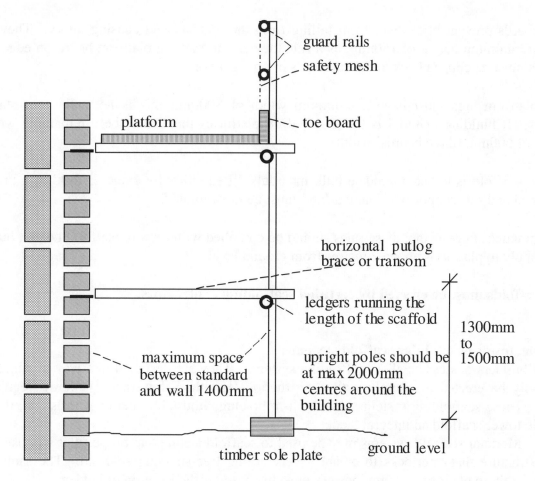

Putlog or building supported scaffold

This type of scaffold is normally only used for new-build or major renovation projects. If your property has lime mortar masonry joints, then this type of scaffold may be used for repairs, as the joints are easily raked out to allow the insertion of the putlog ends.

Scaffold working platforms
Both the previously discussed scaffolds have very similar platforms, with rules applicable to both.

• The boards used for the platforms are of stress-graded softwood, 225mm x 38mm, in various lengths.

• The boards must be free from splits and other defects, i.e. saw cuts and they must comply with BS2482. (Only recognised scaffold 'deals' should be used).

• The boards must be supported along their length by the transoms or putlogs every 1.5 meters.

• At the ends of scaffolding, the overhang of the board must be a minimum of 150mm.

• Where boards overlap along the length of a platform, they must overlap by a minimum of 300mm, and over a support.

• Guard-rails must be provided to prevent falling, usually at a height of 900mm above the platform area. The maximum space between the guard-rails should be 450mm; this also applies to the distance between the toe board and the lower guard-rail.

- Toe boards prevent bricks etc, from falling from the scaffold and causing injury. They must have a minimum height of 150mm, as a rule they are normally a platform board on edge. Toe boards must be clipped back to the standards or up-right poles.

- The platform area must have a minimum width of 800mm; this is normally four standard boards. If building material is to be stored on platforms there must be a remaining working width of 600mm (three boards' width).

- Where scaffold is to accommodate bulk materials, lifted either by crane or forklift, a properly designed and self-supporting 'loading-bay' must be incorporated.

- Best practice suggests that these rules should be complied with for any platform height, but they only apply to platforms above 2 metres from ground level.

- **All scaffolds must be erected by certified scaffolding contractors.**

3. **Mobile, tower or modular scaffold systems:**

Many builders possess smaller scaffolding systems. They are designed in a way in which they can only be erected to comply with Construction (Health, Safety, and Welfare) Regulations 1996. These scaffolding systems have built-in bracing, adjustable feet or wheels and, if it is a mobile tower scaffold an integral ladder.

Modular scaffold systems may be used to scaffold a complete property; it will use a gate type structure that interlocks to create a very strong free-standing scaffold. The same rules apply for these platforms as previous systems, likewise for the location of ladders.

Faults to watch for with modular scaffolds.

Some unscrupulous builders think they are 'Spiderman' and ignore safety measures for both themselves and others. The following points are common and if you encounter them, you must complain and get the scaffold corrected.

- Mobile scaffolds with the wheels not locked, this is crazy it is like working on a giant roller skate, and far more unstable!

- Climbing up the outside of a tower or mobile scaffold, the builder should always climb-up the inside, these have a platform with a hinged trap door to allow access to the working area.

- Modular scaffold systems used on large projects must comply with the same rules as conventional methods.

- Always ensure that the correct platform boards are being used, if the system does not have a custom platform (this maybe made from strengthened plywood), conventional scaffold deals should be used. (**Materials other than the manufacturers' provided, should not be used. They are potentially dangerous, and may well affect any liability insurance**).

Rules applicable to all scaffolding systems.

There are some safety standards that must be complied with in all scaffolds. Common sense should prevail but if a 'cowboy builder' is lurking, standards may slip. It may well be your house insurance policy that has to pay for any injury or damage to third parties; 'cowboy builders' treat insurance like income tax, and avoid it!

* All supporting structures of scaffolds must be free from damage and defects.

* All boards or platforms must be strong, defect free and should be clean.

* All scaffolds must be secure and stable.

* Any stored materials must be distributed evenly around the scaffold, while allowing adequate walkway.

* When the builder is not on site all ladders must be removed to prevent unauthorised access to the scaffold. A plank may be fastened over the rungs of ladders.

* If the scaffold encroaches onto public areas it must be lit at night and the first two metres of vertical standards must have bright or fluorescent tape or paint - although paint can conceal defects! If it is not safe for pedestrians to walk below the scaffold, the whole area must be cordoned off, and appropriately signed.

* Special permission may be required to erect scaffolding on footpaths and public highways if in doubt, check, don't rely on the builder.

Soil or ground testing.

A very complex area of construction. This section is written to give the homeowner an overview of the key issues and problem areas to be aware of. The main reasons for soil tests or investigation are:

- To ensure that the ground is suitable for building upon.

- To decide on the design of building and to cost the foundation.

- To identify and anticipate any problems that might occur during construction, such as natural drainage, and planning for storm water disposal.

- To make sure that the site has not been used for landfill or that there have been no disturbances that could affect the stability of construction.

The ground should be tested within the proposed building area every few metres, if disturbed soil or debris is found further investigations should be undertaken. The most successful methods of checking the history of land are ordnance survey maps, local authority engineering plans, geological survey maps, local historical references and local knowledge, if applicable local mining records and if possible aerial photographs may be inspected.

An aerial photograph can highlight depressions in the ground that are not visible from ground level, these may be a sign of previous building, land-fill or other factors that could pose a potential problem to development. Most building plots do not require this depth of investigation. Always beware when a piece of land is cheap; there is usually good reason for the price!

What do you do if a fault is found during investigation?
As a rule most building sites are thoroughly checked prior to being made available by the vendor. However, it may be that the area on which you intend to build your extension has not been subjected to such a search, or that the plot of land purchased was cheap.

There have been many instances where a garden has been divided to make building land available, and on commencement of building work it has been found that the subsoil has been removed. Often older properties will have had waste disposal pits within their grounds, is your building plot one of these? If so, beware of potential for natural instability.

These are the choices you have:

- Cancel the proposed building!

- Design the project around the problem.

- Use a foundation design that overcomes the problem. (see section on foundations) Raft or piled foundations may be considered.

- Remove soil from the offending area and replace with compacted hard-core.

- If poor drainage is the problem, make alternative arrangements for disposal of storm water other than by soakaway. (see section on drainage)

Always check that every effort has been made to ensure that the ground is suitable for building on, you must ensure that the builder shows you proof, in writing of any findings. If you are unable to confirm or are unhappy with the findings obtain a second opinion.

Remember that if you find the problem with the land after the building is complete, the cost to rectify will be far greater than before the start of a project.

Stairs.

What are the main functions of a staircase?

A staircase has several roles:

- To provide a safe passage between different floor levels in a dwelling.

- An easy passage between floors.

- An effective way of moving furniture to different levels.

- To provide quick escape in the event of an emergency.

What are the names of the component parts of a staircase?

A basic timber flight of stairs will consist of many components:

- **Wall string**   This is the piece of timber stretching from the lower floor to the upper floor, and secured to the wall(s). Its role is to support the treads and risers of the staircase. Stair strings are normally between 25 and 40mm thick.

- **Outer string**   This is the piece of timber that stretches from the lower to the upper floor, between the upper and lower newel posts (the side of the staircase that is open to the room). If a staircase is located away from the wall, it will have two outer strings.

- **Bottom newel post**   This is attached to the outer string(s), and sits on the floor. Its role is to support the handrail and balusters to the outer edge of the staircase. Newel posts are normally a minimum size of 100x100mm.

- **Upper or top newel post**   It is attached to the top of the outer string and serves the same purpose as the bottom newel. This is secured to the upper floor trimmer joist, it is housed out so as it fits over the joist.

- **Outer string capping**   Fixed the full length of the outer string; it sits on the top of the string and is usually grooved or mortised to locate the balusters.

- **Handrail**   This is fixed between the tops of the two newel posts. The underside is normally grooved to locate the balusters. These are sometimes fitted to the wall as well, especially if the staircase is over 1.0 meter wide.

- **Balusters**   This is the in-fill placed between the handrail and outer string capping.

- **Treads**   This is the piece of wood that acts the platform of each step, these are supported between the strings.

- **Riser**   This is the board that fills the space between each tread, a riser and a tread creates one step.

What are the basic regulations applicable to stairs?

Most of the rules that need to be adhered to when stairs are manufactured and installed are straight forward, applying common sense for the safety and structural factors to ensure that the staircase is both safe and durable. These regulations are part of section K of the Building Regulations.

- A staircase must not have a pitch of less than 27.5 degrees or greater than 42 degrees.

- A single flight of stairs should have 14 treads and 13 risers.

- Any straight flight of stairs should never exceed a floor to floor height of 2600mm.

- Each riser must be the same height and be a maximum size of 220mm.

- Each tread must be the same width and have a minimum size of 220mm

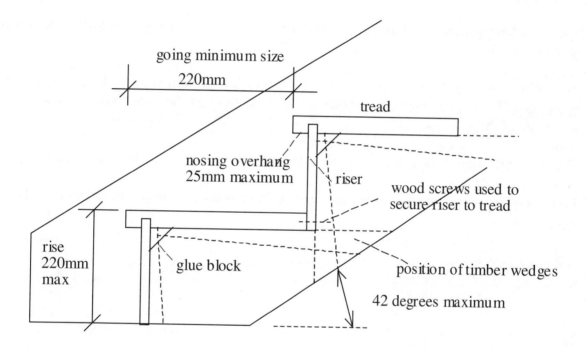

- When the dimensions of the staircase are calculated, twice the rise + the going must = between 550 and 700mm.

- The handrail must be fitted at a height of between 900 and 1000mm, measured from the top front edge of the treads.

- There must be a minimum height of 2.0 metres between the top of the treads and any ceiling areas above the stairs.

- The staircase must be a minimum width of 800mm, measured from the inside edge of the handrail to the wall.

- Any flight of stairs that exceeds a rise height of 600mm (three steps) must have a handrail.

- The spaces between the balusters must be no larger than 100mm.

- The nosing overhang must be no more than 25mm (see drawing above).

Important points when manufacturing a flight of stairs.
There are some points that you will be able to check, prior to the staircase being installed. Once it has been installed inspection of the underside of a staircase may not be possible, as often it is covered in with plasterboard or other material. The techniques listed below are tried and tested, and if not used, may cause permanent faults.

- The treads and risers of a staircase are secured to the string using wooden wedges; these must be secure and glued.

- The joint between the tread and riser should be strengthened using triangular blocks that are glued in position.

- The point at which the tread joins the riser should be secured using at least 5 wood screws across a 800mm wide staircase. These screws pass through the riser into the tread, from the underside of the staircase.

- The risers are often made from 12mm plywood; this is for extra strength and stability.

- Joints between newel post and string are made using tenons, held in position with dowel pins.

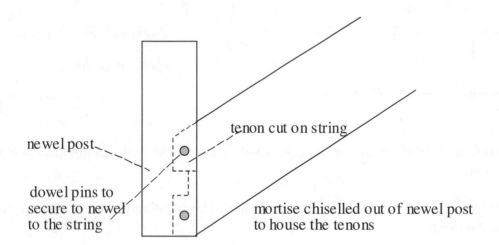

Newel post to stair string joint detail

- The same method is used to secure the handrail to the newel post.

Important installation procedures.

This section covers the areas of installation where problems can occur, explaining the correct methods that should be used.

- Standard flights of stairs are manufactured to fit a standard measurement of finished floor to finished floor size. This is worked out to a pre-set pitch and total length of going. The top or bottom risers must not be cut down to enable the staircase to fit a non-standard situation; all the steps must be exactly the same.

- If stairs are located in a corner of a room, there must be a clear area at the foot of the stairs, the minimum dimensions being 1000 x 1000mm.

- The string against the wall must be securely fixed using the appropriate fixings.

- The top tread must be level with the top surface of the upper floor. This may mean that the underside of the top tread or nosing piece as it is sometimes called will have to be rebated out to fit over the trimmer joist that supports the staircase.

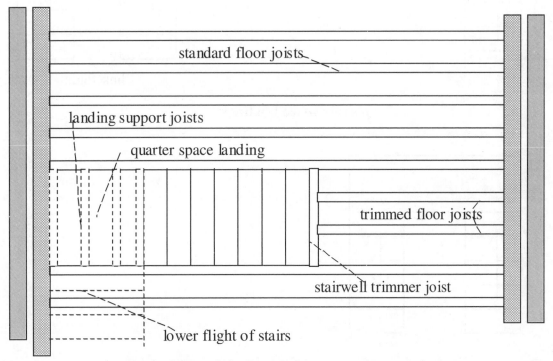

Typical floor joist layout incorperating a staircase

- All the balusters are held into the string capping and handrail using spacer blocks, these must wedge the individual balusters tight and ensure that they are evenly spaced to a maximum dimension of 100mm.

- Any handrails must be capable of supporting the weight of an average adult.

Landings.

A landing serves two purposes. It can be the top area of a staircase, the floor space connecting all the upper floor rooms, or it can be a transitional landing allowing a staircase to change direction. Wherever the landing is situated it must be constructed in the same way as a floor, with joists and floorboards and be appropriately supported using the wall and the storey height newel posts. This is a long newel post that stretches from the floor where the flight of stairs starts, to the handrail height of the landing.

Landings are a good means of fitting a staircase into an area where the length of a single flight will not fit. A quarter space landing allows the staircase to change direction by 90 degrees, whereas a half space landing can permit a staircase to change direction by 180 degrees.

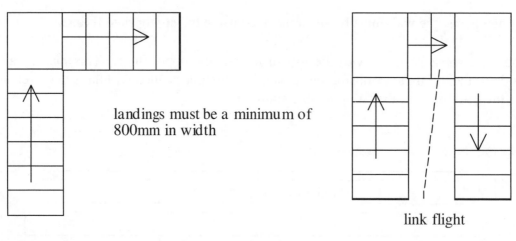

landings must be a minimum of 800mm in width

link flight

Quarter space landings

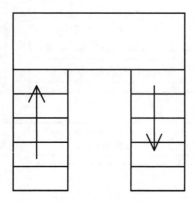

Half space landing

Landings can be placed at any point within the flight, so long as they comply with the regulations shown for stairs, as detailed in part K of The Building Regulations.

Other types of stairs.
Most domestic dwellings use conventional timber staircases such as those already discussed either standard size or made to order. There are other types of staircase regularly used; this gives a brief description and the usual place of installation;

'Grain store' style or open riser stairs.
This type of staircase is used in both modern and older properties for its aesthetic value as part of an open-plan design. There have no real advantage over a conventional staircase other than looks.

     This type of staircase is subjected to most of the rules for conventional stairs, with these additional regulations specially formulated, as stated in section K of The Building Regulations;

- Each tread must overlap adjacent treads by a minimum of 20mm.

- The space between each tread must not have a space any larger than 100mm, the 100mm sphere test is used as with balusters, explained simply a ball of 100mm must wedge in the space, not pass through.

     This rule can pose a problem with stairs that are part of a residential building, so three methods have been designed to overcome the problem, giving the appearance that the staircase is still open riser.

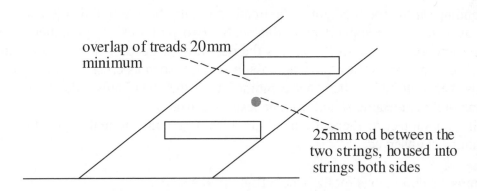

Riser space restricted using timber rod

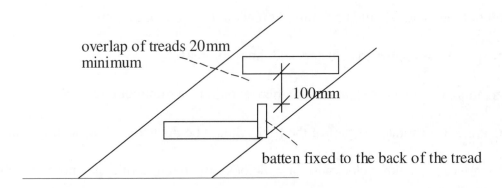

Riser space restricted using batten at the back of the tread.

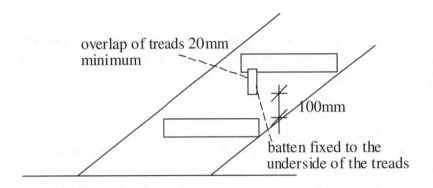

overlap of treads 20mm minimum

100mm

batten fixed to the underside of the treads

Riser space restricted using a batten fixed to the underside of the treads.

Pre-fabricated steel spiral staircases;

These are becoming very common place in warehouse conversions, flats and apartments. They are used because they require very little floor space, and being made from steel, can act as part of the structure of the dwelling. The stairwell where the flight exits the first floor can occupy an area of only 1.7 metres square, whereas a conventional staircase can require a floor area of around 3 square metres.

The treads of a spiral staircase are simply segments of a circle, a flight usually travels through 360 degrees between each floor, but this may vary. As a rule each flight will have either 12 or 16 treads, depending on the room height. The treads normally have a round collar to the centre point, which fits over the centre support pole, this serves two purposes, it strengthens the whole assembly, but more importantly it correctly spaces the rise of each tread. If the stairs are to be left in a natural steel finish, the treads must have a non-slip surface, such as cross-hatching. It is usual to cover the treads with polished timber; this combined with the steel balustrade can give a good aesthetic effect, and dull the metallic sound from pedestrian traffic.

Spiral stairs are subject to the same handrail rules as a conventional flight; these are the additional rules that must observed:

- The handrail must be continuous for the whole flight of the stairs.

- The maximum overlap of the treads at the outer edge must be 150mm.

- The mid-point of the treads should be a minimum width or going of 220mm.

- The 100mm-sphere test applies to balusters and the riser areas.

- Where the tread joins the centre support pole there should be a minimum tread width of 75mm.

- Any landing areas incorporated as part of the flight should be the width of the stairs square.

- A spiral staircase can run either clockwise or anticlockwise, but as a rule they normally climb in a clockwise direction.

- All the nuts and bolts used must be of a locking type.

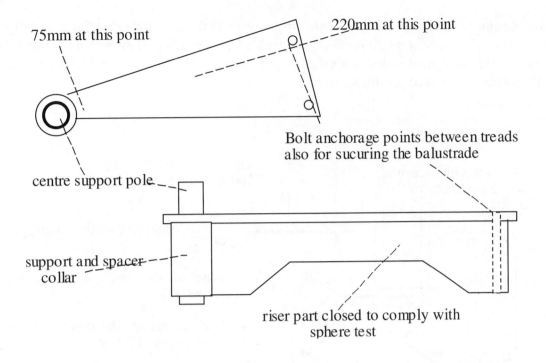

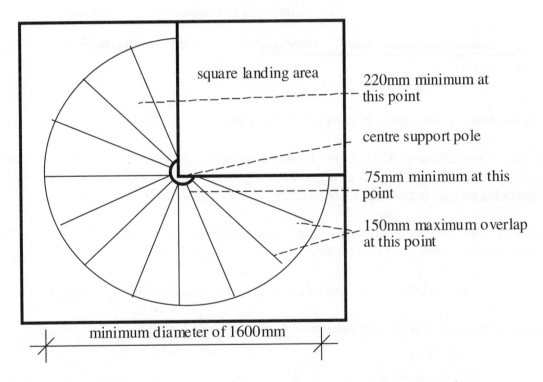

Plan of a typical spiral staircase, showing minimum applicable dimensions.

Steel string stairs.

As industrial premises are converted into residential, the designs used reflect industrial type structures; the result is steel being incorporated in the designs. The attraction of these conversions is the vast space and it is this that allows steel string stairs to be used. The steel string structure allows the staircase to be wide, incorporating large platform landings, with the need for relatively floor joists being used to support landings. This allows a staircase to be the focal point of a room or the centre point of an open plan design.

This design of staircase uses a simple structure of two steel support strings; usually 6mm walled 'box section'. Legs or angle brackets are welded to the string; these are the support points for the treads. This design of stairs is normally open riser, and is therefore subjected to the same Building Regulations as stated for timber stairs.

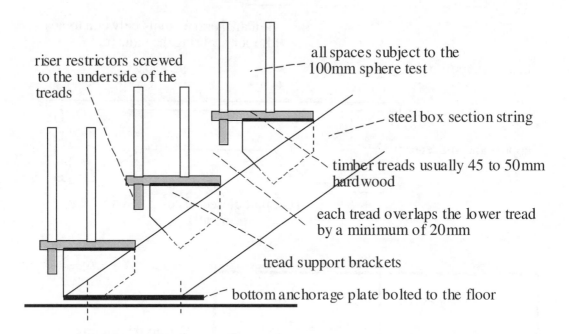

riser restrictors screwed to the underside of the treads

all spaces subject to the 100mm sphere test

steel box section string

timber treads usually 45 to 50mm hardwood

each tread overlaps the lower tread by a minimum of 20mm

tread support brackets

bottom anchorage plate bolted to the floor

Important additional rules applicable to steel string stairs:

- When stairs over 1.0 metre wide, it may be necessary to use a steel brace attached to either tread support bracket to prevent sag occurring when weight is applied to the centre of the treads. The riser restrictor may be increased in size to carry out this task as well.

- Platform or standard space landings should be constructed from steel and bolted to the stair strings, to join the whole structure together.

- Handrails must be located to both sides of the flight, and be continuous from top to bottom.

- All nuts and bolts used in the construction process must be a locking type.

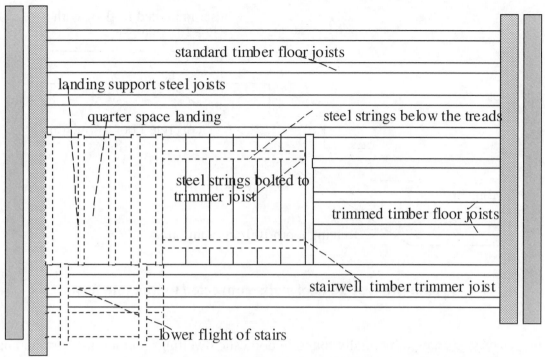

Typical floor joist layout incorperating a steel string staircase
Shows the width increased to around 1600mm

'In situ' concrete stairs:

'In-situ' (built on site) these are manufactured using timber shuttering, steel reinforcing bars and dense concrete. They are not usual in domestic dwellings, but may be used when constructing split level or twin-level apartments and flats, or large prestigious dwellings.

Concrete stairs are subjected to the same regulations as all other stairs and if they are to be used as a fire escape, must comply with Section B of The Building Regulations.

Pre-cast concrete stairs;

This type of staircase is manufactured to match most of the styles of stairs discussed. To make the production of these stairs cost effective they are manufactured to standard sizes, it is the designer or architect's responsibility to ensure that the stairs will fit the design.

This type of staircase uses a very simple construction of mass concrete and steel, shaped in re-useable moulds, this manufacturing process produces stairs that are modular in construction and always made to very precise tolerances. Some manufactures will make this type of stairs to order.

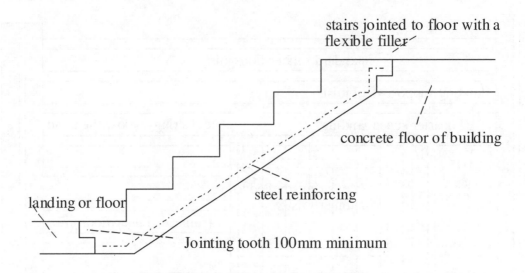

stairs jointed to floor with a flexible filler

concrete floor of building

steel reinforcing

landing or floor

Jointing tooth 100mm minimum

Typical pre-cast flight of stairs connected to concrete floors

These types of stairs are not normally found in domestic dwellings, but are in flats and apartments. Some builders use concrete beam and block systems for house upper floors, especially if the floor span is large. It is for this type of property that a pre-cast concrete staircase is ideal, as it would complement the floor and the cost would be justified on a large property. Again these stairs are subject to the same regulations as all other stairs and, if they are to be used as a fire escape, must comply with Section B of The Building Regulations. The main advantages to these stairs are:

- They are very strong, capable of taking greater loads than timber stairs.

- There is no need to employ a carpenter to build the shuttering.

- Quality is the responsibility of the manufacturer.

- They are a more effective sound barrier.

Common faults to be aware of.
All types of stairs discussed are subject to the same faults, bad workmanship and mistakes. These are common faults:

- Wall string not securely fixed.

- Wall handrails poorly secured, not capable of taking the weight of an average adult.

- Insufficient glue blocks between the treads and risers or wedges that have not been glued cause squeaky treads and risers.

- Top or bottom risers that are a different height from the rest of the flight. This is clear evidence that a 'cowboy' is on the 'ranch', and is the usual shortcut used to allow a standard flight of stairs to fit a non-standard storey height. This is a dangerous practice because someone could trip or lose balance and fall, this fault must never occur or be overlooked during inspection.

- Stair treads that sag under the weight of one person. If the stairs are over 1.0 metre wide, a 'carriage' should be fitted to the underside of the flight, to help take the weight. This will not be visible so it can be constructed from basic framing timber. If the staircase is an open tread type and this fault is evident, it means that the treads are not manufactured to a sufficient thickness, this applies to steel staircases as well.

- Loose newel posts, a very common fault. If this occurs it can have serious consequences because the newel post holds the handrail which in turn holds the balustrade, if one is loose then all three will be. The newel post must be secured to the string using tenons; dowel-pins and glue, failure to use this method will result in a loose newel post.

- Loose balusters, this is just bad workmanship. On a quality staircase it is likely that the balusters will be mortised into the string capping and handrail, this method is very unlikely to suffer from loose balusters. On mass-produced standard flights the normal method of securing the balusters is by spacer blocks between the balustrade, which in turn are located in a groove. If these blocks are not glued and pinned in place firmly the balusters will work loose.

- Handrails at different heights. When handrails are fitted to both sides of a flight of stairs they must be fixed at the same height, a minimum of 900mm from the front edge of the tread.

All of these faults are in breach of Building Regulations, and are unacceptable.

Storage of materials.

Why is storage of materials important?

If food is incorrectly stored, and you have a meal prepared with contaminated Ingredients, you may become ill. The same principle applies to building, if the materials are stored carelessly; the building could have in-built faults. The result in both cases is that you feel pretty 'sick'!

Poor storage of materials on any project, what ever the size or duration is a clear sign that there is a 'cowboy' in the vicinity, and should not be accepted

What will good storage of materials achieve?

There are clear advantages to be gained from good storage:

- Often space is at a premium; good storage will maximise the space available for work.

- Materials should be stored near to their use, where practicable.

- Security of the project is enhanced.

- Site access is made easier, and planned along with the storage area.

- Stock control is easier and more accurate, making budgeting more precise.

- Good storage makes a safer site. Many accidents on building sites are as a result of poor storage and planning.

What are the key areas to watch for?

It would take too long to explain how every building item should be stored. This lists the most commonly used, which are likely to be damaged if stored incorrectly:

- **Bricks**   When bricks are delivered direct, they are packed in a way in which the manufacturer believes they will be best protected. Provided they remain packed in this manner, they require no further attention. For safety this should be stacked no more than three packs high. Most bricks are very strong, but if stored incorrectly they may suffer. When stacked manually on site, bricks must always be placed on their edge, each layer crossing the previous, to keep the stack stable. Stacks must not exceed a height of 2.2 metres and the bricks should be covered with polythene or similar to protect them against mud splashes etc. The area should be level, firm, well drained and free of obstructions.

- **Blocks, lightweight and dense concrete**   These should be treated in the same way as bricks, special attention should be paid to dense concrete to aid lifting and to prevent injury. No manually stacked blocks should exceed seven layers.

- **Timber**   If stored incorrectly, this can be costly. There is no excuse other than the builder is a practising 'cowboy'! Any timber used for building must be dry, and the store should remain dry for the duration of the project. Timber made wet by the weather will take several weeks to dry if it is used in an area of a construction that has inadequate ventilation. A good timber store will be constructed from scaffolding, similar to a free-standing scaffold.

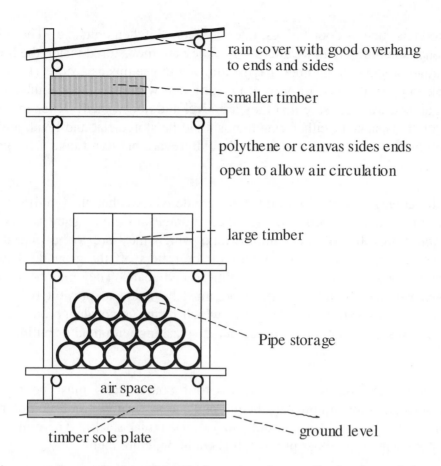

rain cover with good overhang to ends and sides

smaller timber

polythene or canvas sides ends open to allow air circulation

large timber

Pipe storage

air space

timber sole plate

ground level

The diagram shows the heaviest timber stored near the bottom of the rack for stability and to reduce risk of injury through lifting.

- **Roofing tiles**   These are probably the most fragile of the 'hard' building materials. They crack or fracture very easily if stacked poorly and fractures may go undetected. When delivered direct from the manufacturer they are normally bound together on pallets to prevent movement and resulting damage. If tiles are to be stacked loosely on a building project there are important guidelines to prevent unnecessary damage to them and injury to persons near the stacks.

    (i)   The stack is best located against a wall or other strong vertical surface, most tiles are heavy.

    (ii)   Tiles should be stacked on their bottom or top edge, not flat.

    (iii)   Tiles must not be stacked higher than five layers.

    (iv)   Ridge and valley tiles should be stacked on their ends, and not stood on their bedding edges or laid flat.

    (v)   If tiles are going to be stored for a long period, a protective sheet should be placed over them to prevent staining from site spillage and weather.

    (vi)   The ground on which tiles are to be stacked should be covered prior to the tiles being stacked, either with old plywood or pea shingle.

- **External joinery items**   These should be stored flat on firm supports well off the ground. They should be covered with a strong waterproof sheet, weighted down for weather protection.

- **Internal joinery** Products such as door linings, internal doors, kitchen units etc. These should be ordered to arrive once the building is weatherproof. They are then stored inside the building. If the owner has a garage or shed, the builder may be allowed to use this as a store. Doors must be laid flat on suitable support bearers, to prevent twisting and warping. Door linings may be laid flat or stacked against a wall. Ensure that they are level and not twisted! Kitchen units are delivered assembled or 'flat-packed'; either way they should be stored flat and level, and away from 'wet trades'. With all storage, common sense should prevail, but don't take it for granted, some people have little!

- **Roof trusses (pre-fabricated)** Normally roof trusses are delivered when the building is ready to take them, it is prudent to make provision for their storage anyway. They are normally stacked against a wall - probably of the building onto which they are to be placed - and supported by bearers large enough to keep the ends of the rafters off the ground. Failure to support them adequately could result in the joints being forced apart. They may be stored flat on strong bearers well off the ground. Every effort must be made to prevent twisting and stacking under stress; the stack can be to a height at which lifting is not dangerous. All roof trusses are pressure treated so a cover is only necessary if splashing with mud or building waste is likely.

- **Damp-proof courses and membranes** Damp-proof course rolls must be stored on their ends on a flat surface, to a maximum stack height of 1 metre. Damp-proof membrane rolls should be laid flat on a level base, usually an old pallet (a triangular stack). There must be no sharp objects on the storage area for either product, this could puncture them.

- If you are not happy with the storage of any material, question the builder, this is often enough to correct the problem.

Telecommunications

Which parts of your home are part of telecommunications?

It is generally the provision of a telephone supply to a dwelling. Now we have entered the twenty-first century, provision should be made for a personal computer modem and/or Internet connection. With the advent of digital television, telephone and television systems are becoming more closely integrated.

British Telecom, the main provider for 'land-line' telephony in UK, normally provide builders with the cable, ducts and service pipes to supply new developments with a telecommunications network.

Is it standard practice to install telephone cables and extension sockets?

Nearly all new properties have a telephone supply cable routed somewhere inside the building; larger properties may have provision for several extension sockets in various locations around the property.

Is it a compulsory requirement for a builder to make these provisions?

It is not a compulsory requirement for a builder to make these provisions; certain professional building organisations (NHBC) may incorporate this as a part of the standard building code of practice.

Are there rules to be adhered to when installing telephone cables and wall sockets?

There are rules for telephone cable and socket installations, they are different and depend on whether the cables are overhead or underground.

Overhead supply cables:

- A secure wall anchor or hook must be placed on a wall or near the eaves of the roof to support the supply cable. This must be secure and able to withstand the strain of the cable and wind loads. It must also be located high enough so that the cable does not sag and cause an obstruction.

- Near the wall anchor, there must be a 19mm plastic duct (internal diameter) placed in the wall for the cable to pass through and enter the dwelling. Once the cable is in position both ends of the duct should be sealed around the cable using mastic.

- Once the cable is in the loft or roof space it is then routed to where it will be required. Conduit is used to protect the cable where it is covered by plaster and/or render. The same rules apply as with electrical cables, (see section on electric supply)

- Telephone sockets must not be located any closer than 300mm to an electrical socket to prevent interference and problems with computer modems.

Underground supply cables:

- All underground cables must be placed at a minimum depth of 350mm below ground level.

- All underground cables leading to a property must be placed in 50mm plastic duct (internal diameter), this ducting is normally supplied by the local telephone service company (e.g.: British Telecom).

- Once the supply cable duct reaches the property external wall at foundation level, the duct is reduced in diameter to 19mm, this is also usually supplied as part of a 'Telecom' package. The smaller pipe should be inserted into the larger pipe by at least 150mm, and the joint sealed. At this stage it is normal for a small draw rope to be placed in the pipes instead of telephone cable. Once there is no risk of damage as the building work takes place, the cable is attached to the end of the rope and pulled through the duct into the property.

- The smaller duct must pass right through the wall to the over-site area beneath the ground floor, it must not travel up the cavity, these pipes are sometimes called 'hockey sticks' because of their shape. It is standard practice for the duct to come through the floor in the central hallway in line with the face of an internal wall. (see diagram)

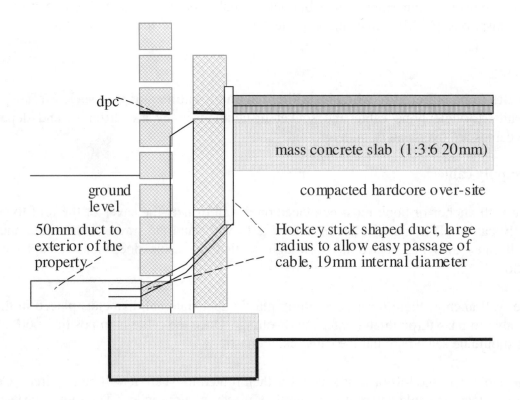

- Once the cable has entered the property, it is routed to where it will be required; conduit is used to protect the cable where it is covered by plaster and/or render. The same rules apply as with electrical cables, (see section on electric supply)

- Telephone sockets must not be located any nearer than 300mm to an electrical socket to prevent interference and problems with computer modems.

Who is responsible for each of the stages of a telephone installation?

This can vary, depending on service provider and region, but as a rule, the ducts draw ropes and cables are supplied by 'Telecom'. These are then laid and built-in to the foundations by the ground-workers. The electrician will usually install any extension cables, and sockets in the rooms throughout the property when the 'first fix' electrical installations are made. The main or first socket must be installed and connected by the service provider (British Telecom or other), and is installed when you take out a contract for their service.

The initial line and socket once connected to a service provider must not be altered in any way, any extension cables and sockets are your property, and the cable and first socket remain the property of the service provider.

Are there any guidelines for telephone installations on existing properties without the provisions for telephone lines and sockets?

The service provider normally completes this type of installation. This will usually include the overhead cable to your property from the nearest telegraph pole, drilling through the wall to allow the cable to enter the property, and the installation of a plug type socket, placed just inside the property.

The service provider is not legally bound to route the cable to where you would like it for your convenience, this type of installation may cost extra, so if, the engineer agrees to place it somewhere other than the standard location, check that there is not an extra charge.

Are there any points to watch for when telephone installations are completed on existing properties?

As a rule Telecom engineers are reliable and conscientious workers, but there are a few common problems that can effect your property.

- Check that the anchor or hook for the supply cable is securely fixed, soft bricks or masonry could present a problem. Sometimes the hook is fixed to the fascia board, where rotten timber or plastic fascia could also present problems.

- A hole should not be drilled through a window or doorframe to allow the cable to enter the property; this is a lazy engineer trying to avoid the lengthy process of drilling the wall.

- Once the cable is in position the gap around the cable must be sealed with mastic.

- The cable should droop below the hole to prevent water running along it into the property.

- Where the socket is fixed to an internal wall it should be secured using masonry plugs and wood screws, normally two per socket.

- If cables have to be secured around a room, it is normal practice to clip them to skirting board and architrave. Cable clips should be placed a maximum of 150mm apart.

- External cables are clipped to the outer walls of a property, secured at a maximum 200mm apart.

- As a rule external cables are black, internal white.

Timber

Various types of timber are used for constructing different parts of dwellings; softwood is the most commonly used.

Softwoods.

- **Redwood** More commonly known as red pine, red or yellow deal or the Scots pine. May be yellow or red in colour, very durable and straight-grained. Strong and used for general joinery and structural building timber.

- **European Spruce** This is very similar to red pine, but is not as tough. It is light yellow or pale pink in colour. Used for simple framework and standard joinery, such as skirting boards or architrave.

- **Douglas Fir** Probably the best all-round softwood, sometimes known as Oregon Pine, normally red to brown in colour. Because of its natural tendency to grow tall without many branches, it has very straight grain, few knots and is very strong. Used for quality joinery and stress-graded timber.

- **Colombian Pine** Similar to Douglas Fir in characteristics, the main difference being that it is normally golden yellow in colour. It has a fantastic fragrance, is excellent to work with, and is normally used to manufacture high-class joinery. It is very expensive and may be difficult to obtain.

- **Pitch Pine** A good all round timber, suitable for most joinery, may suffer from large knots and can sometimes be a very heavy timber.

- **Western Hemlock** A good all-round softwood, mainly used for interior joinery, has attractive yellow, brown or red grain. It sometimes has an unpleasant smell.

- **Parana Pine** Usually in varying shades of brown, sometimes with almost pink colouring to the grain. A good joinery timber that is mainly used for staircases. It can be very heavy, but its character is probably the best of all softwoods.

- **Cedar** Sometimes called 'western red cedar', dark red or brown in colour, with a very pleasant fragrance. It is naturally rot resistant and needs very little if any protection. It tends to be soft and it is not terribly strong; it can be used for cladding, especially for timber 'shingles' (wooden tiles), and is excellent for timber panelling as it keeps it fragrance for many years. It has a natural insect repelling quality, and is occasionally used to line draws (or the backs of wardrobes) to prevent moth infestation.

- **Larch** A very knotty timber, not easy to plane, of average strength. Used mainly for fencing panels, sometimes for cladding.

Hardwoods.

- **Oak (English)**   Most commonly used hardwood in UK. A very durable timber, naturally long-lasting and available in varying sizes, from a fence post to a large structural floor beam for barn conversions. Good quality Oak is expensive. Always check for bad splitting and rot around knots. Steel reacts with the acids in the timber and dark blue/black staining occurs. When used for joinery, it must be well seasoned (air or kiln dried), it takes 1 year for each 25mm thickness of timber to season when 'air-dried'.

- **Japanese oak**   Used solely for joinery manufacture in the UK, it is very expensive, quality is assured. It has very few knots, very straight grain and is easy to 'work' (plane and machine).

- **Mahogany**   Grows naturally in many tropical countries, Cuba, Africa, Philippines, to name a few. Characteristics vary depending on origin. Cuban and African mahoganies are used for cabinet making, whereas Philippine mahogany is sometimes used in window manufacture. All mahogany is very durable, easy to 'work' and low maintenance.

- **Iroko**   Very hard timber, light brown in colour and very heavy. It is used mainly for door cills. Lasts for many years.

- **Beech, Sycamore and Maple**   All very similar in character, very hard, close-grained timber, ranging from white to pale yellow or golden brown, sometimes the grain appears silvery grey. Used for kitchen work surfaces, kitchen-unit doors, its main application is for wood block and strip flooring.

- **Teak**   This is a very hard, strong and long-lasting timber. Its colour ranges from light brown to rich golden yellow. Very expensive timber used mainly for quality door cills, and joinery. Its durability is due to its natural oil content, which makes it almost waterproof. This timber is very difficult to 'work', blunts tools quickly.

- **Sapele**   Very similar to mahogany in character, reasonably hard, making it ideal for internal joinery. It can have better grain than the cheaper mahoganies and polishes very well. Often used as veneer for flush internal doors.

Common timber house components, and the types of wood used.

Floor joists:
Normally softwood, they have to be stress-graded (tested for strength). Various types of softwood are used, such as Spruce or Douglas fir.

Floor beams:
Large beams are constructed from laminated softwoods; this gives them greater strength. Oak is used for most renovation work; if you live in a listed building, any repairs to existing timbers may have to be undertaken with the same type of timber.

Rafters and trusses:
Normally softwood is used for new properties, the same types as for floor joists. Some older properties have oak beams and 'A' frames or trusses.

Timber framed properties:
Old properties may have timber framework, usually of oak. The frame was erected as a guide to which the sections between the timber were filled-in with stone or bricks and mortar. This type of dwelling is normally very old and probably protected with a listed building status, so when repairs are due the timbers must be replaced 'like for like'.

Some new properties are also constructed using timber frames, these are factory-made buildings that are supplied as modules or sections and erected on site. They are usually made from stress-graded softwood, and are available with softwood timber cladding, or a brick outer skin, which is built after the timber frame, has been assembled. This method of building homes is very quick, and requires fewer trades on site.

Window and door frames:
Normally made using good quality softwood, mahoganies, oak and teak are also used.

External doors:
Most new-build properties have painted or stained softwood doors, properties at the top end of the market may have varnished hardwood doors, and mahogany is commonly used.

Skirting, architrave, door stop:
This is made from good quality softwood, some properties have mahogany 'second fix' timber components, but this is very uncommon, due to the fact that it is far more expensive than softwood.

Staircases:
Normally softwood, such as Parana Pine. Larger properties may have oak or mahogany staircases, custom made for the property.

Manmade sheet materials.
These are widely used in construction. Various types are used and are available in sheet sizes of 1220 x 2440mm in thicknesses of between 4 and 50mm. Any sheet materials should be stored flat and dry on stable supports off the floor. Most commonly used types of board are:

- **Plywood**   This is manufactured by laminating thin layers of wood together until the desired thickness of board is achieved. Each layer is laid in an opposite direction, to create strength and stability within the board. Most plywood is bonded together using waterproof PVA, but some more expensive water-resistant boards are glued together using 'urea formaldehyde' resins. If a sheet of plywood is badly warped or stained it should not be used; it is a sign that the board has suffered, either from poor storage, or water damage. Plywood is available in several veneer finishes, both hard and softwood, with board grades suitable for different purposes. Common plywood types are course pine finish for shuttering, mahogany or birch faced for joinery work. Plywood is manufactured in thicknesses of between 4 and 25mm, boards thicker than 25mm are available to special order.

    Common uses of plywood in domestic building are timber door panels, hoarding, walking boards in loft spaces, built-in furniture and bracing plates on structural timber.

- **Chipboard sometimes called particleboard**   Probably the most commonly used manmade board in construction. Its main use is as a flooring material, usually 19 or 22mm thick. It is available as a water-resistant board for bathroom and kitchen floors; this type of chipboard is normally coloured green. Chipboard is available in thicknesses of 6 to 25mm, thicker boards may be specially ordered.

- **Medium Density Fibreboard, MDF**   This is one of the most versatile of all the manmade boards. It is manufactured from wood pulp bonded together with resin. It has a very smooth finish on both faces and is suitable for machine moulding; it can be planed, sanded and cut to almost any shape. It is ideal for most internal joinery, and is sufficiently strong without the need to use a timber superstructure for products made from it. It is available as a water-resistant board for external use, but is not widely used. It is very easy to paint, varnish or stain and once finished becomes very durable. It is available in board thicknesses of 9, 12, 19 and 25mm, with standard sheet sizes of 1220 x 2440 and 1220 x 600mm.

- **Blockboard**   These boards comprise a centre core of glued softwood strips, which are covered on both sides with quality hard or softwood veneer. This veneer is two or three times as thick as that in plywood. Blockboard is ideal for joinery and the manufacture of internal flush panelled doors. There are three types of blockboard available:

    (i)   Laminboard   has an internal core made from softwood strips no wider than 8mm, this gives a uniform thickness board suitable for quality joinery products.
    (ii)   (Battenboard   the core of this is manufactured using strips with a width in excess of 25mm, this does not have a very uniform thickness and is not recommended for quality joinery. Often used for temporary walls and partitions.
    (iii) Blockboard   the core is made from strips of a maximum width of 25mm. The most widely used blockboard, suitable for all joinery, and most building jobs where the board is not part of the structure.

- **Strawboard, sometimes called 'Stramit'**   This is manufactured by compressing heated straw, sometimes a binding agent is used to strengthen the finished board. It is usually spray finished with a colour and left with the natural course finish of the compressed straw. Normally used as a suspended ceiling in-fill panel or as partitioning in-fill. It has good insulation value and is sometimes used as the decking material for a 'warm' flat roof. Sheets are normally between 40 and 60mm thick, and are available in various standard sheet sizes.

Common faults to watch for with sheet materials.
Sheet materials are normally very reliable and give few problems. Problems are normally caused by human error or through damage while in storage. The common faults are:

- **Plywood has distorted face and/or twists within the sheet**   This is caused by stacking incorrectly or prolonged storage in damp conditions. Plywood with this fault should not be used for joinery or finishing surfaces such as door panels, it will require pressure to straighten it and the laminates could separate if moisture were the cause. Sheet material fixed under tension is likely to be forced away from its anchorage.

- **Chipboard with damaged edges and/or corners**   If the sheet is over the size required and the damage can be cut out this may not be a problem. If, however, the damage is on flooring sheets and the tongue and groove edges are effected, this will effect the reliability of the finished floor (see flooring). If there are any stains or discolouring ask the builder what it is. It may be water damage and the sheet could breakdown, also there could be variation in the sheet thickness because of the moisture absorption. The incorrect sheet material   A   common 'cowboy' fault is the wrong type or thickness of sheet material being used. If you suspect a problem check in the section for the particular building area.

- **The incorrect sheet material** A common 'cowboy' fault is the wrong type or thickness of sheet material being used. If you suspect a problem check in the section for the particular building area.

Ventilation requirements.

What does ventilation have to do with your home?

It may not seem so, but this is probably one of the most important areas to consider when designing or altering a property. Correctly planned ventilation can prevent stale air, mould, damp, insect infestation and more importantly unbudgeted cost to the homeowner. Lack of ventilation is the cause of many building faults including, dry rot, mould, damp walls and rotten timber.

It is possible that work completed on your property cheaply may not have measures built-in to provide for sufficient ventilation. It is also possible that work completed by someone that is not properly trained or experienced will suffer from the same problems. Provision must be made when alterations and home improvements take place.

Inadequate ventilation can cause health problems to occupants.

What methods of ventilation are used?

The building industry adopts two methods of creating ventilation:

(i)   Natural ventilation, such as an air brick or trickle ventilator (small vent fitted to window frames), an opening sash in a window, louvres or a door.

(ii)   Mechanical ventilation, such as a kitchen or bathroom extractor fan.

On new properties or where new building improvements are taking place, both these means of ventilation are covered by regulations, (see later).

What areas of your house should have ventilation provisions?

All dwellings must have natural ventilation to all habitable rooms, where rooms are interconnecting they can share the ventilation (see regulations later), This is normally achieved using opening casements of windows. Rooms such as toilets, bathrooms and kitchens may need additional mechanical ventilation, to cope with the condensation and smells that may be produced.

There are many other areas of domestic dwellings that have to be ventilated to prevent moisture and condensation causing damage. Some older properties may not have provision for ventilation at currently accepted levels, this can be provided for, both simply and inexpensively. It is not compulsory for homeowners to make these provisions; however, it is advisable to do so as a preventative measure against problems created by poor ventilation. Areas that should have provision or where improvements can be made;

- Ventilation of pitched roof voids (lofts).

- Ventilation of flat roof voids (the space between the plasterboard and the outer roof covering).

- Roof areas above bay windows and porches.

- Rooms without windows, such as small toilets, storage cupboards and cellars.

- Hollow ground floors (floors with voids beneath them such as a timber ground floor).

- Utility and wash rooms.

Ventilation is covered by part F of the Building Regulations; this part of the regulations also covers the provisions required for condensation.

It is worth noting that many older, unaltered properties have so many draughts that there has always been adequate ventilation. It is often said that modern materials have restricted ventilation in properties and so caused problems that were previously unknown.

What are the regulations?

The best way to explain ventilation recommendations for a domestic dwelling is to go through an imaginary building room by room, giving the minimum requirements of The Building Regulations section F, approved document F1. This gives the minimum window opening area (sometimes called rapid ventilation) for each room, and the minimum background ventilation (controllable airbrick or trickle ventilator located in a window or doorframe).

- **Lounge, dining room and other main living areas** The opening window area for each of these rooms must be equal to 5% of the total floor area of the room, some of this ventilation must be 1.75m above the floor. If the room is 3metres x 2metres, this gives a total floor area of 6 square metres, 5% of this is 0.3 square metres of opening window(s). This would give a minimum window opening casement of 1000mm x 300mm. These minimum requirements can always be exceeded, providing increased ventilation.

  Each room must have background ventilation from a controllable airbrick or trickle ventilator. Whichever is used it must have a minimum venting area of 4,000 square mm. This is a trickle ventilator of 20mm x 200mm, an airbrick measures 215mm x 65mm, giving approx. 5,000 square mm of ventilation, above the minimum requirement.

- **Bedrooms** Must have a minimum opening window area of 5% of the total floor area, calculated as above. Bedrooms must also have a minimum 4,000 square mm of controllable background ventilation.

- **Bathrooms** Must have a minimum opening window size of 5% of the total floor area, calculated as above. They must also have a minimum 4,000 square mm of controllable background ventilation. If the bathroom is internal, (no windows), it must be ventilated by means of a mechanical extractor. This does not have to run continuously, it can be intermittent, as long as it has a 15-minute over-run. This type of extractor is normally connected to the light pull-cord, so that it has to operate once the light is switched on.

- **Toilets or other sanitary accommodation areas** These rooms should have rapid ventilation by means of opening windows of a minimum size of 5% of the total floor area and also have a minimum 4,000 square mm of controllable background ventilation. If the room is internal, (no windows), it must be ventilated by means of a mechanical extractor. This can be intermittent, as above so that it gives the room three air-changes per hour. This type of extractor is normally connected to the light pull-cord. These extractor fans must have a minimum output of 15 litres/second.

- **Kitchens** These should have a minimum of 5% window ventilation and 4,000 square mm of background ventilation. In addition it is recommended that there be additional rapid ventilation by means of mechanical extractors. This can be achieved by a wall extractor with a minimum output of 60 litres/second, or by a cooker hood extractor with a minimum output of 30 litres/second, both these methods can be intermittent, when cooking takes place or when there is excessive steam.

- **Hallway or landings**   There is no set minimum requirement of ventilation for these areas, but it is a good idea to have the minimum background ventilation by means of a trickle ventilator, if an external wall or window frame is available.

- **Pitched roofs greater than 15 degrees**   This is covered by Approved Document F2 of the Building Regulations and applies to roofs where the insulation is placed directly above the ceiling, this is applicable even if the ceiling is pitched such as a roof that has dormer bedrooms. All pitched roofs must be cross-ventilated, achieved by placing permanent vents in the eaves, either side of the roof.   The area of the vents must be the equivalent of a 10mm wide gap running the total length of each side of the roof. These vents are normally located in the soffit board, and are covered with fly screens to prevent insects and small birds entering the roof void. Occasionally additional airbricks are place in the gable ends of roofs, just above the ceiling level insulation and just down from the ridge, as a means of extra ventilation for a large roof.

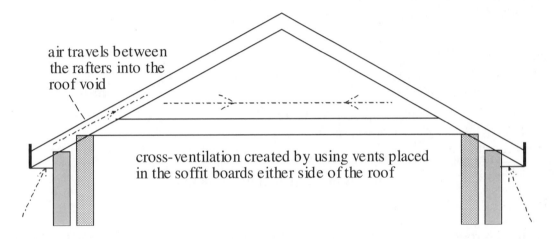

air travels between the rafters into the roof void

cross-ventilation created by using vents placed in the soffit boards either side of the roof

In a mono-pitched (lean-to roof) such as found above a bay window or extension, it is ventilated in the same manner at eaves level. Additional vents must to be introduced to create the cross-ventilation effect. This is achieved by using a vent-tile located at the highest point possible without causing obstruction to flashing.

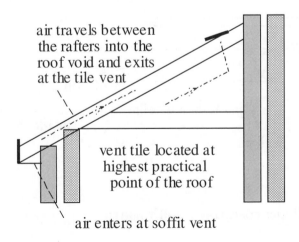

air travels between the rafters into the roof void and exits at the tile vent

vent tile located at highest practical point of the roof

air enters at soffit vent

The vent must have an area equivalent to a 5mm gap running the length of the lean-to roof.

Steeply pitched roofs may be vented by means of a ridge tile ventilator, normally used where living accommodation is located within the pitched area of the roof and the remaining void above the ceiling is small.

- **Flat roofs or those with pitches less than 15 degrees**   This type of roof is notoriously difficult to ventilate adequately. Because of the smaller volume of air contained within the roof void they are also more susceptible to moisture saturation. Cross-ventilation is be created by venting both sides of the roof. Ventilation area in the eaves must be equivalent to a 25mm gap running the full length of each side of the roof to create sufficient cross-flow of air.

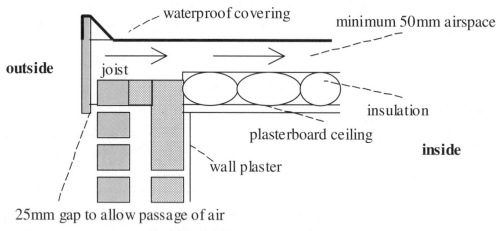

Conventional flat roof eaves detail

If the flat roof is in a location between other buildings and cross-flow cannot be created, a soffit can be incorporated to allow larger vents to be installed (conventional flat roof designs do not use a soffit). Where location is a problem and cross-ventilation cannot be ensured, an alternative design of roof should be considered, while not compulsory, it is strongly advised.

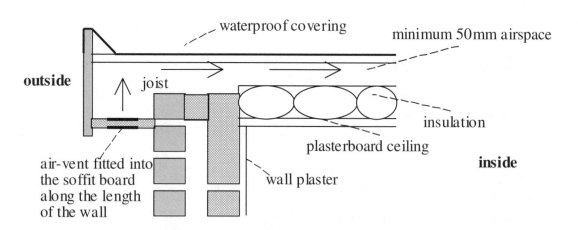

Flat roof eaves detail incorperating a soffit board

If the joists are placed at right angles to the airflow, 50mm battens should be placed across the joists to allow the passage of air. These are fixed securely to the top of the joists to support the decking sheets.

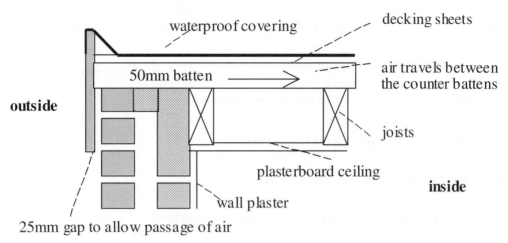

Flat roof eaves detail with joists running at right angles to the air-flow

Common faults and bad practices to watch for.

Poor ventilation is caused when several different building events take place, often through bad training or just lack of care by the company carrying out the work. There are many home improvements, which if carried out without the provision for ventilation, will cause horrendous problems, resulting in very costly repairs to correct the fault and to rectify the damage caused simply by the lack of ventilation.

Installation of replacement uPVC windows.

This is one of the main causes of damage when building alterations take place. In most cases old windows in your property are constructed from metal or timber, they may will not have casement seals and as a result may be draughty and allow heat loss. However, the unwelcome draughts will have helped air to circulate within the property, thereby preventing stale air pockets in the corners of rooms. In addition to this, many properties built prior to 1990 were constructed without background ventilation, and it is the combination of these two factors, which compounds the problem.

When uPVC windows are installed to replace old windows, provision must be made to create sufficient ventilation; this can be achieved by one of two methods:

- By installing air-bricks in the external walls of all occupied rooms, or,

- By installing trickle ventilators in the frames of the new windows.

N.B.: "Cowboy" window manufacturers may not include trickle ventilation in their frames, to keep costs down. This is a false economy and contravenes building regulations. Such windows should not be accepted.

Whichever method is used, it must match or exceed the minimum requirements already discussed. If there is poor background ventilation in your property it is advisable to install trickle ventilators to all window frames. The opening casements of replacement windows must comply with the "5% of room floor area" minimum regulation.

When provision is not made the following signs will soon become apparent:

- Wallpaper peeling away from the wall in corners of the rooms.

- Black mould growing in the bottom corners of rooms.

- Black mould growing on the reveals of windows.

- Stale mouldy odour in rooms when doors are closed for a period.

Flat roof repairs.

This is another instance where if the job is not done properly, it will not last. All work should comply with Building Regulations. Most bitumen felt covered flat roofs break down and leak because the decking boards become moist and sag. Once the deck becomes unstable, joints in the felt force apart, allowing more water in and creating leaks. The initial problem of sagging boards is a result either joists being too far apart, and/or air not being able to circulate within the roof void. Remember, roofing felt is black and absorbs the heat from the sun, which in turn exacerbates the problem; moisture is locked in and when heated spreads by evaporation.

These precautions must be taken out to ensure that new flat roof coverings last for the estimated 25-year lifetime:

- All old felt covering must be removed.

- Any water-damaged decking must be removed and replaced.

- If insulation material within the roof void is damp, it must be removed and replaced.

- If there is not a gap around the perimeter of the fascia board as shown in the earlier diagrams, the fascia board must be removed. The ends of the joists will need to be extended to create a gap allowing air to enter the roof void. The fascia is then re-attached.

- The whole roof should be protected in adverse weather while this repair process takes place.

Important: (see section on roof construction).

Installation of background ventilation wall vents (airbricks).

There is a proven method of installing air-bricks that must be followed, failure to use this method will result in the air-brick or vent not working correctly:

- Most airbricks are the same size as standard bricks, 215mm x 65mm. Installation is a matter of drilling several holes in a brick and carefully removing it. Some air vents are round and special masonry drills are needed to create a neat hole for the vent to fit into. When the air-vent is being installed in a cavity wall the same procedure is repeated to the inner leaf of the wall.

- Before the two faces of the vent are fixed in place either side of the wall, a plastic link sleeve is inserted in the wall. This is to ensure that air passes through the wall without obstruction and, more importantly, in a cavity wall the sleeve prevents moisture in the cavity entering the room.

- Silicone sealant must be placed on the ends of the sleeve prior to the faces being pushed into position.

- Once in position the faces of the airbricks are held in place with mortar externally and bonding plaster internally.

- It is good idea to ensure that the internal air vent has a controllable shutter, so that the flow of air can be controlled.

- Airbricks should never be covered!

Installation of fossil fuel boilers and room heaters:

Very important:
Any room with a fossil fuel boiler or room heater must have adequate ventilation. This allows any noxious fumes to escape and more importantly, the room would be starved of oxygen during combustion, if the room were inadequately ventilated.

The rules that must be adhered to are:

- All rooms that have a boiler or room heater in must be ventilated, even if the boiler is located in a hallway where building regulations do not require a vent normally.

- The vent must be the minimum size of two standard bricks, (215mm wide by 135mm high approximately).

- The inner face of the vent must not be controllable as with normal background ventilation. It must be clear and fully open at all times when the boiler/room heater is operating.

- Boilers or heaters that have balanced flues (horizontal flues through the wall directly behind the place where they are located) do not require vents for the combustion process to take place. For safety reasons it is still advisable to install a single brick sized air-vent as a precautionary measure.

Wallpapering

This is an area of building that has no set way or techniques for application but does have set standards and levels of quality that are reasonable to expect from a builder or painter. Normally wallpapering is carried out by a painter and decorator, and as a rule they do a good job. This book will not explain how to apply wallpaper but will explain what faults to look for, and what might be considered a reasonable standard.

- All walls must be smooth and free of loose material such as flaky paint and old crumbly plaster, prior to application of wallpaper. Failure to ensure this could result in bumps or tears in the paper.

- Any holes should be filled and rubbed down to ensure that the wall surface is even.

- Any uneven or walls with very porous plaster should be painted over with stabilising solution or PVA glue thinned with equal parts water.

- If the walls are old, not of cavity construction and are prone to winter damp, an alternative to wallpaper should be considered. The paper will probably peel off the wall, but more importantly it will prevent the wall from 'breathing' and drying out.

- A new property, with 'wet' plastered walls must not be wallpapered for 6 to 8 months, the moisture within the plaster must be allowed to dry out completely. In winter months if new walls were papered it would probably come off very quickly.

- When thin wallpaper is used, if the walls are not smooth a satisfactory finish may not be possible. To resolve this lining paper is be applied to the wall prior to hanging the finishing paper. Lining paper can also be used prior to applying emulsion finish to walls and plastered ceilings.

- To avoid raised or prominent joints when a wall is going to receive both lining and finishing paper, the lining paper should be hung horizontally. The top paper is then hung vertically to create a cross pattern of the layers.

- Lining paper is normally hung horizontally starting from the skirting board, working up the wall to the ceiling.

- When finishing paper is hung, best results are achieved by working from the main window of a room towards the internal walls. Most professional paper-hangers work from left to right, in other words clockwise around a room, away from the natural light source.

- To ensure that paper is hung level, a line should be drawn on the wall at the starting point. It should be drawn from skirting to ceiling using a spirit level as a guide. The builder or decorator should not assume that the room corners are vertical, as occasionally they are anything but!

- Where the paper meets the skirting, ceiling, window frames, door linings or any other raised surface, the paper should have a straight cut edge against that which it is abutting. The best results are achieved by using a 'Stanley' or art knife, using the corner or edge of the surface as a guide for the knife, to ensure the cut matches the joint between the wall and adjoining surface.

  A blunt edge can be pressed along the edge to be cut; the paper can be drawn away from the wall and scissors used to cut along the mark. This is just as effective as the earlier method but takes longer, and is not favoured by professional paper-hangers. Whichever method has been used the paper should not sit on the abutting surface.

- Where paper is hung around sockets or light switches the electricity should be turned off at the fuse board and the face of the socket or switch should be carefully unscrewed and drawn away from the wall. This is to allow the paper to pass under the face by about 4 to 8mm; this gives a more professional and neater finish to the wallpapering and avoids any unsightly cutting at easy to see points around the wall.

- Wallpaper varies in weight, texture and paper quality, for this reason the manufacturers' instructions should be followed. This is likely to state glue type, soaking time, whether the paper is ready pasted.

- All patterned papers have codes on them; this is to ensure that the colour and patterns match. Wallpapers are manufactured in batches by the factories and each run will probably have a different code. Ensure that all the rolls have the same code, an unscrupulous decorator may buy paper with different codes to save money, but will charge you the full rate!

- While paper is being hung, it is normal for air bubbles to appear under the paper. These should decrease as the paper begins to dry; none should be visible once the paper is completely dry.

- There should be no creases, this is a sign that the paper has been stretched or that one edge is not vertical. A good paper-hanger will overcome this problem by tearing randomly across the fault and smoothing the paper so that it lays flat with no crease. The excess paper of the crease is hidden below the top piece of the tear.

- Joints in wallpaper should not overlap, there is no excuse for this, and is clearly the sign of a 'cowboy'.

- A typical fault is lack of glue to the edges of the paper, there is no excuse for this as it makes the edges vulnerable to being caught and torn.

- When patterned papers are used every effort must be made to match the pattern, some allowance may be made for variation in the pattern but most papers are relatively accurate.

Water

For use with building material.

Any water used for construction must be of drinking water quality. Pond, stream or collected rainwater should never be used for mixing with building materials. There may be impurities in the water that could affect the building materials with which it is to be mixed.

Water in excavations.

This can be a problem in areas where the water table is high. Water will not prevent building work from taking place but precautions must be made to prevent problems. These are the common instances where water on a building project can cause problems:

- A water logged over-site area can create serious problems, e.g. the subsoil to 'puddle'. This means that it becomes unstable and no longer provides a firm base for the hardcore, making compacting of the hardcore difficult. Water should be removed with a pump prior to filling the over-site area with hardcore.

- This problem can also cause difficulties in excavations as well.

- Water in excavations can also wash away the sides of trenches, in an extreme case this could cause the sides of the trenches to collapse, especially in sand or gravel based subsoil.

A waterlogged site.

- A waterlogged site can be very dangerous; every effort must be made to create natural drainage from a site before building work takes place.

- If the site is extremely wet, temporary hardcore paths and vehicle hard-standing areas should be provided, this will save time later when the surrounding land has to be returned to garden.

- Electric cables must be supported away from water and mud, this is advisable even if the supply is 110 voltage (this is the Health and Safety recommended electric supply for building sites).

Windows

The purpose of a window is to provide natural light and a means of ventilation in a dwelling. Both have minimum requirements that are part of standard Building Regulations (see local Authority Building Control department). (See section on ventilation)

Windows must be in keeping with the design of the property and if the windows are part of an extension to a property the new windows should match those on the existing part of the dwelling. Windows must be designed so that they meet with the minimum requirements for safety, security, weather tightness, sound insulation and heat loss as stated in Building Regulations.

Windows are available from builders' merchants in various standard sizes and styles, if non-standard windows are required a local joinery workshop will normally make them to order.

Components of a window.

Most windows have similar components, they may vary in profile but all serve the same purpose. The drawing below identifies the parts of a window.

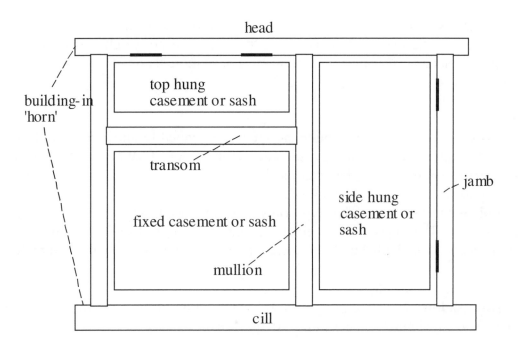

Types of window.

This refers to the way in which the window operates; the most common types are:

Casement windows:

These are windows that have an outer frame with a rebate that houses the inner frame or casement. Normally the opening casements have weather seals to prevent draught and penetration of rain; some have a stepped rebate - known as a storm-proof casement window.

- **Fixed light**   This is a window with no opening parts, if a casement is used to match other windows in the building it will be secured into the frame or the glass will be directly glazed into the frame.

- **Top-hung casement window**   This is a window with the opening section hinged from the top, the casement opens outwards.

- **Side hung casement window**   This is a window with the opening section hinged on the side, the casement opens outwards.

- **Bottom-hung casement window**This is a window with the opening section hinged along its bottom edge, the casement opens inwards.

Sliding windows:

These are used where conventional opening windows may cause problems due to restricted space, they give good controllable ventilation and can be constructed as a high performance window, suitable for exposed areas or flats where the elements may have a greater effect.

- **Vertical-sliding sash or double-hung balanced window**   This is a window that has two casements or sashes that slide vertically within the frame. The sashes are fixed to cords and weights or spring mechanisms; the purpose of these is to hold the sash in the desired position.

- **Horizontal sliding sash**   This type of window is designed on the same principle as the vertical sliding sash, the main difference being that there are no weights or springs, just low friction guides or runners. This type of window may have more than two sliding sashes.

Pivot windows:

These are used where space is at a premium, and are often pivoted to allow cleaning from inside. They can be manufactured to give high performance weather specification, however this type of window is more expensive than a standard casement.

- **Horizontal pivot window**   This type of window pivots from the centre of its vertical uprights or jambs. They may have internal locking 'restrictors' to allow ventilation but not unauthorised access. In high buildings these 'restrictors' are a standard feature for safety reasons.

- **Vertical pivot window**   These pivot from the centre point of the window frame's head and cill, the specification will match that of the horizontal pivot window.

Ventilation or louvre windows

This type of window is seldom used in domestic properties, they do give good ventilation and security, but have very poor insulation qualities. If used they normally consist if an outer frame to which the louvre mechanism is fitted, this is then fitted with glass blades or paddles that can be opened or closed using one lever. When closed the paddles or blades overlap one another to provide a weather-tight barrier.

The different materials that windows are made from.

Timber is the main material used to manufacture windows, most are made from softwood, but increasingly hardwoods are being used for greater durability. Some new properties are fitted with plastic or uPVC windows, normally at the expensive end of the market. However most uPVC windows are fitted as replacements windows, to existing properties.

Metal windows:

Metal windows are occasionally used for domestic building; they are made from steel BS6510 or more commonly aluminium BS4873. Metal windows are prone to condensation because of the 'coldness' of the metal surfaces; this has been overcome on aluminium windows by incorporating a thermal break or barrier in the components of the window.

The thermal break consists of insulating material that prevents condensation. 'Thermally broken' aluminium windows are very expensive compared with timber, they are very strong and can be finished in almost any colour using 'powder' or 'stove-enamel' coatings. This finish should last the life of the window, making them a good choice for flats where maintenance can be costly for wooden windows.

Plastic windows:

Plastic or uPVC windows are normally good value for money. They can be made to almost any size, or style and take varying thicknesses of sealed glazing units. When fitted to new properties, they are not built-in as the brickwork progresses. Simple timber 'buck' or 'profile' frames are used to lay the bricks to, once the brickwork is complete the temporary profiles are removed and the uPVC windows are fitted in place.

Timber windows:

Most houses have timber windows fitted when new; some replacement windows are timber as well. Timber is very flexible and all of the different types of window are available in timber. Softwood is the main timber used for window manufacture, it is inexpensive, strong, and if treated with preservative and decorated regularly, long lasting. There are some houses with softwood windows that are over a hundred years old, and because of regular maintenance are probably quite capable of lasting for several more decades.

Very often timber windows are not painted or stained properly, or are painted in wet or cold conditions. This shortens their life dramatically. Most 'high performance' timber windows are manufactured from hardwood, generally Mahogany, which is very stable and reasonably inexpensive. When finished with stain these tend to require less maintenance than softwood. (See section on timber).

Common faults with windows and their installation.

On new property, the building control process should pick-up on faults, however sometimes problems can be overlooked. This is not the case with alterations or extensions, where 'building control' may not be involved, so you will have to ensure that either the builder or you adopts a quality procedure to ensure that problems do not arise.

• All timber windows must be primed prior to fitting, with either base coat paint or stain.

• All joints, where different parts of the window intersect, must have no gaps. This applies to windows whatever they are made from.

• All timber windows should have a well-sanded smooth finish, with no sharp edges, splits or knots that have fallen out.

• If glazing beads are used, the corner joints should be tight and without gaps. Shaped or moulded beads are mitred; square beads may be butt-jointed.

- Most windows are not fitted by using the horns as shown at the beginning of this section, this was the traditional method, and is now superseded by modern techniques. Most windows installed as the brickwork progresses are now secured to masonry using frame ties, sometimes called 'owlets'. There should be one of these fixed to the frame jambs top and bottom and every 5/6 course of bricks.

- The distance from the face of the brick and the face of the window frame must be equal all around. (see drawing below)

Inside

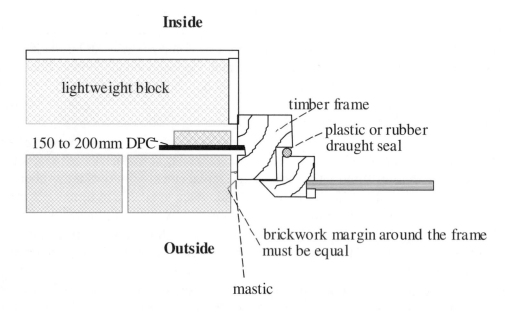

lightweight block

150 to 200mm DPC

timber frame

plastic or rubber
draught seal

brickwork margin around the frame
must be equal

Outside

mastic

- A neat mastic seal should be applied all around the frame.

- Any mortar spillage should be removed as they occur, failure to do this could result in stain marks on unpainted windows. This rule must be applied to plastic or 'stove-enamelled' windows, because when the mortar dries it may damage the surface when it is eventually removed.

- Storm-proof or 'high-performance' windows must comply with British Standard requirements, this will be labelled on the window or in the builder's specification, ask to see it, or ask for reassurance that the window complies with the minimum standards.

Window replacement.
This is probably the main area of building that causes problems for homeowners; it is a very big area of the construction industry, which is very lucrative for window replacement companies. This area of construction also has the largest number of complaints, some of which are never resolved, definitely 'cowboy' territory!

Because of the vast profits to be made from window replacement, especially uPVC windows, unscrupulous people are attracted to form companies offering window replacement. Always check the background and trading history of the company. Reliable companies are around for a long time and rely on good 'word of mouth' recommendation.

Once the initial sales 'nightmare' is over and you have contracted to buy a company's windows, they will send a surveyor to your home to measure accurately the window openings or external reveals. (Always remember if you agree to buy windows from a salesperson in your own home, there is an automatic 'cooling off' period of seven days, in which, if you want to, you can cancel the order).

The surveyor's job is to ensure that, when made, the windows fit the openings snugly, with a 6 to 10mm tolerance all around, which is sealed with low modulus silicone. Poorly fitting windows, that are out of level, or have large mastic seals to get over bad surveying, should not be accepted, Complain! The surveyor's most important role is to look for faulty brickwork, existing structural windows (see bay windows) and other areas that could present difficulties to the fitters. They should put this on a written report, and if there are problems, the window company should notify you in writing in advance. Any problems like this are not normally covered in the cost of the windows, so make sure that any quotes to rectify these problems are confirmed in writing before window fitting commences. If your property has bay windows extending to all floors, seek advice from a structural engineer, these are normally structural windows and replacements must be constructed accordingly.

Some window companies employ poorly trained fitters, some even have little or no basic construction training, and this is where the real problems arise. Good window replacement companies employ bricklayers and carpenters, both normally have the experience and skill to fit windows properly. Another problem with the replacement window industry is that the people at the various stages of the contract are paid on a commission or percentage basis. Most sales people are paid on commission, surveyors usually get paid a percentage of the total price, as do the fitters, it is this that generally causes the problems. Because window fitters usually receive a fixed price for the job, it is in their interest to finish the job as quickly as possible and to move on to the next job. The risk is that the job is hurried, and shortcuts are made.

Common replacement window faults.

- Most faults or damage occur to a property when the existing windows are removed. There is a tried and tested method for removing existing window frames, so that no damage occurs to the surrounding structure. When the existing frames are timber, removal should be reasonably straight forward;

    (i)   Where there are casements, they should be opened and a saw cut made right the way through the frame, this should be repeated further along the frame so that a section can be removed. If there are no opening casements the pane of glass should be removed and the same procedure applied.

    (ii)   A nail bar or suitable lever should be inserted between the window jamb and wall, carefully prising the timber section away. As soon as it has moved enough for a hand to get under the frame the nail bar should be removed, the timber sections should be firmly pulled towards the middle until they come loose. The frame should not be forced outwards or inwards as this will increase the risk of forcing bricks loose or cracking plaster.

    (iii)   Further saw cuts may be required to enable complete removal of the window frame, the more cuts that are made, the easier removal of the frame will be.

- Any repairs to brickwork should be done before the replacement window is installed; this allows complete access to the reveal and lessens the risk of damage to the new window.

- Modern window profiles are much smaller than those on older timber windows; this creates the problem of paint lines on brickwork or internal gaps in the plastered reveals. The best solution in this instance is to place the outer face of the new window over the paint line; this allows the mastic to cover the old paint giving a much neater finish to the job. The gap in the plaster reveal can be re-plastered or if acceptable, plastic cover trims can be fitted to hide the gap, using the trims is the easy option, not favoured by good tradesmen!

- Large window frames will probably have large casements, and if manufactured from plastic, there is a special method of positioning the sealed unit to ensure that the casement remains square and that the weight of the sealed unit does not cause the casement to bind or drop. This is known in the trade as 'toeing and heeling', it means to place packing between the sealed unit and rebate, thereby tightening the casement and allowing it to fit the frame accurately, this procedure 'squares' the casement. If you have a plastic window or door that doesn't close easily, this is probably the reason why.

- Plastic windows have joints that are bonded using heat, these are then finished using one of three methods:

    (i)   A raised nib joint, straight from the jointing machine,
    (ii)   A sanded and polished joint, this gives the impression of no joint,
    (iii)   A grooved joint, a 4 to 6mm shallow groove is machined over the joint as a feature in every corner.

Whichever method is used, the joints must be strong with no visible gap. If the polished method is used, the joints should be seamless and invisible. Grooved joints if made correctly, look attractive, but they should be no deeper than 1mm, as this will weaken the joint.

Conclusion

Builders should not take the blame, and neither should they be expected to, for cheapskate homeowners. There is an old saying that tell us that 'the consumer is always right'. Where a builder has been asked to do work by the homeowner which does not conform to standard building practices, the builder should not be held responsible for any consequences. Another old saying tells us 'that it is not possible to fashion a silk purse from a sow's ear'. It is unreasonable to expect a high-quality result from poor or cheap construction materials!

Legally and - perhaps more importantly - morally, homeowners can only expect a reasonable quality of work and workmanship from their builder. Anything better than reasonable should be regarded as an unexpected bonus - even rewarded as such!

Genuine, quality 'bona fide' builders have nothing to fear from the contents of this book. It has been written as a guide to and endorsement of quality work and workmanship, and as a guide to identifying faulty work and workmanship.

Much has been said in the media about the 'cowboy builder' in recent months, and rightly so. There are many issues, not least safety, which if ignored of overlooked may result in a sub-standard product and disappointment. However, it should be noted that there are many awkward or difficult customers - homeowners - whose expectations are unrealistic, whose whims change almost with the weather and whose demands are impossible to satisfy.

Special attention should be given to the contract found at the back of the book. This simple document provides the means of formalising the expectations of both parties. It sets out clearly the important points and gives both the builder and the homeowner a simple, easy to follow procedure that can enable either party to reach satisfaction.

As in any situation, it is poor communication that leads to a breakdown in relationships. It is the responsibility of all parties to ensure that good communication is maintained. More projects and relationships fail through poor communication than from almost any other cause.

As a final comment, I would like to suggest to those who may think that they can use the contract without permission from the publishers, that should they then encounter problems and need to enter into legal proceedings, they may find it more difficult to fight a case on a stolen contract. You have paid for the four copies of the contract as part of this book and you are free to use them to employ the services of builder(s), please remember that one copy each time is for you and one copy for the builder(s).

As a homeowner, I will use this book; as a builder I should have!

Tom MacKeown, Editor.

Glossary of building abbreviations and trade jargon

These are abbreviations and trade jargon that you need to familiarise yourself with, as they are use widely by genuine builders and can help to identify the 'cowboys'. Some are explained in the sections applicable, others will be found in this section.

- **Ballast** term used to describe aggregate, which is to be added to cement to create mortar or concrete.
- **Balustrades** in-fill and supporting components beneath the handrail on a staircase, not the newel posts.
- **Baluster** individual upright components beneath a staircase handrail.
- **Benching** term used to describe the shaping of mortar or concrete in a manhole, around posts, around kerbs and path edgings. It is normally a sloped face.
- **'Bulk-out'** a term used to describe the process of increasing the volume of a mix of concrete, plaster or other mixed building material.
- **'Cans'** this describes the plastic or steel boxes that sit in walls behind electrical sockets and switches, their role is to house the wiring behind the socket and to hold the face of the socket or switch by means of screws.
- **Circuit breaker** electrical device that in the event of a fault cuts the electrical supply in fractions of a second.
- **Conduit** plastic or steel covers used to protect electric cables.
- **Commission or commissioned** term used to describe the testing of an appliance, i.e. gas boiler, prior to the handing over to the homeowner.
- **Earth bonding** for safety reasons, the earth bonding of metal sinks and taps to prevent electric shock, denoted by yellow and green wiring and labelling.
- **Earth pole or stake** metal pole driven into the ground outside a property to earth the electrical supply, identified by yellow and green wire attached to it that passes from the pole into the property.
- **Fascia board** board fixed vertically to the bottom edge of rafters. Its purpose is to close the roof space to the elements and to give a fixing point to guttering; it also holds the front edge of the soffit board.
- **First fix** term used to describe the carpentry, electrical and plumbing work that is done in the first stages of constructing a house, if you like, the 'skeleton of the house'. Items that fall into this category are; roof, internal door linings, floor joists, stud-work walls, window and door profiles, plasterboard ceilings and walls, wiring, socket and switch 'cans', water and heating pipes, service installations and support work in roof spaces.
- **Going** describes the rise and distance travelled by a staircase.
- **Ground level** used to describe the natural level of the topsoil around a property, or the manmade level of the ground, suiting building that has been placed on the site.
- **Hang and hanging** used to describe the action of fitting a door, to hang a door, the door is hanging on the left-hand side of the frame.
- **High modulus** Term used to describe the setting property of mastic and silicone sealants. High modulus sealants dry to give a seal that has an even consistency. Usually for areas where a reliable waterproof seal is required, i.e. around a bath or sink.
- **'Muck'** bricklayers jargon for mortar.
- **Leading edge** term used to describe the edge of a door to which the handle, lock or latch is fixed, the opposite edge to the hinges.
- **Low modulus** Term used to describe the setting property of mastic and silicone sealants. Low modulus sealants dry to give a seal that has a firm outer skin with a soft centre, these types

of mastics are more flexible for areas where movement is great. Usually around a window frame or in an expansion joint in a wall.

- **Plasticizer** powder or liquid added to mortar making it more workable for pointing and shaping, usually when a roof is being pointed between the tiles and brickwork on the gable end of a roof or if decorative pointing of a wall is taking place.
- **Plumb**   to describe something as upright , checked for level, applies to all 'uprighting', i.e. door frames, windows, walls, etc.
- **Pointing**   describes the trowel action applied to the joints in brickwork.
- **Pointing iron**   specially shaped steel tool used by a brick layer to shape the joints in brickwork, some brick layers use a shaped piece of 15mm copper plumbing pipe.
- **Screed**   name used to describe the 50mm layer of fine aggregate concrete applied to dense concrete floor slabs. Sharp sand (aggregate) is used with the cement to give a smooth finish to the floor, not obtainable using concrete made with 20mm pre-mix aggregate.
- **Sealed-unit double-glazing**   two pieces of glass separated around the edge by an aluminium spacer bar. The airspace between the two pieces of glass can be filled with an inert gas to improve its thermal value. These are fitted to window frames with special deep rebates.
- **Secondary double-glazing**   Glazing fixed within a frame separate from the main window frame, fitted internally to retain heat and to improve sound insulation.
- **Second fix** term used to describe the carpentry, electrical and plumbing work done in the second stages of constructing a house, i.e.; after the wet trades like plastering and 'artexing' have been completed. A sample of the items that fall into this category are the skirting board, architrave's, internal doors, fitted kitchen, electrical socket faces, fuse boards, heating radiators, water tanks etc.
- **'Sets'**   Another name used to describe brick or concrete 'pavers', used on paths and driveways. (e.g.: Square sets)
- **Soffit board**   board that is fixed at right angles or horizontally to the bottom edge of the fascia board, generally made from man-made board such as 'master board' or plywood. It is identified by its grey cement coloured appearance if it is a cement-based product.
- **Stop cock (tap)**   Tap for turning the mains water supply on and off, there is one inside a property usually under the kitchen sink and the local water supplying company will install one outside the property, if the property is recently built
- **Speculative building**   term used to describe new building development, the properties are offered on the open market to the general public.
- **Timber stud(s)**   describes the timber component parts of a studwork partition wall, the skeleton of the wall.
- **Trunking** trade jargon for the ducting or covers used for surface mounted electric's and telecommunication cables.
- **Valuations**   term used to describe the calculation of work completed or materials on site. When a project is to run for a period of more than two weeks it is normal for the builder to be able to take interim payments calculated on this basis.
- **Wet trades**   used to describe the trade persons who use wet materials to do their job, trades like bricklayer, plasterer, 'artexer', floor layer etc.

Glossary of Legal terms

These are legal terms that you need to familiarise yourself with as they are used widely when discussing English law and when construction written contracts are made. Some are explained in the sections applicable, others will be found in this section.

- **'Agent'** person who has been appointed by another (the Principal) to act on their behalf, usually to negotiate a contract between the principal and a third party. Provided that the agent discloses they are acting for a principal they are usually not liable personally for any results of the contract or to benefit from it.
- **Bona fide** in good faith
- **Caveat emptor** (Latin: let the buyer beware), means a purchaser cannot claim their purchases are defective unless he protected himself by obtaining express guarantees from the vendor. This common law maxim has now been modified by the Sale of Goods Act 1979(see section on contracts)
- **Condition** principal term of a contract, a term that goes to the roots of a contract, the sum and substance of the contract. Breach of a condition constitutes essential breach of the contract, which in turn allows the injured party to treat the contract as discharged.
- **Consideration** an act, promise, payment of money or services or provision of goods in exchange. There must be consideration by both parties to a contract, payment for work done or service given in exchange for goods are some of the examples. Put simply 'this for that'.
- **Damages** sum of money awarded by a court as compensation for breach of contract, awarded as a lump sum for any losses incurred by the injured party. The award will aim to put the party in the state they were in before the breach occurred. They are not supposed to profit from the award.
- **Disposition** transfer of property by some act by its owner, e.g. by sale, gift, will or exchange.
- **Ex parte** on the application of one party, no notice given to the other party(s).
- **Express term** provision in a contract, agreed to by the parties in words, written or spoken. It may be a condition or a warranty of the contract.
- **Injured party** in a contractual sense the party to a contract who has lost out as a result of the breach or non-performance of a contract.
- **Implied term** provision in a contract not agreed to by the parties in words but regarded by the courts as a necessary element of the contract to make the contract work. It could be that it is a statutory requirement, as in the sale of Goods Act, see 'caveat emptor' (see above).
- **JCT contract** normal commercial standard form of contract. Stands for Joint Contracts Tribunal.
- **Locus standi** (Latin - a place to stand), the right to bring an action or challenge a decision of a court.
- **Performance** to carry out the obligations given to the parties of a contract, complete performance by both parties will discharge the contract completely. The obligations means work done by one party, payment by the other party. Performance by one party discharges them alone.
- **Prima facie** at first view, taking into account known facts at that time.
- **Principal** person who the 'agent' acts for when contracts are made, the builder being the agent and the site manager being the principal.
- **Privity** relationship that exists between people as a result of their taking part in a transaction or agreement.

- **Privity of contract** relationship that exists between the parties to a contract, only parties to a contract can sue or be sued, it is not possible to confer rights under the contract to another person as this would create (jus quaesitum tertio--right acquired for a third party) English law does not recognise such a right.
- **Quantum meruit** entitled to be paid a reasonable sum for the work done, as much as the builder deserves.
- **Rescind** to revoke or cancel a contract.
- **Rescission** setting aside of a voidable contract, therefore treating it as though it never existed.
- **Representee** someone who receives or believes an untrue fact or information as part of a contract
- **Representor** someone who makes an untrue fact or gives information that is not correct as part of a contract.
- **Undue influence** influence that prevents someone from exercising an independent decision with regard to an agreement.
- **Tort** wrongful act or omission for which damages can be obtained in a civil court by the person wronged, mainly for personal injury and damage to property caused by negligence.
- **Ultra vires** (Latin: beyond the powers) describes an act by a public authority, company or other body that goes beyond the limits of the powers conferred on it.
- **Vicarious liability** liability imposed on one person for tort(s) committed by another, usually employer is responsible for tort(s) committed by employee. This can also apply to independent contractors and agents. A person made vicariously liable is not personally at fault , the act must have happened during normal duties of the employee for the employer to be held liable.
- **Void** to have no legal effect
- **Void contract** contract that has no legal effect from the moment it is made, an example might be where a mistake has been made or the contract is in some way illegal.
- **Voidable** capable of being set aside.
- **Voidable contract** contract which, when made, may have been valid, but is now liable to be thereafter set aside, may have been caused by mistake or undue influence
- **Warranty** term or promise in a contract, breach of which will entitle the injured party to damages, but not to treat the contract as discharged.

Linear measurement	Alternate metric	Imperial equivalent
1 millimetre		= 0.039 inch
1 centimetre	= 10mm	= 0.394 inch
1 decimetre	= 10cm	= 3.94 inches
1 metre	= 10dm	= 1.094 yards
1 decametre	= 10metres	= 10.94 yards
1 hectometre	= 100 metres	= 109.4 yards
1 kilometre	= 1000 metres	= 0.6214 mile

Square measurement		Imperial equivalent
1 square centimetre		= 0.155 sq. inch
1 square metre		= 1.196 sq. yards
1 are	= 100 sq. metres	= 119.6 sq.yards
1 hectare	= 100 ares	= 2.471 acres
1 square kilometre		= 0.386 sq. mile

Cubic measurement		Imperial equivalent
1 cubic centimetre		= 0.061 cu. inch
1 cubic metre		= 1.308 cu. yards

Weight		Imperial equivalent
1 kilogram	= 1000g	= 2.205 pounds
1 tonne (metric ton)	= 1000kg	= 0.984 (long) ton

Index

Aggregate	1
types of aggregate	2
Appearance	3
key things to watch for	4
Architect	5
Bay window	6
Bill of quantity	8
Blocks and block work	9
Bricks and brickwork	12
bonding	14
bad practices	13
Bricklayer	15
Building contract	17
elements of a contract	17
capacity to make a contract	18
terms of a contract	19
privity of a contract	20
mistake	20
exclusion clauses	21
remedies	22
applicable legislation	23
conclusion	25
standard contract	26
Building regulations	28
who controls them	29
Cavity walls	30
faults	31
Carpentry	33
standards	33
Carpenter	36
Ceiling textures	37
Cement	38
different types	38
storage	38

Ceramic tiling	39
trade skills	39
Chimneys and flues	41
rules	41
chimney pot details	43
metal flues	44
maintenance	44
flue liners	44
Concrete	45
mixtures	45
faults	46
pre-mixed	47
Coving	48
Curtain battens	49
Damp-proof course	50
purpose	51
other uses	51
failure	53
types of material	53
Damp-proof membrane	54
Doors	56
external	56
internal	58
sizes	58
Door linings	59
fixing	60
Door frames	62
Door sizes	58
Drains and drainage	64
storm-water	64
soakaway	65
foul water	67
inspection chambers	69
manholes	70
Dry lining	72
problems	73

Electrical installations 75
looking for faults 75
circuit rating 77
cable sizes 77
supply 78

Floors and floor finishes 79
materials 79
floor structures 80
timber joists 80
dense concrete slab 80
suspended concrete slab 81
pre-cast 82
faults 82
ceramic tiles 87

Foundations 88
strip 88
ground movement 89
trees 89
step 91
trench-fill 92
raft 93
piled foundation 94

Gable 96

Gas supply 97

Glass and glazing 99
glass types 99
glass measurement 100
glazing compounds 100

Guttering 102

Hard-core or hoggin 104
types 104
faults 105

Heating boiler maintenance 106

Insulation 107
water system 108
walls 108
floors 108
roof 109
faults 109
improvements 110
draught-proofing 111
thermal bridging 112

Ironmongery 114
different type 115

Joinery 117
faults 118

Kitchens 120
installation 120
faults 121

Lead and zinc flashing 125
faults 126

Masonry 127
bad practices 128
correcting faults 128
identifying faults 129

Mastic and silicone sealant 130
different types 130
faults 132

Nails 133
types of nail and use 133
nail length 135
identifying faults 135

Openings in walls 139
beams and lintels 139
requirement 140
openings in existing walls 140
problems 141

Painting 143
types 143
application rules 144
preparation 145
different surfaces 146
common faults 146
life expectancy 147

Partition walls 149
roll of internal walls 149
types of partition wall 150
identifying wall type 150
insulation 150
advantages/disadvantages of
each system 151
faults 152
pre-formed walling systems 154

Plans and drawings   157
rules   157

Plasterboard   158
types   158
faults   159

Plastering and rendering   160
types of plaster   161
preparation   161
sequence   162
faults   163

Plumbing and plumbing systems   165
fresh water supply   165
cold water systems   166
hot water systems   167
water supply rules   170
pipe-work materials   171
pipe-work problems   171
pipe sizes   172
pipe-work joints   173
common faults   174
central heating   175
central heating faults   177
sanitary fittings and waste
water   180
waste water rules   183

Quality and service   184

Quantity surveyor   185

Roofs   186
role of   186
components   187
pitched roof rules   188
roof trusses   190
repairs   191
loft conversion   192
pitched roof faults   193
roof coverings   194
flat roofs   204

Safety   212
site secerity   213
hoarding rules   214

Scaffolding   215
types   215
platforms   217
rules   219

Soil testing   220

Stairs   222
components   222
regulations   223
installation   225
floor joists   225
landings   226
other types   227
spiral   228
steel string   229
concrete   231
faults   232

Storage of materials   234
why   234
key areas   234
timber store   235

Telecommunications   237
rules   237
underground cables   238
installation guide   239

Timber   240
softwood   240
hardwood   241
types of timber used   241
manmade sheet materials   242

Ventilation   245
methods used   245
where must ventilation be   245
regulations   246
flat roof   248
plastic window problems   249
flat roof repairs   250
boiler ventilation   251

Wallpapering   252

Water   254
building use   254

Window   255
components   255
types   255
materials   256
replacement faults   259

Conclusion   261

Contracts for Homeowners and Private Occupiers.
(For building works, repairs and maintenance only)

This building contract is between ……………………………………………..…...(Home owner)
and ………………………………………………………….(Builder)
……………………………………………….(Builder's Address)
……………………………………………………………………………
……………………………………………………………………………

The address where the building work is to take place is:

………………………………………….(Home owner's address)
……………………………………………………………………………
……………………………………………………………………………
……………………………………………………………………………

The contract is for ……………………………………………………………....
……………………………………………………………………………………
……………………………………………………………………………………………
…………………………………………………………………….(nature of the work)

All plans, specifications, variations must be attached to this document, and will comply with all current planning and building regulations

The agreed sum for the completed work is……………………………………………….

The contract is to commence on………………………………………………………..

The contract will be completed by………………………………………………………..
Unless a further date is agreed to in writing by the parties

Payment will be made to the builder within 14 days of the completion of the contract. If the contract is to run for more than 28 days then there will be weekly payments made to the builder from the commencement of the contract, on a valuation of work completed basis, paid a week in arrears

Any changes to the specification must be made in writing with a minimum of seven working days notice.

If the builder/home owner is going to incur delays then they will give the homeowner/builder a minimum of seven working days notice.

The homeowner may retain 10% of the total contract value for up to 28 days after completion and this will be paid when both parties have inspected the work and satisfactory completion has been agreed.

Builder……………………………………………….   (Signature)   as per terms over the page

Homeowner………………………………………….   (Signature)   as per terms over the page

This contract was agreed and signed on this……………………………………………….(date)

Terms and conditions of the contract

(1) The homeowner will provide any 'mains' services required enabling the builder to carry out the work. If unusual requirements are needed the builder will give reasonable written notice.

(2) The homeowner will, where practical, make sure that there are no obstructions that will prevent the work from taking place, such as a blocked access or internal furniture and fittings.

(3) The builder will be fully responsible for all the work undertaken by himself, his operatives and any other sub-contractors that he appoints. If sub-contractors are to be used the builder must notify the homeowner of this intention in writing. (minimum of 7 days notice)

(4) It is the builder's responsibility to ensure that they comply with the minimum insurance requirements to undertake building works for a homeowner. This is to include cover to provide for injury to a third party, or their property in the form of public liability insurance. Proof of this insurance must be shown at the time the contract is agreed.

(5) The builder will be responsible for all aspects of Health and Safety for the duration of the contract in accordance with the current regulations laid down by the Health and Safety Executive.

(6) Payment details are as agreed to on the front page of the contract, unless another agreement is made at the time of contracting.

(7) All waste that is the result of the building work is the responsibility of the builder, they are responsible for its safe disposal and for cleaning the site area when the building work is complete.

(8) When the building work commences the builder must give a guarantee to complete the work to a satisfactory standard, or to a standard a reasonable person would expect. Any faults or bad workmanship will be the responsibility of the builder and they will be responsible for any costs incurred by this bad workmanship for a period of two years, to commence once the work is completed.

(9) The contract can be terminated in writing by the home owner if;

    (i)   The work is not being completed with reasonable care, skill or if the work is not being completed in the time scale agreed to; or

    (ii)   There is failure to follow the homeowner's written instructions within a reasonable time (reasonable can be determined by the agreed duration of the initial contract).

(10) The contract can be terminated in writing by the builder if;

    (i)   They are delayed from completing the said works by the home owner without reasonable cause; or

    (ii)   The homeowner does not make the payments to the builder as agreed this includes any stage payment agreements as specified on page one of this contract.

(11) In the event of sections 9 or 10 taking place the home owner must pay for work completed and materials purchased for the work, up to the time of the termination, this will be calculated on a 'quantum meruit' basis.

(12) If, when the work is completed, there is disagreement as to whether the work is completed to a satisfactory standard, a 'third' party, qualified to inspect the work should be called in to adjudicate the decision (adjudicator must be acceptable to both party's). The cost of the inspection should be taken out of the retention payment, and when a decision has be made, if it is decided the work is of a satisfactory standard the cost of the inspection should be paid for by the home owner. If it is found that the work is sub-standard the builder should correct it, or in the event that they will not do the work the retention should be used to pay another builder to complete the work. Should any funds be left after the faults have been corrected they must be paid to the original builder.

Contracts for Homeowners and Private Occupiers.
(For building works, repairs and maintenance only)

This building contract is between ……………………………………………...(Home owner)
and ……………………………………………………(Builder)
…………………………………………….(Builder's Address)
………………………………………………………………………
………………………………………………………………………

The address where the building work is to take place is:

…………………………………………..(Home owner's address)
………………………………………………………………………
………………………………………………………………………
………………………………………………………………………

The contract is for …………………………………………………………...
………………………………………………………………………………………
………………………………………………………………………………………………
……………………………………………………………….(nature of the work)
All plans, specifications, variations must be attached to this document, and will comply with all current planning and building regulations

The agreed sum for the completed work is…………………………………………………

The contract is to commence on…………………………………………………………..

The contract will be completed by……………………………………………………..
Unless a further date is agreed to in writing by the parties

Payment will be made to the builder within 14 days of the completion of the contract. If the contract is to run for more than 28 days then there will be weekly payments made to the builder from the commencement of the contract, on a valuation of work completed basis, paid a week in arrears

Any changes to the specification must be made in writing with a minimum of seven working days notice.

If the builder/home owner is going to incur delays then they will give the homeowner/builder a minimum of seven working days notice.

The homeowner may retain 10% of the total contract value for up to 28 days after completion and this will be paid when both parties have inspected the work and satisfactory completion has been agreed.

Builder……………………………………..………… (Signature) as per terms over the page

Homeowner……………………………………… (Signature) as per terms over the page

This contract was agreed and signed on this……………………………………………(date)

Terms and conditions of the contract

(1) The homeowner will provide any 'mains' services required enabling the builder to carry out the work. If unusual requirements are needed the builder will give reasonable written notice.

(2) The homeowner will, where practical, make sure that there are no obstructions that will prevent the work from taking place, such as a blocked access or internal furniture and fittings.

(3) The builder will be fully responsible for all the work undertaken by himself, his operatives and any other sub-contractors that he appoints. If sub-contractors are to be used the builder must notify the homeowner of this intention in writing. (minimum of 7 days notice)

(4) It is the builder's responsibility to ensure that they comply with the minimum insurance requirements to undertake building works for a homeowner. This is to include cover to provide for injury to a third party, or their property in the form of public liability insurance. Proof of this insurance must be shown at the time the contract is agreed.

(5) The builder will be responsible for all aspects of Health and Safety for the duration of the contract in accordance with the current regulations laid down by the Health and Safety Executive.

(6) Payment details are as agreed to on the front page of the contract, unless another agreement is made at the time of contracting.

(7) All waste that is the result of the building work is the responsibility of the builder, they are responsible for its safe disposal and for cleaning the site area when the building work is complete.

(8) When the building work commences the builder must give a guarantee to complete the work to a satisfactory standard, or to a standard a reasonable person would expect. Any faults or bad workmanship will be the responsibility of the builder and they will be responsible for any costs incurred by this bad workmanship for a period of two years, to commence once the work is completed.

(9) The contract can be terminated in writing by the home owner if;

    (i)   The work is not being completed with reasonable care, skill or if the work is not being completed in the time scale agreed to; or

    (ii)   There is failure to follow the homeowner's written instructions within a reasonable time (reasonable can be determined by the agreed duration of the initial contract).

(10) The contract can be terminated in writing by the builder if;

    (i)   They are delayed from completing the said works by the home owner without reasonable cause; or

    (ii)   The homeowner does not make the payments to the builder as agreed this includes any stage payment agreements as specified on page one of this contract.

(11) In the event of sections 9 or 10 taking place the home owner must pay for work completed and materials purchased for the work, up to the time of the termination, this will be calculated on a 'quantum meruit' basis.

(12) If, when the work is completed, there is disagreement as to whether the work is completed to a satisfactory standard, a 'third' party, qualified to inspect the work should be called in to adjudicate the decision (adjudicator must be acceptable to both party's). The cost of the inspection should be taken out of the retention payment, and when a decision has be made, if it is decided the work is of a satisfactory standard the cost of the inspection should be paid for by the home owner. If it is found that the work is sub-standard the builder should correct it, or in the event that they will not do the work the retention should be used to pay another builder to complete the work. Should any funds be left after the faults have been corrected they must be paid to the original builder.

©Lastresortpublishing.com

Contracts for Homeowners and Private Occupiers.
(For building works, repairs and maintenance only)

This building contract is between …………………………………………………...(Home owner)
and   …………………………………………………(Builder)
                                      ……………………………………………….(Builder's Address)
                                      ……………………………………………………………………
                                      ……………………………………………………………………

The address where the building work is to take place is:

                                      …………………………………………….(Home owner's address)
                                      ……………………………………………………………………
                                      ……………………………………………………………………
                                      ……………………………………………………………………

The contract is for   …………………………………………………………………....
………
………………………………………………………………...…………………………………………
……………………………………………………………………………………….(nature of the work)
All plans, specifications, variations must be attached to this document, and will comply with all current planning and building regulations

The agreed sum for the completed work is…………………………………………………………

The contract is to commence on………………………………………………………………………..

The contract will be completed by……………………………………………………………………..
Unless a further date is agreed to in writing by the parties

Payment will be made to the builder within 14 days of the completion of the contract. If the contract is to run for more than 28 days then there will be weekly payments made to the builder from the commencement of the contract, on a valuation of work completed basis, paid a week in arrears

Any changes to the specification must be made in writing with a minimum of seven working days notice.

If the builder/home owner is going to incur delays then they will give the homeowner/builder a minimum of seven working days notice.

The homeowner may retain 10% of the total contract value for up to 28 days after completion and this will be paid when both parties have inspected the work and satisfactory completion has been agreed.

Builder……………………………………..…………   (Signature)   as per terms over the page

Homeowner……………………………………………   (Signature)   as per terms over the page

This contract was agreed and signed on this………………………………………………………(date)

Terms and conditions of the contract

(1) The homeowner will provide any 'mains' services required enabling the builder to carry out the work. If unusual requirements are needed the builder will give reasonable written notice.

(2) The homeowner will, where practical, make sure that there are no obstructions that will prevent the work from taking place, such as a blocked access or internal furniture and fittings.

(3) The builder will be fully responsible for all the work undertaken by himself, his operatives and any other sub-contractors that he appoints. If sub-contractors are to be used the builder must notify the homeowner of this intention in writing. (minimum of 7 days notice)

(4) It is the builder's responsibility to ensure that they comply with the minimum insurance requirements to undertake building works for a homeowner. This is to include cover to provide for injury to a third party, or their property in the form of public liability insurance. Proof of this insurance must be shown at the time the contract is agreed.

(5) The builder will be responsible for all aspects of Health and Safety for the duration of the contract in accordance with the current regulations laid down by the Health and Safety Executive.

(6) Payment details are as agreed to on the front page of the contract, unless another agreement is made at the time of contracting.

(7) All waste that is the result of the building work is the responsibility of the builder, they are responsible for its safe disposal and for cleaning the site area when the building work is complete.

(8) When the building work commences the builder must give a guarantee to complete the work to a satisfactory standard, or to a standard a reasonable person would expect. Any faults or bad workmanship will be the responsibility of the builder and they will be responsible for any costs incurred by this bad workmanship for a period of two years, to commence once the work is completed.

(9) The contract can be terminated in writing by the home owner if;

    (i)   The work is not being completed with reasonable care, skill or if the work is not being completed in the time scale agreed to; or

    (ii)   There is failure to follow the homeowner's written instructions within a reasonable time (reasonable can be determined by the agreed duration of the initial contract).

(10) The contract can be terminated in writing by the builder if;

    (i)   They are delayed from completing the said works by the home owner without reasonable cause; or

    (ii)   The homeowner does not make the payments to the builder as agreed this includes any stage payment agreements as specified on page one of this contract.

(11) In the event of sections 9 or 10 taking place the home owner must pay for work completed and materials purchased for the work, up to the time of the termination, this will be calculated on a 'quantum meruit' basis.

(12) If, when the work is completed, there is disagreement as to whether the work is completed to a satisfactory standard, a 'third' party, qualified to inspect the work should be called in to adjudicate the decision (adjudicator must be acceptable to both party's). The cost of the inspection should be taken out of the retention payment, and when a decision has be made, if it is decided the work is of a satisfactory standard the cost of the inspection should be paid for by the home owner. If it is found that the work is sub-standard the builder should correct it, or in the event that they will not do the work the retention should be used to pay another builder to complete the work. Should any funds be left after the faults have been corrected they must be paid to the original builder.